The
Complete Guide to
Sex & Loving

The
Complete Guide to
Sex & Loving

Dr David Delvin

Consultant Editor
of *General Practitioner*

Medical Consultant to the
British Family Planning Association

Ebury Press
London

First published in 1985 by Ebury Press
an imprint of Century Hutchinson Ltd
20 Vauxhall Bridge Road
London SW1V 2SA

This revised edition published in 1990

British Library Cataloguing in Publication Data
Delvin, David
  The complete guide to sex and loving.
  1. Man. Sexual intercourse. Techniques
  I. Title
  613.9'6

ISBN 0-85223-843-6

Designed by Graham Dudley
Illustrated by Patricia Ludlow
Tessa Land
Peter M Gardiner

Cover photograph by Carrie Branovan

Printed and bound in Yugoslavia

I'd like to thank Eric Bailey for his help and
encouragement over the years; Frank Phillips,
Anna Selby, Suzanne Webber and Robert Smith
of Ebury Press for their patience; the artists,
for the really beautiful illustrations; Valerie
Woods, for her typing – and her sense of
humour.

Finally, my gratitude to F.F.R. of Paris without
whom the chapter on the various positions of
love-making wouldn't have been the same...

Contents

Introduction

Love, sex and health – who isn't interested in these three subjects?

For love is perhaps the most important thing on Earth – and sex and health aren't all that far behind!

So this book is about those three topics:

- *Love* – and in particular, the importance of romance (for I reckon that there's been far too little romance in people's lives in recent years)

- *Sex* – and in particular, the need for laughter in sex (for laughter in bed is a precious thing, more valuable than 1,000 orgasms)

- *Your health* – and in particular, how to maintain it (for the fact has to be faced that there are important health problems connected with sex and contraception – especially in this age of alarming new sexual infections).

Also, there are two new – and I think, quite important – features to this book.

The first is that it stresses the increasingly widely-accepted 'New Role' for men: a much more caring and sharing role (in bed and out of it) than the old *macho* one which has caused so much trouble and unhappiness in the past.

Secondly, the book quite frankly acknowledges the fact that nowadays women are more and more frequently taking their sexuality into their own hands (if you'll forgive the phrase).

Today's woman is *not* the passive creature of yesteryear, who let men take all the sexual decisions – and who just lay back and hoped for the best (which she very rarely got …).

No, today's woman is much more sexually independent, challenging and forthright about her sexual needs – and very good luck to her too! No wonder that it's being claimed that it's the *men* who're beginning to fake multiple orgasms these days.

One final point: *please* don't take this or any other sex book too seriously! Bear in mind what I've said about concerning the vital importance of laughter. When the pair of you are hopelessly entangled in Position Number 27A (Romance Rating 3; Sensuality Rating 5; Pregnancy Rating 131.4), and you've just dropped the book on the bedroom floor, so you can't work out how to escape – well then, the only thing to do is laugh together.

So, make love – and make laughter. That's the message of this book.

1

The Seven Sexual Ages of Woman– and Man

Sexual development through life—1 Infancy to puberty—2 Puberty—
3 After puberty—4 Sexual maturity and promiscuity—5 Settling down—
6 Middle age—7 Old age—A lifetime of loving

Sexual development through life

We're all sexual beings throughout our lives. Some people try and deny this, but in fact some form of sexuality is present in almost every human being, although it changes and develops throughout life.

It's a tragedy that very often, the development of a person's sexuality is 'blighted', so that she or he ends up frustrated, unhappy or bitter—or indeed violent, or sexually perverted in some other way. (Violent sex is, of course, one of the all-too-common sexual perversions. Yet, at the moment, you won't find 'Rape' in any medical textbook on perversions!)

Ideally, the development of a person's sexuality should be smooth and untroubled, but as we look at what I've called 'the seven sexual ages', we'll see that many things can go wrong.

These 'seven ages' are:

- infancy to puberty
- puberty
- immediately after puberty
- sexual maturity (which often includes a phase of promiscuity)

- the 'settling down' period

- middle age

- old age.

1 Infancy to puberty

Rather surprisingly, small babies and toddlers do have some degree of sexuality. For instance, baby boys have erections, and small children of both sexes will stroke themselves—apparently deriving some sort of comfort and pleasure from doing so.

It's important to realize that there's nothing *wrong* with this: it's just a natural part of their development.

However, many people do get irrationally upset about these harmless manifestations of infant sexuality. Long ago, Bertrand Russell lost his job at an American university for saying that a baby shouldn't be slapped for touching its genitals! Even today, there are parents who belt their childen for doing just that—or who furiously tell them that their sex organs are 'dirty' (something which, medically speaking, isn't true—see Chapter 2).

It's far better to pay no attention to your child's innocent manifestations of sexuality. But it's important, too, that no one should take advantage of a child's sexuality.

Sadly, recent surveys have made it clear that sexual molestation of young children—and of older ones too—is very common. I'm in little doubt that such interference does quite often affect boys or girls for life, making it very difficult for them to develop a normal sexuality. Certainly, many women who have serious marital problems eventually reveal to their doctors that they were interfered with as young children—and have since carried a great burden of guilt.

So, be very careful whom you pick as a baby-sitter for your toddler, or indeed your school-age child. The most surprising people turn out to be untrustworthy. (One very recent survey claims that, for some reason, men in uniform are the most likely to be dangerous to children.)

As the child grows into her or his school-age years, the outward manifestations of sexuality grow less obvious—though up till about six or seven, it's quite common for boys to declare that they're 'going to marry Mummy', or try to look up her skirt.

This sort of 'let's try and get a squint at the knickers' attitude is harmless and universal in small boys. I remember—at about the age of four—approaching a dummy in a clothes shop and discreetly lifting its skirt. *Very* unfortunately, it turned out *not* to be a dummy after all! (Luckily, this experience didn't blight my subsequent life—though it might have done so if she'd been a bit faster with the clout she aimed at my ear with her handbag...)

By about the age of seven or eight, a child has learned that an outward display of sexuality is not acceptable to adult society.

At school, things may be different—and it's undeniable that many children (both male and female) find amusement in 'dirty talk', and also in rude games of the 'I'll show you mine if you'll show me yours' variety. While nearly all teachers and parents gently discourage this kind of behaviour, it's important not to make a fuss about it, nor to make your child feel that she or he's some kind of potential pervert because she passed on a rude joke to the child sitting next to her or him.

One thing that is very important is to give your child *reasonably adequate information about sex*. Again and again, people who have serious sexual difficulties (for example, being unable to consummate their marriage) say that they were told nothing about sex by their parents. Even today, some girls know absolutely nothing about the subject of sex till they have the shattering experience of finding themselves bleeding when their first period arrives.

Do give your children enough information to let them cope with this extraordinary, bewildering world, in which little human beings are somehow manufactured as a result of something that big human beings do to each other! Quite a lot of parents are still embarrassed about telling their children 'the facts of life'—indeed, through no fault of their own, they may lack the knowledge to do so.

If you're in difficulty, don't hesitate to get your child a sensible, well-illustrated book on the subject. Plenty of these are now available in public libraries and bookshops, and they can do a very useful job in preparing the child for the next stage of life: puberty.

2 Puberty

One of the miracles of existence is the fact that somewhere in all our brains is some sort of *biological clock*. Through some strange mechanism, this clock bestirs itself when a human being reaches a certain age, and makes the pituitary gland (that's at the base of your brain, as you can see from Figure A) send signals down to your sex glands to start them working. They in turn start sending out hormones—via your bloodstream—and these have the most dramatic effects on your body: in short, the changes of puberty occur.

At what age does this remarkable biological clock fire off? It's important to realize that it varies greatly from person to person, as you can see from Figure B. Young people worry terribly about the fact that they don't seem to be reaching puberty at exactly the same time as their friends and classmates: but the truth

At puberty, the pituitary gland (at the base of the brain) sends hormone signals to the sex glands to start them working.

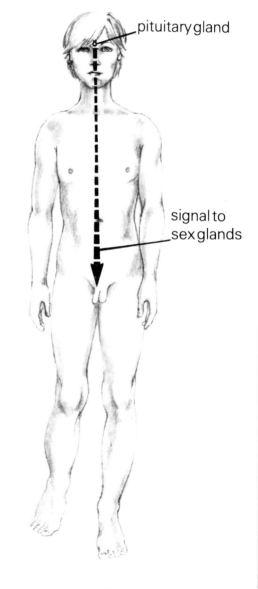

pituitary gland

signal to sex glands

Fig A

is that there's no exact 'right time'. In practice, most children reach puberty between 12 and 15, but a proportion reach it a bit earlier (at 10 or 11) or a bit later (at 16 or 17). A very few alarm their parents—and themselves—by reaching puberty at nine or even earlier.

An appalling statistic is that the world's youngest mother was a poor little South American girl who was raped at the age of four—regrettably, the unfortunate child had already reached the early stages of puberty, and gave birth the next year. In China, round about 1904, a boy of nine and a girl of eight somehow managed to conceive a child.

In contrast, a few boys and girls don't really reach puberty till about 18. In general, if a youngster doesn't seem to have reached puberty by 16 or 17, it's best to have a discreet word with the doctor; in the same way, you should seek medical advice if a child reaches puberty before 10.

Incidentally, it doesn't seem to be true that youngsters reach puberty far earlier in the hot countries, as so many westerners believe! There isn't actually any evidence to prove this. Certainly, in some tropical countries it's the practice for girls or boys of 13 or 14 to get married—something we in the West find rather distasteful. Rich boys of 13 in India may be given concubines by their parents as birthday presents (certainly a startling contrast to Hornby train sets!) but there's no scientific research to suggest that they're any more mature than boys in the West.

Nor is there really much basis in that other popular myth: *that boys and girls are reaching puberty much earlier today.* We often forget that in Britain and other western countries, marriage at 13 used to be quite legal—something we'd find appalling today!

What are the main changes which occur at

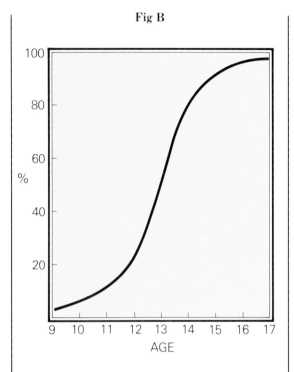

Fig B

The great variation in the age at which youngsters reach puberty.

puberty? They're summed up in Figure C.

In girls, the principal changes are:

- 'budding', and then full development, of the breasts
- growth of pubic hair
- development of other body hair (e.g. armpits)
- increase in width of the hips
- changes in complexion—e.g. spots

- rapid increase in weight and height
- development of adult-type sweat glands
- start of periods
- interest in boys (variable!).

These changes occur in varying order. In addition, some rather bizarre things can happen, which can worry a girl considerably. For instance, she may have one or two periods—then nothing more for several months. One breast may develop well before the other one—so that the poor girl is left for months with one perfectly developed, the other still a bud! No wonder young girls get a bit confused, and need all the help and reassurance they can get.

What about boys? The changes they experience are also shown in Figure C.

Briefly, they're as follows:

- enlargement of the testicles
- enlargement of the penis
- growth of pubic hair
- development of other body hair
- breaking of voice (this may be gradual—it's not always sudden, as many people think)
- development of beard—which may take several years
- complexion changes—spots, acne—due to hormones
- rapid increase in height and weight

Fig C

Stages of development in boys and girls.

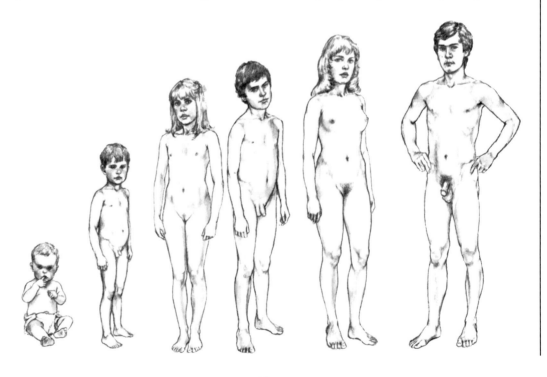

12

- development of adult-type sweat glands (with, alas, resultant BO problems!)

- start of 'wet dreams'

- start of masturbation

- interest in girls.

As with females, these manifestations of puberty occur in a varying order. Perhaps the most startling (even bewildering) changes for the boy are the frankly sexual ones: his sudden interest in women, which can be mild in some boys but overwhelming in others; the arrival of 'wet dreams'—orgasmic dreams which he can do nothing to prevent; and the beginning of masturbation. It's important to realize that virtually all boys (and quite a few girls) do masturbate, and that there's nothing abnormal about this. Indeed, many parents are only too grateful that their teenagers find sexual release in this way—rather than going out and having intercourse, with all its dangers at this age.

You can see that amongst all this chaos, young people can become bewildered—especially if their friends are whispering all sorts of myths in their ears (e.g. 'It'll make you go blind'!). Anything you can do to help and reassure your youngsters at puberty will be much appreciated. Girls, in particular, need help to cope with the embarrassing mysteries of sanitary towels and tampons.

3 After puberty

The years after puberty can also be difficult for both sexes. During this time, girls tend to feel intensely romantic—and boys tend to feel intensely sexy! Girls may sometimes feel very sexy too, and this may have disastrous results.

Figure D shows quite clearly that this is the time of a man's life when the sexual drive reaches its height. Contrary to what many people imagine, boys of this age are having more orgasms than might be suspected! It's a difficult time. Although our society doesn't want young males and females of this age to have intercourse, they're exposed to sexual stimuli all the time—from the media, from advertising, and from people of their own age.

I think that it's a good idea to make clear to them that until they're more mature, sexual intercourse should be regarded as 'out'. But you've got to understand that the frustrations (romantic as well as sexual) which they

Fig D

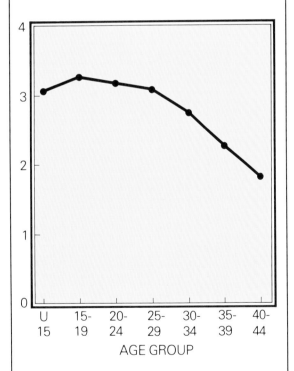

Men's sexual drive at various ages—expressed as average number of orgasms per week.

experience as a result may quite understandably lead to very 'difficult' behaviour.

A boy whose glands are driving him constantly to outlets for his sexual desires, or a girl whose mind is full of romantic fantasies about pop stars, can hardly help being a bit grumpy and irritable sometimes, when it's quite obvious that those desires and fantasies are going to remain unfulfilled!

In addition, parents need to bear in mind that the sudden increase in height, and in length of limbs, that has been mentioned above do very frequently make a teenager gawky and uncomfortable. When your arms and legs have suddenly become about 20% longer, they can be a bit difficult to control! This can easily exacerbate feelings of shyness and uncertainty.

Then there's the fact that the outpouring of hormones from the sex glands very often messes up the teenager's complexion badly, just at the time when she or he desperately wants to look good.

An additional problem is that many youngsters do undeniably go through a brief bisexual or even homosexual phase at this time of their lives. Certainly among girls, 'crushes' are very common indeed—though they are usually just temporary.

These teenage years can therefore be very trying indeed for the young adult. It's vital for parents to understand that inside nearly every young man or woman is a continuous emotional/physiological clash—between the glands saying *yes* and the pressures of society saying *no*.

Inevitably, many young people do eventually give in to the drive of those hormones. Whether we like it or not, recent surveys have shown that by the end of the teenage years (at 19), an astonishingly high proportion of today's men and women are no longer virgins.

This early sexual experimentation is associated with quite a high casualty rate in terms of: abortions, unwanted babies, VD and 'shotgun' marriages (28% of all teenage brides in Britain are pregnant).

So teenagers need all the help they can get. Many parents do find this difficult to provide, but fortunately there are now Youth Advisory Services in many cities (see Chapter 20 for details), where young men and women can get friendly counselling, plus advice about sexually transmitted disorders and (if necessary) contraceptive help. Quite a lot of young adults have been saved from emotional and physical disasters by this sort of commonsense support.

4 Sexual maturity—and promiscuity

With the coming of adulthood, most people start establishing sexual relationships. Of course, some *don't* – for a variety of reasons, including religious or moral conviction, or just plain shyness. And a minority of women and men (though admittedly a substantial minority) find out that they are 'gay'.

The average age for marriage in most western countries these days is around 24. But statistics indicate that by the early twenties, the majority of people have had some sexual experience. Unfortunately, some of them become (at least temporarily) sexual *casualties* as well, since they may have run into trouble with unplanned babies, abortions or VD.

Happily, most men and women do seem to 'muddle through' their early twenties somehow—though it can't be denied that early adulthood is frequently a difficult time, with its often very complex tapestry of flirtations, steady relationships and separations.

First sex

One of the worrying things about this period of life is that so many people—the great majority, according to most surveys—have their first experience of sex *with absolutely no protection against pregnancy*. No wonder then that many 'first times' are rather disappointing—especially for the woman. She may have grown up believing that her first love-making will be a marvellous and miraculous experience, with stars bursting, trumpets playing, the earth moving—in fact, with *all* the things that happen in the most exciting novels! In practice, her first time may be something of an *anti*-climax—especially if her partner is inexperienced or incompetent, uncaring or insensitive, and she may well spend the next week or two hoping desperately that she's not pregnant.

One important point to make is that, contrary to what many women expect, it is very unlikely that she will have an orgasm the first time. Indeed, if you look at Figure E, which is based on the intrepid researches of Dr Alfred Kinsey (of 'Kinsey Report' fame), you will see that the ability to reach orgasm is surprisingly

Fig E

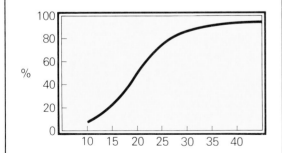

Women's ability to come at various ages. Note that the proportion of women who can come continues to increase until well past 40.

low in women in this age group—but that it increases as a woman gets older.

Promiscuity

The fact has to be faced that promiscuous sexual behaviour has now become very widespread in this age group—in women as well as in men.

Figure F is based on the researches of the distinguished British sociologist Michael Schofield. He studied a large group of 25-year-olds, some of whom were married.

As you can see, he found that:

- almost one third of them had had *no* sex partners in the previous year

- almost one third had had only *one* partner in a year

- a tiny proportion had had just *two* partners in a year

- but a full third had had *three or more* partners (sometimes many more) in the course of a year.

So Schofield found that nowadays a very large proportion of women and men in their early-to-mid twenties do go through a decidedly promiscuous phase. It cannot be denied that the rise in VD in western society—and the emergence of new and alarming types of sexually transmitted disease—is related to the fact that people do have many more partners these days.

Regrettably, there are a lot of men in this age group who have a quite extraordinarily aggressive appetite for sexual conquest, and who will quite cheerfully have sex with 200 partners per year or more, if let loose. Anyone with even a passing acquaintance with

Fig F

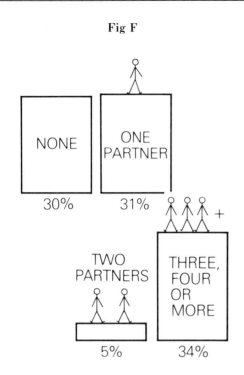

NONE
30%

ONE PARTNER
31%

TWO PARTNERS
5%

THREE, FOUR OR MORE
34%

25 year old British men and women: number of sex partners in 12 months.

bacteriology will realize that this sort of foolish, irresponsible behaviour unfortunately provides a sort of perpetual Christmas party for germs!

Happily, most men and women who go through a rather promiscuous phase between about 20 and 26 do eventually get over it and settle down to a monogamous—or at least relatively monogamous—relationship which they intend to be life-long.

5 Settling down

Perhaps fortunately for the future of humanity, the great majority of women and men regard it as desirable to settle down with one partner for life, either in marriage or, if that's impossible, by living together.

It was Bernard Shaw who said that the popularity of marriage was due to the fact that it 'combines the maximum of temptation with the maximum of opportunity'. And it was his *inamorata* Mrs Patrick Campbell who defined its attraction thus: 'After the hurly-burly of the *chaise-longue*, the deep, deep peace of the double bed!'

Most couples—even those who have played the field for some years—are only too glad to settle into a mutual loving relationship in which they devote themselves to each other permanently—and have sex only with each other.

How often should they have sex? I wish I had a pound for every time somebody has written in asking me this question! The answer is that there are no very definite rules. Couples vary very greatly—from those who make love only once a month to those who have sex every night.

Dr Kinsey was the first to establish that the 'average' couple made love 2.4 times a week. At the beginning of 'settling down', couples tend to make love a little more often than this, later it's a little less. Figure G shows the variation in the frequency with which couples make love, according to Kinsey. Other surveys over the last 40 years or so have confirmed that he was right. But the important thing to realize is that as long as *both* partners are happy, it doesn't matter how often they make love.

The real problem arises when (as is so often the case) one partner wants to have sex frequently, while the other doesn't. This often happens, and when a woman who likes intercourse four times a week marries a man who only likes it once a month (or, indeed, *vice versa*), then trouble is brewing! Indeed, under

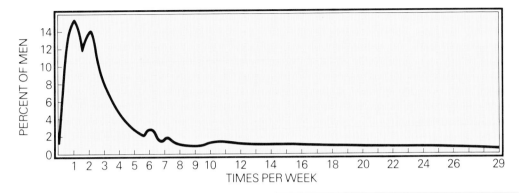

Fig G

The great variation in frequency of love-making. Note that most people report 1, 2 or 3 times per week—while a few, a very few, claim figures of 10, 20 or even 30.

these circumstances it's quite unusual for the marriage to survive. It is therefore important to try to marry somebody with more or less the same amount of interest in sex. Otherwise, by the end of the 'settling down' period you will probably both have decided to settle for totally different partners.

Fig H

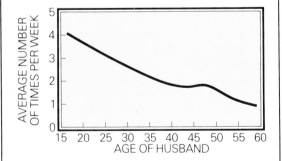

Average frequency of love-making per week— note the slight increase in the late 40s.

6 Middle age

As you can see from the graph in Figure H, frequency of intercourse does diminish a bit as the years go by—but it diminishes far less than many people imagine, and the curve shows a small but encouraging bump upwards in the late forties! Indeed, in middle age most women are very, very sexy. All surveys seem to confirm this fact. Women in their middle years have a greater ability to reach orgasm than younger women do.

Figure E (earlier in the chapter) shows clearly that the proportion of females who cannot reach a climax is much higher at 20 than it is at 40. In addition, the capacity for *multiple* orgasms is much higher in women over 40 than it is in those of 25 or 30. This is very encouraging, particularly if you have been taught the myth that 'sex is all over by 40'. You may also have been told that 'sex finishes by the menopause'. There are no reasons why a woman shouldn't be just as sexy after the menopause as she was before it; indeed, some women are more keen afterwards because the worry of pregnancy has been removed.

Another common myth which surrounds this age group concerns hysterectomy. In many western countries, at least one woman in five has a hysterectomy—usually in middle age. And many of them are told (often by well-meaning friends) that this indicates the end of their sexuality. Others may be told that 'all the sex organs will be taken away'. As you can see from Figure I it's just the *womb* that is removed in a hysterectomy—not the vagina. This means that sex is not only possible, but in fact just as much fun as before. Some women report that the climax feels 'different—but just as nice'.

Naturally, if a woman has been suffering from a womb disorder, like a prolapse (fallen womb) or bulky, uncomfortable fibroids, then it is likely that the removal of the trouble will

Fig I

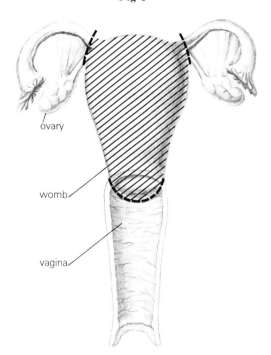

What happens in a hysterectomy: note that it's only the womb (shaded area) which is ordinarily removed.

make her sex life more enjoyable. However, hysterectomy is certainly not a minor operation, and always involves some pain and discomfort. In some countries—particularly the USA—there is little doubt that too many hysterectomies are done. The phrase 'hip pocket hysterectomy' is common in the States—the hip pocket being the one where the surgeon keeps his wallet!

No woman should undergo the operation unless she has discussed it carefully with her doctor and (where possible) with a woman's hysterectomy support group too.

7 Old age

Some years ago, I went to a marriage guidance counsellor's course, at which surprisingly explicit videotapes were shown. The one which provoked most astonishment was the tape of a fit and sprightly-looking old couple who were still wildly enthusiastic lovers at the age of about 75! I think this gave

> *Problems do occur if the partners' sexuality wanes at different rates*

many of those present a certain amount of fresh hope.

In fact, all recent research shows that if a couple love each other and they are in reasonably good health, there is really no reason why they should not go on making love for as long as they want to. Of course, many people are not particularly interested in sex during their later years, and are quite happy with the companionship of a loving partner, with no need for actual sexual activity. However, problems do occur if the partners' sexuality 'wanes' at different rates. For instance, I quite commonly get letters in my advice column postbag from grandmothers who are still feeling sexy—even though their husbands are not.

In such cases, it is obviously important for the *less* sexy partner to do his or her best to help the other one find sexual release. This may have to be through love-play (petting) if actual intercourse is difficult or impossible.

Incidentally, some couples in this age group experience difficulties because intercourse in their usual position is too uncomfortable or painful. Very often, a simple switch to one of the many positions shown in Chapter 10 will help.

Where a less sexy partner is unable or unwilling to satisfy his or her spouse, then the best answer may be masturbation or the use of a vibrator. This is also the answer for many widows and widowers. I get quite a few letters from widows in their sixties or seventies who still have very strong sexual feelings, and who wonder if self-stimulation is all right. Fortunately, a good many couples are able to enjoy a loving old age together. It is true that the man is not as virile as he was in his youth. He has to accept that the frequency of erection is probably not going to be quite what it was, and he has to accept that sometimes he will need a bit of a helping hand—either from his partner or himself—to achieve that erection.

As you can see from Figure J (which is also based on the work of Dr Kinsey), the vast majority of men of 65 are still sexually potent. Even at 70, over 70% of males remain potent. And as the curve shows, even at 75 years of age, roughly half of all men are still capable of intercourse.

Finally, a word of warning to old gentlemen who pursue young ladies, in the firm conviction that they are now 'too old' to have children! If you can still have sex, you are probably still capable of fathering a child. Men in their eighties do quite often get ladies pregnant. The most extreme case of elderly fatherhood is, according to record books, that of Thomas

> *If you can still have sex, you are probably still capable of fathering a child*

Fig J

Men's potency at various ages. Note that most men are potent till well past the age of 70.

Parr—a notorious Elizabethan philanderer who got a poor maidservant in the family way when he was 104!

A lifetime of loving

In conclusion, then, a loving couple can usually continue with the amount of physical love *that suits them* for as long as they want to. They may have to make some adaptations as they get older. And they should not expect to 'perform' in the way that they did at 25! But if they concentrate on keeping romance and laughter in their lives, then the sexual side should remain good.

Just as I was completing this book, the *New England Journal of Medicine* published a report on a massive new survey of thousands of elderly American couples. It confirmed that a very large proportion of these people (who ranged up to 93 in age!) are still sexually active in some way with their loved ones. What is notable, says the report, is the high 'quality, quantity, variety and enjoyability of their sexual activities'.

It's interesting that a major conclusion of the report is that those who are most likely to have a happy marriage 'are persons who enjoy having sexual relations with their spouses'. And jolly good luck to them, too.

2

A Conducted Tour of the Sexual and Erogenous Zones

The similarities between men's and women's bodies—Why you both need to know about the erogenous zones—WOMEN and their bodies—
The breast—The nipple—The ovary—The Fallopian tube—The womb—
The cervix—The vagina—The vulva—The clitoris—The G-spot—
The female buttocks—The pelvic floor muscles—MEN and their bodies—
The male nipple—The testicles—The vas deferens—The penis—
The prostate gland—The male bottom

The similarities between men's and women's bodies

Rather surprisingly, the sex organs of men and women orginate from the same basic tissues, during early life inside the womb. So, quite a few of them are the exact equivalent of each other in males and females:

WOMAN	MAN
Clitoris	Penis
Ovaries	Testicles
Labia	Scrotum
G-spot	Prostate
Female nipple	Male nipple

These pairs of organs tend to behave in very much the same way as each other in response to sexual stimuli. Perhaps the most important point to note—and all couples should be aware of this—is that the woman's clitoris is the exact 'match' of the man's penis. *That's why this is really the sexiest part of a woman, and why everybody should know precisely where it is.*

But we all know that men's and women's bodies are very different too. The really striking difference is in their *attitudes* to their own bodies.

nipple

areola

breast

pubic hair

Fig A
Female and male sex organs.

SEXUAL AND EROGENOUS ZONES

nipple

pubic hair

penis

glans

scrotum

Why you both need to know about the erogenous zones

It's a rather depressing fact that many men and women don't understand their own anatomy or their partner's anatomy either. From a sexual and romantic point of view, this is obviously bad. A man who has no idea about the beautiful and intricate design of the female genitals is quite clearly going to be a bad lover. Similarly, a woman who doesn't understand the basic sexual workings of her partner (including what excites him and what is likely to *hurt* him) can't be a good lover.

Furthermore, it's important to have a basic understanding of your own anatomy. This is because the sexual regions of the body are so important from a health point of view. For example, a woman who wants to protect her own health really does need to know something about her breasts, her cervix and her womb—and particularly about the symptoms which can indicate trouble in those organs.

Women and their bodies

Women, as I've already said above, do have certain surprising physical similarities with men—though of course, men's bodies tend to be much firmer and more solid. But one of the biggest differences between the sexes is their totally differing *attitudes* toward their own bodies! Men do tend to look at their own bodies in a fairly crude and mechanical way— and far too many males think that the same attitude can be applied to women's bodies. It's vital for men to realize that a woman nearly always reacts badly to any basic, mechanistic approach to her body. Any man who thinks that a woman is just like a car ('Press the right button, and off she goes...') must be prepared for disappointment!

A woman sees her body in much more romantic and mysterious (sometimes even mystical) terms. She may have all sorts of interesting fantasies about the way it is made. Only the man who treats her body as she wants it to be treated will be really successful in satisfying her needs.

The breast

Breasts loom very large in women's emotions—as anybody can see by considering the terrible grief which so many women feel if they have to lose a breast, or the distress of women who reach adulthood without developing any breasts.

As you can see from Figure B, the breast is really a mass of milk gland tissue, embedded

> *One of the biggest differences between the sexes is their totally differing attitudes toward their own bodies*

in fat, and attached to the front of the muscular wall of the chest. From the glands which produce milk, a large number of milk ducts lead down to little milk sinuses (or collecting areas) just behind the nipple. In between the milk ducts, there's a network of fibrous tissue which gives the breast support and its firm outline. This fibrous tissue does tend to stretch a bit with the years, particularly if the breasts are very big and heavy.

The size of the breasts depends on the amount of fat and glandular tissue contained in them, and this is to a large extent controlled by a woman's own hormones. It's difficult and dangerous to try to change breast size by giving hormone treatment. Nowadays, it's not too difficult to enlarge abnormally small breasts (or to reduce abnormally large ones) by plastic surgery.

Disorders

The most important breast disorders are benign swellings and malignant (cancerous) ones. Benign swellings are incredibly common; some are fibrous, some are fluid-filled. Their cause is not known, but is thought to be linked to hormone imbalance. The Pill tends to lend protection against such swellings, contrary to what many people think.

Malignant swellings (breast cancers) are not as common—but an alarming *one out of every 17* women suffers from this disease. Again, the cause isn't known, but a woman's chance of developing breast cancer is increased by certain 'risk factors' which include:

- having your first baby after the age of 30

- having a very strong family history of breast cancer

- just possibly the Pill.

But *all* women should check their breasts for lumps.

The illustrations in Chapter 5 Figure A show you how to do this. I suggest that you carry out these checks once a month, after a period. If you think you feel a lump, always ask a doctor to check it out within a few days.

Fig B

The breast.

This is one area where your life may, quite literally, be in your own hands.

The nipple

The nipple is one of the most sexually sensitive areas of the body—*in both women and men*. Quite a few women can actually reach a climax just through having their nipples stimulated, although I don't know of any males who experience this.

Most people use the word 'nipple' wrongly—they think it means the *whole* of the pigmented disc in the middle of the breast, but it is, in fact, only the central protuberance; as you can see from Figure C, the disc which

Fig C

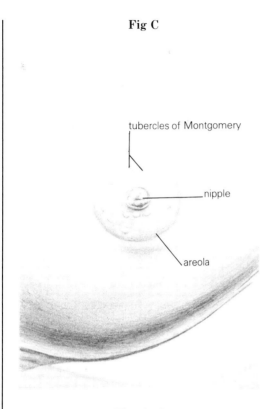

tubercles of Montgomery

nipple

areola

The nipple.

surrounds it is called the areola. The areola is quite sensitive too, but it does not have as many nerve endings as the nipple. The areola may be pink, brown or black—depending on your general colouring. It can be anything up to 12.5 cm (5 ins) across, and there's no 'normal' size. People are sometimes worried by the little 'blobs' which often run round the areola but these are perfectly normal structures called 'the tubercles of Montgomery'.

The nipple itself contains the openings of the 15-20 milk ducts which are directly connected to one of the most important emotional regions of your brain. That's one reason why both suckling a baby *and* sexual stimulation of the nipple both tend to have a very immediate emotional impact on almost all women.

Disorders

Inturning (inversion) of the nipple is common, and is *not* a disorder if you've had it all your adult life. If it makes breast-feeding difficult, then your GP can prescribe you some 'nipple shells', which may help. A sudden and unexplained inturning of the nipple *is* a potentially dangerous symptom, since it may indicate that a growth is pulling the nipple inwards. An urgent medical check is necessary.

Similarly, blood (or a brown discharge) coming from the nipple can be a danger sign. It may only indicate a small papilloma (benign swelling) in a milk duct but a check-up is required.

Finally, a raw, or weepy eczema-like patch on the nipple in the over-45s must also be investigated *fast*, since it may indicate a malignant disorder called Paget's disease of the nipple.

The ovary

Tucked away inside your pelvis are two ovaries—little pinkish-white ovals, each about 3.5 cm (1½ ins) long and 2 cm (¾ in) across—just a bit smaller than a man's testicle, in fact. The comparison with a man's testicles is apt, because the ovaries are the exact female equivalent, and are formed from the same tissues in the early human embryo. However, nature very sensibly tucked the ovaries away where they can't be damaged.

Only someone with fairly long and fairly skilled fingers can feel them: they're just about palpable through the upper part of the side wall of the vagina—and some women do like having them gently stroked during love-play. You can see what I mean from Figure D.

The ovaries probably contain about 100,000 eggs each, but only one egg is released each month, making a grand total of about 400 during your reproductive lifetime.

Apart from releasing eggs (ovulating) the ovaries are also important sources of a woman's sex hormones—although not the only sources. If the ovaries have to be removed, some female hormones are still manufactured in other parts of the body.

Disorders

Disorders of the ovaries are frequently difficult to diagnose, simply because of their inaccessibility.

Fig D

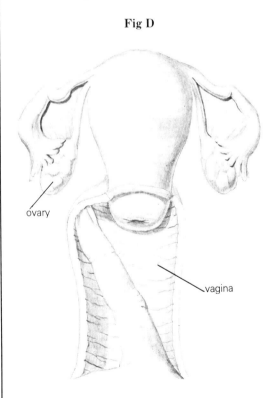

Stroking the ovary during love play.

Cysts are very common, particularly in younger women. Many cysts produce no symptoms at all, but others can cause pain which can be mistaken for appendicitis. By some quirk of nature, a few ovarian cysts when removed turn out to contain teeth.

Contrary to what many people believe, cysts of the ovary are not caused by the Pill. In fact, the Pill tends to protect you against them.

Cancer. Sadly, cancer of the ovary is quite common, and kills rather more women than the much better-known cancer of the cervix. The cause is not known, but again there is now evidence that the Pill helps to protect you against it.

Symptoms tend to be rather vague, and include persistent low abdominal pain and bleeding after the menopause. Let me stress that the disease is rare under the age or 45.

There's a very new screening test for cancer of the ovary—it is done by ultrasound, is painless and takes only ten minutes. If you're over 45, it's well worth having. Unfortunately, it's only available at a limited number of hospitals at present.

So for the moment, your best protection against cancer of the ovary is:

- to use the Pill (though, of course, this has health drawbacks too)

- to have a regular internal check-up from a clinic or doctor. This can usefully be combined with your regular 'smear' test.

The Fallopian tube

These are among the most vital organs of your body because, until very recently, it was completely impossible for a baby to be born unless his or her mother had at least one healthy Fallopian tube. Unfortunately, the Fallopian tubes are often far from healthy. So what *are* the Fallopian tubes? As you can see from Figure E, they are the little bits of tubing which link your ovaries to your womb. (Incidentally, the word 'Fallopian' comes from the sixteenth-century Italian medic called Fallopius.) There's a left tube and a right tube, as you can see from Figure E. Each one is about 10 cm (4 ins) long. The outer end makes a sort of funnel shape which points towards your ovary, and when an egg is released from the ovary, it'll go into the funnel and find its way down the tube and into your womb. Fertilization usually happens in the tube.

Fig E

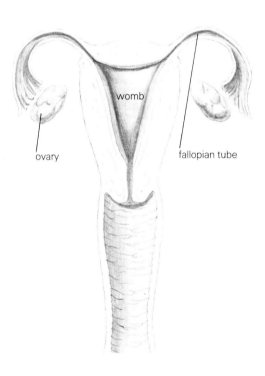

The Fallopian tubes.

Disorders

Unfortunately, the narrowness of the Fallopian tube makes it very vulnerable to blockage. Blockage is usually caused by a common disorder of the tubes: infection. These days, literally tens of thousands of women find themselves unable to have babies because of blocked tubes.

The infection—which may be introduced through sexual activity—often produces no immediate symptoms, though in some cases, severe lower abdominal pain and fever can result. This is called 'salpingitis', and if it's diagnosed in time and treated with the right antibiotic, it can be stopped immediately.

If a tube infection does lead to blockage, then the outlook for future pregnancy is bleak. However, the last few years have seen the development of two techniques to overcome the problem: microsurgery to 'clear' the blocked tube, and the test-tube baby technique, which bypasses the blocked tube altogether.

The womb

The average woman's womb is only about as big as her clenched fist. As you can see from Figure F, it's very like a small pear, turned upside down, with the tip of the pear representing the cervix, or neck of the womb. The womb is actually a little bag of muscle which is powerful enough to push a baby out—and it's the contraction of this muscle fibre which produces the pains of labour. However, the womb is not all muscle. Inside the walls, there's a thin lining which is shed every month when a woman has her period.

Disorders

There are very many disorders of the womb. This is one reason for the quite extraordinary fact that about one out of every five women eventually has her womb removed.

The main disorders are:

Fibroids. Benign swellings which develop in the muscular wall. Incredibly common, particularly in the over-thirties and in women who haven't had children. The cause is unknown and the symptoms are pain, or heavy periods, or difficulty in passing urine. If they don't cause symptoms, they can usually be left alone. But troublesome fibroids may have to be 'shelled out' (an operation called

Fig F

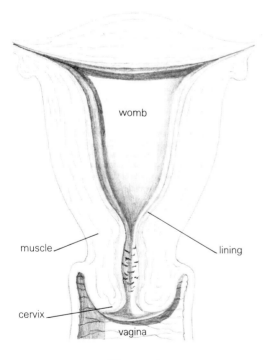

The womb.

myomectomy)—or a hysterectomy may be necessary.

Prolapse. Prolapse of the womb means that it comes down into the vagina, and may even come outside. It's caused by weakening of the supports of the womb during childbirth. It's less common than it used to be because women are having fewer babies and it's curable by a repair operation, or if necessary a hysterectomy.

Endometriosis. Painful nodules in the wall of the womb, and elsewhere in the pelvis. Treatable with hormones or, if necessary, surgical removal.

Cancer of the womb lining. Womb cancer (which is quite different from cancer of the cervix) kills about 1,000 British women each year. It usually starts in the womb lining, and can be triggered off by excessive stimulation with oestrogens. The warning sign that every women should know about is *unexplained bleeding after the menopause.* Cure is possible by hysterectomy.

Unfortunately, there is as yet no widely available screening test for cancer of the womb. Smear tests (for cancer of the cervix) do *not* detect cancer of the womb—as many people imagine. There is a test, called 'out-patient curettage', but at the moment, cost prevents it from being widely used.

The cervix

Every woman should be familiar with her own cervix. One of the many good things about the women's liberation movement is the fact that self-help groups have encouraged a lot more women to be conscious of their own cervixes—and of the medical problems which can affect the cervix.

As you probably know, the cervix is widely referred to as 'the neck of the womb'. In fact, it's the tip of the womb—as you can see from Figure G. It's the very point of the womb, which projects down a few centimetres into the vagina.

A narrow tunnel runs up through the cervix and into the cavity of the womb itself. This is the only way into the womb from the exterior. Sperm passes up through this canal into the womb immediately after intercourse. Naturally, menstrual blood passes down it. And during childbirth the baby has to pass through this hole through the middle of the cervix. Fortunately, the cervix has the remarkable property of opening up to a quite extraordinary extent during labour—enough to let the baby's head through.

Fig G

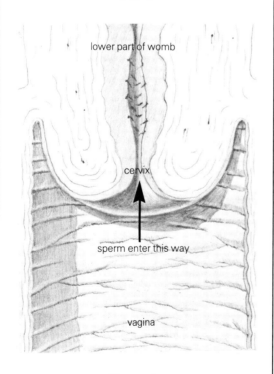

The cervix.

Functions

It's difficult to say what the function of the cervix is—except to provide a useful sort of expandable entrance and exit to the womb. Some women do derive considerable sexual pleasure from having it touched—particularly during the last 'surge' of intercourse—but others do not have any special feeling there. This may be owing to individual variations in nerve supply to the cervix. Some women feel no pain when their cervix is touched by a surgical instrument.

In this century, the cervix has developed one important new function—as a sort of useful hatpeg on which to 'hang' a contraceptive cap. Any woman who uses a cap must be able to feel her cervix with her fingertips.

Disorders

There are three important disorders of the cervix which every woman should know about—erosions, polyps and cancer.

Erosions of the cervix. These are raw places on the cervix, and millions of women have them. They're especially common in pregnancy, and in women on the Pill. If they're not producing symptoms, they're usually left alone. But they can cause discharge, bleeding and occasionally pain on intercourse—in which case they should be cauterized.

Polyps. These are little fleshy out-growths, which can be felt projecting from the cervix. They often cause bleeding, and they should be removed (usually by a gynaecologist).

Cancer of the cervix. This tragic condition causes over 2,000 deaths a year in Britain—and countless more in other countries. Nearly all would be prevented if every adult woman were given a regular smear test ('Pap test').

The vagina

The vagina is a warm, pink, well-cushioned sheath (the word 'vagina' is actually Latin for 'sheath'), which is absolutely perfect for its intended function in life. And that function is to fit snugly and lovingly round the penis, so that the sperm is deposited in the right place, and so that both partners derive the maximum possible enjoyment from the act of love.

Regrettably, a lot of people don't realize that the vagina is such a capacious and comfortably-upholstered channel. Instead, they think it's a very tight passage, up which a penis can only be forced with difficulty and with pain. In reality, there's a vast amount of room inside the vagina. It 'balloons out' and lengthens quite dramatically during romantic and sexual excitement, as you can see from Figure H. The vagina *has* to be a distensible organ, because it must be able to open up widely enough to let a baby's head pass through. In addition to being remarkably distensible, it can also contract (especially at orgasm) to fit perfectly round the man's penis.

The vagina's other function is to produce the 'love juices'—the erotically-induced secretions which lubricate the movements of intercourse. Using an 'intra-vaginal camera', the great American sex researchers, Masters and Johnson, have shown that when a woman becomes sexually aroused, it's the *walls* of her vagina which suddenly start pouring out these juices, almost like water squeezing out of a sponge.

Disorders

Life-threatening disorders of the vagina are fortunately rare. But here are some common vaginal problems:

Vaginismus. A fairly common emotional

Fig H

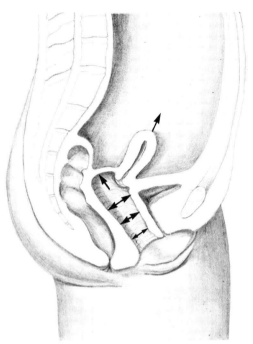

How the vagina widens and lengthens during sexual excitement.

condition in which the vagina tightens up whenever any approach is made to it. It also fails to 'lubricate'. This tends to make sex either difficult or impossible. Doctors at Family Planning Clinics have achieved first-class results in treating it with simple psychotherapy and relaxation techniques. More details in Chapter 11.

Vaginal infections. These are fantastically common, and I am afraid that most sexually active younger women seem to acquire one or other of them these days. The most frequently encountered ones are caused by thrush (also known as candida or monilia) and a parasite, trichomonas. Details of these and other infectious organisms are given in Chapter 5.

Post-menopausal vaginitis. This is a frequently-met condition, in which the drop in natural hormone production after the menopause causes vaginal dryness and soreness—and hence painful intercourse. Application of a vaginal hormone cream usually puts things right. Again, more details are given in Chapter 5.

The vulva

The vulva—which is the actual opening that leads to the vagina—is also a beautifully-designed structure. It's tragic that so many women (and, indeed, men) grow up 'conditioned' to regard the vulva as 'ugly' or 'nasty-looking'.

I get a lot of letters from women who are deeply distressed because they think that their vulvas are mis-shapen or abnormal. In practice, it's almost unknown to find a patient with a mis-shapen or deformed vulva. Usually, when people think their vulvas are abnormal, it's just that they do not know enough about normal female anatomy (see Figure I).

Starting at the top of the drawing, there is the *pubic hair.* This is usually crisp and crinkly. It doesn't necessarily have to be in the shape of a neat triangle, contrary to what you might think from looking at pin-up pictures! Its colour is usually black, ginger or 'mousy'—even in natural blondes, a genuine platinum colour is very rare. Next is the clitoris which is dealt with in the next part of the chapter, and then we come to the outer lips and inner lips *(labia majora* and *labia minora).* These provide a sort of 'seal' for the opening of the vagina. During sexual excitement, they open out like a flower to welcome the tip of the penis and they also swell up a little, so as to make a sort of snug collar around it. It's very impor-

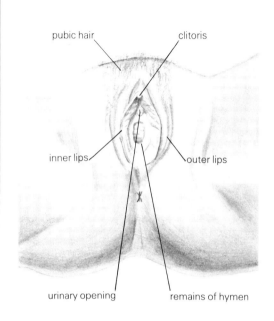

Fig I

pubic hair   clitoris

inner lips   outer lips

urinary opening   remains of hymen

The parts of the vulva.

tant to know that these lips *vary greatly in length from woman to woman.* So if one of yours is longer than a friend's this does *not* make you abnormal.

The urinary opening (urethral opening) is just below the point where the inner lips meet at the front. It's small—usually less than ½ cm (¼ in) across. People occasionally do stupid things like pushing an object up it; the end result is likely to be an operation to remove a hair-grip from the bladder.

Finally, as you can see, around the actual entry to the vagina, many women tend to have the remains of the hymen (or 'virgin's veil')—the thin membrane which partly closes off the vagina in virgins.

If you're not too sure about your own anatomy, it's well worth getting a mirror to compare yourself with this drawing.

Disorders

Serious disorders of the vulva are rare. Varicose veins of this area are common in pregnancy, but usually subside after delivery. Small viral warts are extremely common, but are easily removable through application of a special paint by a doctor.

Cancer of the vulva is a great rarity. Benign moles are quite common, but are easily removed.

The clitoris

From studying overseas editions of previous books of mine, I have been able to discover what the clitoris is called in various tongues. In German, it's *die Kitzler*, in Dutch it's *de clitoris*, in French it's *le cli-cli* – and in the Hebrew edition of one of my books it's represented by something that looks like the figures '72727', followed by a picture of Stonehenge!

As can be seen from Figure J, the clitoris is located just in front of the pubic bone—so it will be gently compressed and squeezed during intercourse. It's only the size of a little button—even when it swells up during sexual excitement. Close examination of it reveals that it's in fact almost identical in structure to a man's penis, so it's not surprising that it's more plentifully supplied with 'pleasure-producing' nerve endings than any other part of the female body.

More about clitoris-stimulation techniques which can help women to obtain sexual fulfilment in Chapter 8. But male readers may like to note that during love-play, many women

Fig J

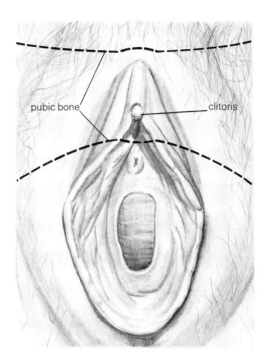

The clitoris—located in front of the pubic bone.

(not all) do prefer to be stimulated along the *side* of the clitoris, rather than directly on top of it.

Disorders

Disorders of the clitoris are very rare. Occasionally, women seek medical advice because of a sudden and alarming *swelling* of the clitoris. This swelling appears to be due to a collection of blood—and it soon bursts, leaving no ill-effects.

Some years ago, I described the condition in *World Medicine*, and promptly received a number of letters from doctors who had also seen it. Two of them had discovered that their patients had actually caused the swelling by wrapping a cotton thread round the clitoris during masturbation—clearly, this is *not* a very sensible idea!

The G-spot

Controversy still rages about whether the 'magic female G-spot' really exists or not. I am inclined to think that it *does* – and that stimulation of it can help some women who have difficulty in getting sexually aroused, or in reaching a climax. It may also be connected with the curious phenomenon of 'female ejaculation'.

My knowledge of the G-spot goes back to a time several years ago when I wrote in my column that it was a 'complete myth' that women ejaculated a fluid at the moment of orgasm. I was immediately flooded with protest letters from readers who said that they *did* do this. One lady even sent me a sample of the liquid, but the plastic container broke in the post.

At this stage, two readers wrote to me to point out that an obscure US sexological journal had just published a series of research papers which indicated that women had something called a G-spot (named after its discoverer, Ernst Grafenberg), and that stimulation of this newly-discovered organ could produce a climax—a climax which was sometimes accompanied by a squirt of some mysterious sexual fluid.

You can see the alleged location of this organ in Figure K. It's located in very much the same situation as the male prostate gland. It's interesting that US and Canadian researchers have claimed that the liquid which it's supposed to produce is in fact very similar in chemical composition to the secretion of the prostate. So it's claimed that the 'G-spot' is a sort of 'homologue' (i.e. an exact anatomical equivalent) of a man's prostate gland.

Books have recently been written about this structure—notably the world best-seller *The G-Spot*, by Alice Ladas, Beverly Whipple and John D. Perry. I notice that the blurb of the book describes Mr Perry as 'an ordained minister, psychologist and sexologist, specializing in vaginal myography and other innovative applications of biofeedback'.

Not altogether surprisingly, the new 'anti-sex movement' in the USA has been claiming that the G-spot doesn't exist at all. But whether it does or not, searching for it may actually help some women with sexual

Fig K

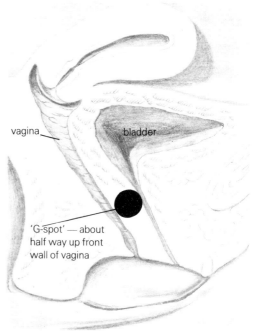

vagina

bladder

'G-spot' — about half way up front wall of vagina

The alleged location of the G-spot.

difficulties. If you or your partner gently rub an area about half-way up the front wall of your vagina with a soft fingertip, you'll rapidly be able to draw your own conclusions as to whether the G-spot is real—or just a fig-leaf of somebody's imagination. . .

The female buttocks

The female bottom has always been a subject of great interest to the male sex—as any woman who has ever endured the indignity of a stroll along the Via Veneto will know. But the buttocks are undoubtedly an erogenous zone of the body—so much so that some women can reach orgasm through having their bottoms patted or even slapped. There are so many sexually-tuned nerve endings in that area of the body that a firm stimulus—like gentle slapping—is almost bound to fire off a few sensual circuits somewhere in the nervous system.

It also has to be admitted that the anal area is even more rich with sexually-tuned nerve endings. This is why anal love-play ('postillionage'—see Chapter 8) and even anal intercourse are so common. The recent *Playboy* sex survey indicated that a rather alarming 54% of those couples who took part in the survey had tried rectal sex. I say 'alarming' because of the hygiene risks of this practice—outlined later in this book.

The pelvic floor muscles

Lots of people don't really understand what the pelvic floor muscles are. Indeed, recently I had a slightly surreal conversation with an otherwise highly-informed woman who thought that pelvic floor exercises were so called because you had to do them on the floor!

The pelvic floor is a cleverly-interwoven basket of muscle which forms a network that supports the organs in the pelvis—including the womb, ovaries and bladder. You can get a rough idea of the size and shape of the muscles of the pelvic floor simply by holding your two hands palms upwards in front of you. Then slide the two hands together, so that the fingers interlock. The resulting shallow basin is quite like the pelvic floor. Imagine that it's supporting your pelvic organs—and imagine too that (as in Figure L) there are two apertures in the basin, through which pass the vagina and the rectum.

It's very important for all women to know about this pelvic floor musculature because in so many females, childbirth leads to serious

Fig L

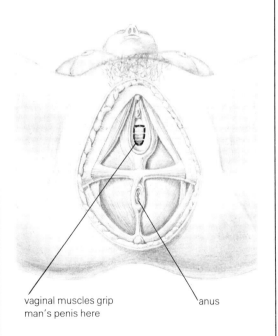

vaginal muscles grip
man's penis here   anus

The pelvic floor muscles.

weakening of these muscles—with unfortunate consequences for love-life and health. Repeated childbirth and *prolonged or difficult* labours are particularly likely to do this. As far as her sex life is concerned, a woman is likely to find that her vagina seems to have become slack and loose. Either she or her partner (or both) are liable to feel dissatisfied because things are not as snug as they once were.

Furthermore, severe weakness of these muscles can lead to *prolapse* (descent of the womb); much more frequently, it simply causes problems with urination and the woman may find that she has embarrassing incontinence, especially when she coughs or laughs.

Gross weakness of the pelvic floor muscles can usually be put right, with one of a variety of surgical repair operations. Obviously, it's much better to avoid surgery altogether, and this can be done by means of pelvic floor exercises, also known as Kegel exercises (after their inventor).

Every women should do these exercises daily for several months after the birth of a child, in order to prevent problems. Any woman who feels that her vagina is a little too loose can do these exercises—they are quite good fun, and they may prevent the need for a vaginal repair operation later on in life. The exercises develop the muscles just where they surround the vagina, and where they grip the penis during intercourse (as you can see from Figure L).

Indeed, the exercises can and should be done during intercourse: this is enjoyable, and your partner will find it pleasant too. Once these muscles are strengthened, you'll discover that doing the exercises creates an agreeable sort of 'milking' sensation in his male organ. But it's no good just doing the exercises during love-making. As with any other 'muscle building' exercises, *you need to do them for about 20 minutes twice a day—over at least six months*.

You can do the two exercises while you're at work, or pushing a pram, or sitting in the bath—no one will know you're doing them. Here they are.

Exercise one: make a real effort to tighten up the *front* part of your pelvic muscles, by 'tightening up' as if you were trying to stop yourself passing water. Hold the contraction for 10 seconds, then release for 10 seconds. Continue for 10 minutes.

Exercise two: make a similar effort to con-

Fig M

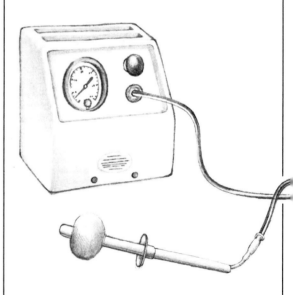

A perineometer, invented by a US gynaecologist. The woman puts the bulb in her vagina, flexes her muscles—and then reads off the strength of the contraction on the dial.

tract the back part of your pelvic floor muscles by 'tightening up' as if to hold back a bowel movement. Again, maintain the contraction for 10 seconds, than relax for 10 seconds—and repeat for 10 minutes.

There are now numerous devices which are supposed to help people do Kegel exercises. One of them converts your vaginal muscle contractions into electrical impulses and records them on a chart, and another plays them back to you on a loudspeaker!

There are also very sophisticated American devices, like the one shown in Figure M, which enables you to read off the strength of your vaginal muscles from a dial.

Men and their bodies

As we said earlier in this chapter, men have quite a different attitude to their own bodies as compared with women: a much more basic—perhaps even mechanical—attitude.

In particular, a man tends to see his own penis (and the stimulation of it) as just about the most important thing in the world! Obviously, this is a pretty daft point of view. But all women should be aware of it.

Quite often, things do go wrong sexually between a couple, simply because the woman hasn't realized how 'penis-orientated' men's sexual behaviour is. In other words, she hasn't stimulated her partner's penis enough.

If that makes men sound selfish, I should make one important point. Many males—particularly nervous ones and older ones—simply *can't* make love unless they have had their penises stimulated fairly energetically beforehand. The sex life of a lot of middle-aged and elderly couples tends to founder merely because the man isn't getting an erection, while the woman doesn't realize that she could help him by taking time to stimulate him.

The male nipple

A man's nipple is a sexually excitable organ. That's because it comes from the same basic tissues which go to form the *female* nipple, and has much the same nerve supply. The only thing that makes the female nipple different is that female hormones have made it grow and develop—and have made the breast form around it.

If you give a man female hormones, he too will develop female-looking nipples and breasts. (Indeed, many trans-sexual males who want to be women take female hormones for just this purpose.)

The fact that the ordinary male's nipple has such a rich nerve supply means that a woman can produce a very good reaction in her partner by stroking it, kissing it, or teasing it gently with her tongue—in fact, just what most women like men to do to *their* nipples.

The testicles

It's fairly important for a woman to have a working knowledge of the male testicle—if only because it's so awfully easy for her to hurt it in bed! So be careful where you put your knees. . .

The testicle (also known as the testis) is an incredibly pain-sensitive part of the male body. This fact is vital to remember if you're *attacked* by a man. If at all possible, hit him as hard as you can in the testicles—and then run, because the disability is only temporary!

The testicle is, of course, the source of the millions of tiny sperm whose aim in life is to unite with a ripe ovum from the woman's ovary, and so form a baby. You can see from Figure O how sperm which are produced by the testicle find their way up through a man's 'plumbing', in order to be ejaculated at the moment of climax. Anything up to 500 million of these are produced in a single orgasm.

The two testicles have another function, which is to produce the male sex hormones, which give the secondary male sex characteristics of hairiness, muscularity, aggression, and so on.

As you can see from Figure N, each testicle is rather like a flattened ping-pong ball in shape and size. Average dimensions are about 4 cm (1¾ ins) long, 3 cm (1¼ ins) deep, and 2½ cm (1 in) thick.

A curious property of the testis is that it will 'retract' rapidly upwards if it's 'threatened' in any way. Try poking the inside of your partner's thigh with a pencil and you'll see

what I mean! Don't be *too* rough.

Testicles occasionally have to be removed because of accident or disease. These days it's possible to replace a lost testis with a plastic one which feels very like the real thing.

Although testicles are pain-sensitive, men do like them to be held by women—but gently! You shouldn't actually rub your partner's testicles; but if you hold them gently—particular during intercourse—you'll find he'll appreciate it.

The vas deferens

Here's an important organ which is not very well known to the public. It's the vas

Fig N

The testicle—rather like a flattened ping-pong ball.

Fig O

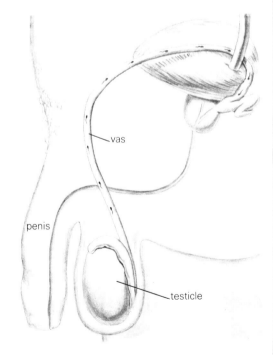

vas

penis

testicle

The vas (vas deferens), carrying sperms up from the testicle.

Fig P

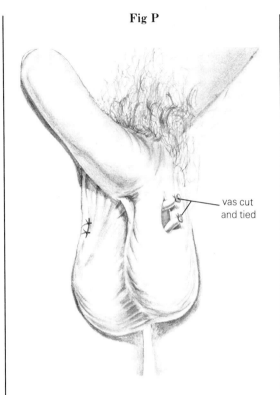

vas cut
and tied

Vasectomy.

deferens—more commonly referred to as 'the vas' (usually pronounced 'vass', rhyming with 'lass'). 'Vas' is Latin for 'vessel', and 'deferens' means 'bringing'. And the vas deferens is the tube which brings sperm up from the testicle towards the penis, as you can see from Figure O.

A man normally has two of these tubes; a few men have three, but this is not an advantage to them as we shall see. The vas looks very like a thin piece of spaghetti. It can be felt with the fingertips through the skin of a man's scrotum as—with its accompanying blood vessels—it runs up towards the groin.

The reason why there is such a lot of interest in the vas these days is that *it is the bit that is cut in a vasectomy.* Vasectomy just means 'cutting through the vas'—as you can see from Figure P.

This popular operation (well over a hundred thousand are being done world-wide every year) just involves making two tiny incisions in the skin of the scrotum, working through them to cut through each vas, and tying the ends.

Why are men who have a *third* vas at a disadvantage? Because the surgeon probably will not realize they have an extra vas deferens, and will fail to cut it. In such cases, the vasectomy won't work! However, the sperm test which is done a couple of months or so after a vasectomy will detect the fact that there is another vas deferens, still sending up vast supplies of spermatozoa. The third vas can then be cut and tied off too.

The vas deferens does *not* seem to have any hormonal function. So, cutting through it doesn't interfere with a man's production of sex hormones, or with his virility. It just gives him a great feeling of confidence that he is no longer exposing his female partner to the risk of unwanted pregnancy.

The penis

Now to the organ which so many people get concerned about: the penis.

It's surprising that this particular organ generates such a lot of emotion, embarrassment and even outrage. For after all, it's a somewhat unimpressive little structure, comparing rather unfavourably in dimensions with a decent-sized *andouillette*.

However, one has to face the fact that many men and women do have hang-ups about the penis. In the case of men, vast numbers have an extraordinary obsession about penis size—and are firmly convinced that their own is too small. In the case of women, a surprising number of females feel frightened or disgusted by the idea of a close encounter with a male organ. You may be surprised to hear it, but some wives are so emotional about this matter that they cannot bring themselves to touch their husbands' penises.

Perhaps life would be easier if everybody understood a few of the basic facts about this organ. The penis is the male equivalent of a woman's clitoris. It's equipped with a great many 'pleasure receptors' which, when stimulated, produce very agreeable sensations in the man's brain.

The average penis in its non-erect state is quite a bit smaller than most people imagine.

Fig Q

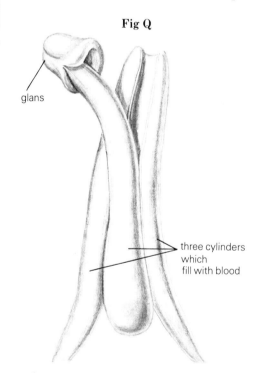

glans

three cylinders
which
fill with blood

The penis—'split up' to show that it's made of 3 cylinders which fill with blood in order to produce an erection.

In general, it measures between 8.5 cm (just over 3 ins) and 10.5 cm (just over 4 ins)—but it varies a lot, depending on the weather.

Masters and Johnson have discovered a curious fact of which few men are aware. Though penises vary quite a bit in size in the non-erect state, they are nearly all about the same size when they are erect. So though many males feel inadequate about the size of their penis, this is all quite unnecessary—especially as most women are not remotely interested in the size of a man's organ.

You can see the anatomy of the penis in Figure Q. It's a very simple structure in comparison with the female genital organs. It consists of three 'cylinders' of tissue, which are capable of filling with blood (thus causing an erection), when a man thinks about sex.

On the end of these three cylinders is the cone-shaped glans, which is the most sexually sensitive part.

The only other thing to say about the penis is that contrary to what so many women (and men) imagine, it's actually a pretty clean structure. Provided a man washes regularly under his foreskin (if uncircumcized) there should be nothing 'dirty' about it at all.

The prostate gland

The prostate is a gland about the size of a chestnut—with a hole through it.

What does it do? Its only known function is a sexual one. It adds a contribution to the fluid which a man ejaculates when he has a climax. The prostatic secretion is thought to give impetus to the sperm in some way—and the added volume probably does give a certain boost to his sensual satisfaction.

From a sexual point of view, prostatic stimulation is possible and (I gather) widely practised in exotic parts of the world. It's done

Fig R

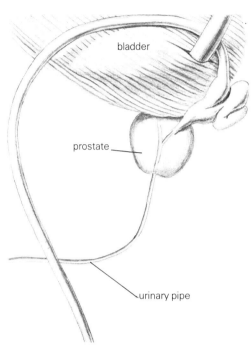

The prostate gland.

by gentle finger massage with a well-lubricated finger, and tends to produce a more intense climax with a more powerful ejaculation. However, as the massage has to be via the bottom, there are serious hygiene risks involved.

Disorders

There are two main problems to which the prostate gland is subject: *enlargement* and *cancer*.

Enlargement. In most men, the gland increases markedly in size after about the age of 50. For fairly obvious reasons, this tends to interfere with the waterworks. Indeed, if the enlargement is too great, it may become impossible to pass urine.

Prostate trouble is so very common that two recent British Prime Ministers have had theirs removed. As an alternative to removal, there is a newer and less serious operation, a 'TUR' (it stands for 'Trans-Urethral Resection')—in which part of the gland is simply nibbled away with a slim instrument pushed up the urinary pipe.

Cancer. Cancer of the prostate is of course far more serious. It's treated (often very successfully) by removal of the gland, plus hormone therapy and possibly radiation.

The male bottom

As with the female bottom, the male one is a sexually arousable area. In other words, most men like having their buttocks caressed. And as with some women, some men also like having it gently slapped or spanked. With a minority of men, this seems to go a great deal further: in other words, they actually enjoy being caned, even though it hurts a good deal. I cannot account for this male tendency (for it *is* largely confined to males), but it seems to be a very widespread one. Most large cities in Anglo-Saxon countries seem to have sizeable 'spanking industries'—including parlours where, for suitable remuneration, young ladies will wallop gentlemen across the buttocks with canes. In London, this kind of thing has recently become semi-respectable, with the advent of several spanking restaurants, where male diners get 'punished' by 'Matron' for not eating up their dinners. There may be something in the widespread theory that all these men have been deeply influenced by the repeated bottom canings they experienced at school. (But since corporal punishment has become so rare in recent years, it's surprising that the trend has not died out.) There is certainly no harm in a little honest bottom smacking in bed, but there is no point in going in for it unless you really want to.

The other extremely sexual area of the male bottom is the anus. Just as is the case with the female back passage (see earlier in this chapter) this is a region where there appear to be a lot of erotic nerve endings. A lot of people think that it's only homosexual males who get sexual pleasure in this way but that is not true. In Britain, the USA and many other western countries, it has become the smart thing for sophisticated women to slip a lubricated finger inside the man's rectum while making love, or having oral sex. Sometimes a woman does this to stimulate a man's prostate gland, but mainly it's just to stimulate the back passage itself.

It can't be denied that this widespread practice (which is called 'postillionage') gives a lot of men pleasure, and that it may be useful if a man's virility is flagging somewhat. However, there seem to me to be real risks in doing it, if you're not *very* careful about washing your hands immediately afterwards. In particular, some of the alarming 'new' sexual infections which are spreading across the world may well be transmitted by this sort of play.

Finally, let me add that there is one other quite common way of stimulating the male (or indeed female) bottom. This is with the 'rectal vibrators' which are widely sold in sex shops. I mention these only to say that *you should not use them*. Vaginal vibrators are quite a different thing, but rectal vibrators can sometimes vanish inside you!

Summing up

Sorry to have concluded this chapter on such a bum note! But as I hope you'll have gathered from this swift gallop round the female and the male anatomy, I feel that the sexual parts of the human body are among the wonders of the universe: beautifully designed, and incredibly good fun to use.

3

How the
Sex Organs Work

A blooming miracle!—WOMEN first: ovulation—Fertilization—
Menstruation—How the vagina works—Orgasm—Micturition—
Masturbation—MEN: physiologically the simpler sex—How the testicles
work—How the plumbing works—The strange phenomenon of erection—
The man's climax—Fitting it all together

A blooming miracle!

Yes, it really *is* a miracle that anything as complicated as sex works so remarkably well. As a doctor, I'm constantly astonished that sex is so efficient at doing three things:

giving people babies

giving people enormous pleasure

giving a loving couple such a splendid way of *expressing* their love.

This chapter concentrates on the *physiology* of sex—in other words, how it all works;

and more specifically:

how it all works to give you babies (if you want them)

how it all works to give you sexual pleasure.

Women first: ovulation

I shall begin with women because their physiology is so much more complicated than men's. Let's start with the functions of the *ovary*.

It's really got two functions. As I said in Chapter 2, it produces female sex hormones—

43

chemical messengers which flow through a woman's bloodstream and help to give her those typical female characteristics, such as breasts, curvaceous hips, and the common sense not to behave as aggressively as we males.

The ovary's other function is ovulation—which means of course the release of an ovum (egg) from the ovary. It happens once a month—usually about 14 days before the start of your period. You can see what I mean from Figure A: a 'ripe' ovum bursts from the surface of the ovary, makes an extraordinary 'long jump' across the enormous gap which separates the ovary from the Fallopian tube, and then makes its way down the tube on the off-chance of meeting any sperm coming up the other way.

Not long ago, I was at a meeting which was being addressed by Dr Robert Edwards—who (with Mr Patrick Steptoe) invented the test-tube baby technique. He revealed that he and Steptoe have now found that ovulation nearly always takes place in the early afternoon.

Indeed, when his American patients come to Britain to undergo the test-tube baby technique, he finds that they're ovulating at about 3 p.m. New York time or San Francisco time, or whatever. But after a month or so in Britain, they start ovulating at around 3 p.m. Greenwich Mean Time!

Edwards' announcement prompted a rash of speculation that early afternoon might therefore be the best time to get pregnant. But you needn't make any arrangements for post-lunch love-making just yet! For if you think about it, the ovum usually takes a day or two to make that journey down the Fallopian tube. So if you make love *around* the day of ovulation, there's a good chance of conceiving.

Ovum release is caused by a hormone signal

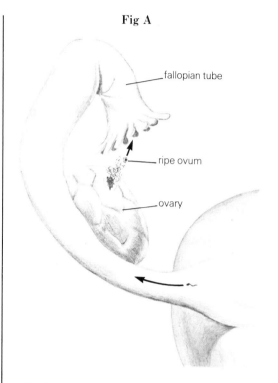

Fig A

fallopian tube

ripe ovum

ovary

Ovulation: a ripe ovum (egg) bursts from the surface of the ovary.

which travels once a month from the pituitary gland (at the base of your brain) to the ovaries. Emotional stresses—or even a sudden change of work or diet—can interfere with that signal, which explains why irregularity of the menstrual cycle often happens in women who've had a recent upset.

By the way, you may have noticed that you get a slight pain in the lower abdomen midway between periods: this is caused at the moment of ovulation by the egg being released. It's called *mittelschmertz*, which is actually German for 'middle pain'. For some women, it's a useful sign that they are ovulating.

A monthly temperature chart—as shown in Figure B—is another way of confirming that

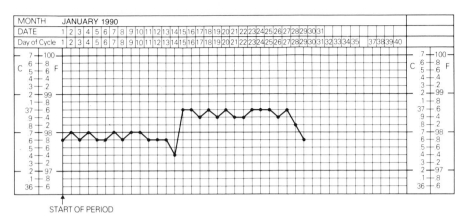

START OF PERIOD

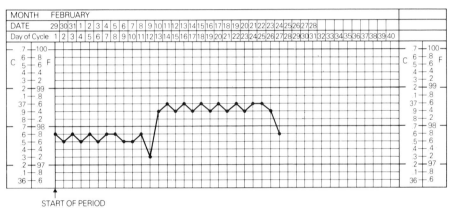

START OF PERIOD

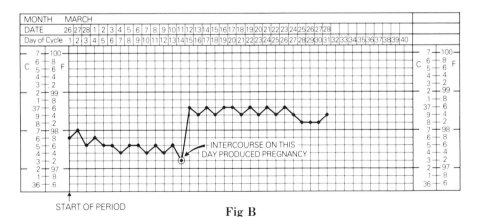

START OF PERIOD

Fig B

*A monthly temperature chart, indicating the approximate day of ovulation—
where the graph kicks upwards.*

Fig C

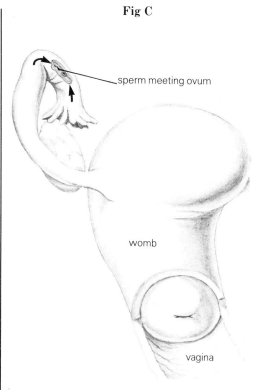

sperm meeting ovum

womb

vagina

Fertilization: the sperm meeting the ovum in the tube.

ovulation is actually happening and fixing the day on which it occurs. But really *precise* estimation of the day of ovulation requires careful laboratory measurement of a woman's hormones.

Unfortunately, there's as yet no cheap, mass-produced method of detecting ovulation. As soon as there is, the Rhythm Method of birth control (see Chapter 7) will become much more accurate.

Fertilization

Fertilization means the union of a man's sperm with a woman's ovum. It's thought that it usually occurs in the outer part of a woman's Fallopian tube, as you can see from Figure C. I say 'usually' because fertilization can in fact occur just about anywhere.

Many eggs (ova) must be fertilized by sperm in the vagina—but by then, they're far too low down to stand any chance of a pregnancy occurring.

Nowadays, fertilization can of course also occur in the *laboratory* – though not in a test-tube, as people tend to imagine. (One newspaper reporter breathlessly asked the mother of the first 'test-tube' baby: 'Did you actually *see* your baby in the test-tube, Mrs Brown?') In practice, the husband's sperm and the mother's ovum are united in a sterile glass dish in the laboratory.

The moment an ovum has been fertilized by a sperm, an impenetrable shielding layer closes round it. So from that instant, no other sperm can enter.

An important point to bear in mind is that once fertilization has occurred, that doesn't automatically mean you're pregnant. A very high percentage of fertilized ova fail to implant in the lining of the womb—so that the woman simply menstruates, and never even realizes that her ovum was fertilized that month.

Menstruation

Nearly all women menstruate—as a rule, between the ages of about 12 and 49. A woman menstruates on average 13 times a year, so she has to put up with something like 480 periods during her lifetime. That wasn't always the case. Until the present century, many women had so many children (and therefore spent so much time either pregnant or breast-feeding) that they got through life with only a couple of dozen periods!

A woman's first few periods are often painless. But once she has menstruated a few times, the odds are that she will get at least some pain. In the past, male 'experts' have tended to dismiss the idea of menstrual pain, and to suggest that it's all in the mind. This is nonsense, of course. It's now thought that at least five million women in Britain, and at least 25 million in America, suffer from some degree of period pain (or 'dysmenorrhoea', to give it its posh name).

It's also important to realize that at least a fifth of that number suffer from menstruation which is *too heavy* or *too prolonged*. This is why so many women (in contrast to men) become anaemic: they lose too much iron in heavy or prolonged periods, so that the blood becomes weak.

Happily; modern treatment *can* help a woman combat painful, heavy or prolonged periods. In particular, I have to say that the fact that there are countless millions of women on the Pill has made a great difference to the world-wide problem of period pain and appallingly heavy periods. Despite its possible side-effects, the Pill is remarkably good at:

abolishing period pain

lightening the menstrual flow

shortening the duration of menstruation.

But in view of the fact that menstruation causes women so many problems (I certainly can't blame them for calling it 'the curse'!), you may ask why on earth a woman has to be bothered with it all. The cause is fairly straightforward. Each month, the womb builds up a rich lining, ready to receive a fertilized egg. This lining is filled with blood vessels. However, if *no* fertilized egg embeds itself in that rich lining (i.e. if the woman doesn't get pregnant that month), then her body's hormone balance 'tips' in such a way that the lining breaks up.

The break-up of the blood-rich lining naturally causes bleeding, and that's the period. The reason it looks a bit different from 'ordinary' blood is that it's mixed with debris and secretions from the womb lining.

How the vagina works

The vagina is really incredibly well-designed for its function—which is mainly to give both of you a great deal of pleasure.

When you think about it, it's quite surprising that, most of the time, it's a *closed* tube—so that a woman remains perfectly 'watertight' when she takes a bath or goes for a swim. But as soon as she gets sexually excited … well, that's a different matter. What happens—according to the work of Masters and Johnson and their extraordinary vaginal camera—is this: within 10 to 30 seconds of a woman starting to think about sex, her vagina starts to produce the lubricating 'love juices' which are so essential for the preparation for sexual intercourse.

Then, as you can see from Chapter 2 Figure H, the next thing that happens is that the woman's vagina suddenly starts widening and lengthening quite dramatically. This is partly because the muscles round the opening of her vagina start to relax, and partly because her womb starts moving upwards, in anticipation of the possibility that something may be about to enter the vagina.

As the woman becomes still more sexually excited, the result is that the outermost part of her vagina swells up to form a snug collar around her partner, thus increasing his pleasure.

As she reaches orgasm, something almost

Fig D

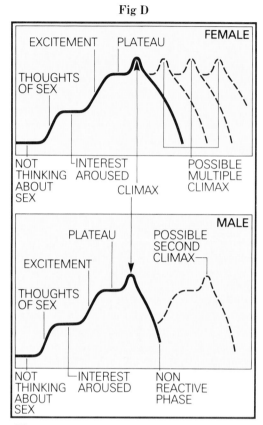

The stages at which men and women reach their climaxes.

seems to explode in the outer part of her vagina. What happens is that the congested outer third of the vagina (the part which has swelled up) is shaken by a series of contractions—which are of course associated with feelings of great pleasure.

These contractions occur just a little faster than once a second. Sometimes there may be only about three or four of them, and sometimes ten or even fifteen—with the middle or later contractions being associated with the highest point of ecstasy for the woman.

By the way, virtually the same changes

seem to take place in the vagina if the woman becomes sexually excited and has her orgasm *without* intercourse.

Orgasm

At the medical journal where I work, we still get a steady flow of letters from a small number of doctors who firmly believe that women don't reach orgasm.

As most readers will be aware from personal experience, this is manifestly not true! Female orgasm is a widespread and intensely pleasurable experience, judging by the descriptions which women give of it ('the moment when all the fuses blow' and so on).

Studies by Virginia Johnson and Dr William Masters seem to confirm without the slightest doubt that most women do reach a climax, in much the same way as men do.

Figure D shows exactly what Johnson and Masters found out about climaxes. The top half shows the stages in which a woman reaches *her* orgasm. The lower part shows the stages in which a man reaches *his*.

You'll notice one immediately obvious difference. Women have a great advantage over men in that—in theory at least—they're capable of second, third, fourth, or fifth climaxes in quick succession. For most men, this is no more than an unattainable dream.

But we mustn't get this business of multiple orgasm out of proportion. Kinsey's statistics indicated that only about one woman in seven has these multiple climaxes. I'd say that a few more women have multiple orgasms nowadays, but most of them are perfectly content with one orgasm at a time.

Now there are also many women who don't reach a climax at all—and who get very upset about it. About 20% of younger married women say that they haven't yet experienced an orgasm—though the percentage is far less among women of more mature years.

I would like at this point to dispose of the old myth that orgasm originates from stimulation of only one part of the body—and that anything else is wrong. Orgasm can in fact result from stimulation of your vagina, your clitoris, your G-spot, your buttocks, your breasts—or indeed your ears, if enough sweet nothings are whispered into them.

Micturition

Although micturition (passing urine) is not part of a woman's *sexual* functions, the urinary apparatus (see Figure E) is so closely linked with the sex organs that I thought it had better be dealt with here.

Micturition is one bodily function about which there's still a lot of embarrassment. Even today, a lot of women (and indeed men) find it difficult to discuss the subject with their doctors.

In an attempt to reduce the general embarrassment about this subject, let me explain just how micturition works. As you can see from Figure E, you have a urinary bladder which is located just in front of the upper part of your vagina. It's filled by two tubes (the ureters) which come down from your kidneys. And when it empties, the urine passes out through the short tube called the urethra.

Normally, you are quite unaware of any sensation of your bladder until about 150 ml (or little over ¼ pint) of urine has accumulated in it. At that stage, the nerves which run upwards from your bladder to your spinal cord and brain start sending a few mild signals that the bladder will shortly need emptying.

If more and more urine accumulates in your bladder, you begin to feel discomfort. When the quantity reaches 600 ml (a little over a

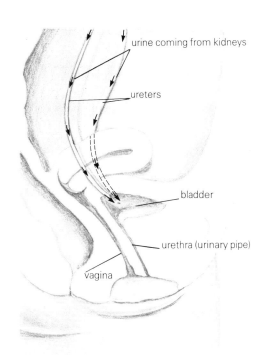

urine coming from kidneys

ureters

bladder

urethra (urinary pipe)

vagina

A woman's urinary apparatus.

pint) the signals coming upwards become very urgent! If you tried to hold out much longer, you simply wouldn't be able to.

Curiously enough, in pregnancy a woman *can* hold out much longer. The pregnant woman seems to have a sort of special dispensation so that her bladder can hold at least twice as much.

When you finally decide that it's time to empty your bladder, nerve signals come down from your brain and make your bladder contract. They also relax the sphincters (the muscles which close off the opening of the bladder).

Masturbation

As we work our way down through the female sex organs, the other 'function' which I feel we should deal with here is masturbation—mainly because so many women get worried about it. A surprising number still think that there's something wrong or shameful about it—and a few still believe that it has harmful effects, like damaging your eyesight!

Even today, I regularly get letters in my postbag which say: 'I'm worried because I have to undergo a gynaecological examination shortly. Do you think the doctor will be able to tell that I have masturbated?' To which the answer is:

- no, he or she won't be able to tell

- he or she couldn't care less anyway!

But I think most people are now aware that masturbation is completely harmless. It's also well known that survey after survey has shown that the majority of women have masturbated at some time.

Indeed, this widespread knowledge has itself led to a new source of confusion. There are now quite a few women who think they're 'abnormal' because they don't masturbate! Nothing could be further from the truth. Though the sex surveys do show that the majority of adult females have masturbated at some time or other, the fact is that a very substantial number *haven't*. And even among those women who *have* gone in for it, there are many for whom it's just a very intermittent sort of pleasure—often amounting to little more than a comforting stroke through the nightdress on a cold winter's evening.

So medically speaking, the point about masturbation is that it's entirely up to you.

Whether you do it or not, you're definitely not 'abnormal'. It's true that many sex therapists do now believe that masturbation is a help to a lot of women: as a reliever of tension; as an aid when there's difficulty in reaching orgasm; and even in relieving period pain. But no one is obliged to do it!

However, just a few words of warning:

women (like men) sometimes do rather silly things when masturbating. For instance, a doctor friend of mine treated a young woman who'd done appreciable harm to her vagina by putting an electric toothbrush inside it. Similarly, I've recently had several letters from doctors about patients who have caused injuries to their clitorises by over-violent

Fig F

Using a massager alongside your clitoris.

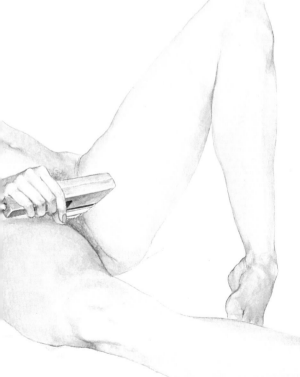

manipulation with various objects. And there are also occasional cases of women who very unwisely try to masturbate by pushing things like hairgrips in and out of the urinary pipe. This is madness—there's a high risk that the object will vanish up into the bladder!

So if you want to masturbate (and for many women—especially single, divorced or widowed women—it's undoubtedly a pleasant and soothing experience) it's best to stick to gentle rubbing alongside the clitoris, using either a finger or a vibrator, as you prefer (see Figure F). Never feel guilty about it—and remember that its one great advantage is that it can't make you pregnant!

Men: physiologically the simpler sex

And now on to the men. Physiologically speaking, we are by far the simpler sex so there's not so much to say about the workings of the male body.

Here we go then, on our brief survey of male physiology.

How the testicles work

The testicles do two things. First of all, they produce the male hormones, the chemical messengers which travel round the bloodstream and give a man his male characteristics.

Secondly, they produce the sperm— millions and millions of them. In the moment when a man 'comes', anything between 300 million and 500 million are released, all in search of an ovum to fertilize. But what actually happens to the testicles as a man gets sexually excited? Well, they're drawn upwards so that they press hard against his body. The work of Johnson and Masters indicates that if his testes do *not* do this, then he probably won't reach orgasm.

A practical point here is that if the woman caresses the man's testicles with her hand during intercourse, this will help him to reach a climax. A good method of stimulation is called 'Florentine intercourse' and it's shown in Figure G.

Fig G

Florentine intercourse: the woman uses her hand to stimulate the man's testicles and penis.

How the plumbing works

You can see what I mean by the 'plumbing' from Figure H. As you'll observe, it's quite a complicated system of tubes which carry the sperm up from the testicles to the tip of the man's penis.

Regrettably, not a lot is known yet about the way this plumbing works. It's thought that the tubes probably contract in waves in order to drive the sperm upwards, but this isn't certain.

What *is* certain is that a very large number of sperm lurk around in the upper reaches of these tubes—possibly for weeks at a time. This point is important: for if a man has a vasectomy, the presence of so many sperm in the upper parts of all this piping means that he will *not* be 'safe' for some weeks at the very least—see the section on vasectomy in Chapter 7.

You'll notice that along the upper reaches of the tubing, there are various structures, such as the seminal vesicles, Cowper's gland and the prostate gland. Oddly enough, we know remarkably little about these glands and what they're there for, but it's thought that they produce fluids which nourish the sperm and provide a suitable medium for them to swim in.

Certainly, the prostate gland does release a good deal of fluid just as the man's orgasm starts. The prostate gland can be felt to contract rhythmically as the climax proceeds, and this is certainly part of the pleasure of a man's orgasm.

The strange phenomenon of erection

It's important for women to realize that men are absolutely obsessed by the phenomenon of erection. Which isn't surprising really—because it's very frustrating and embarrassing if it doesn't happen.

In fact, when I consider how complicated the human body is, I am absolutely astonished

Fig H

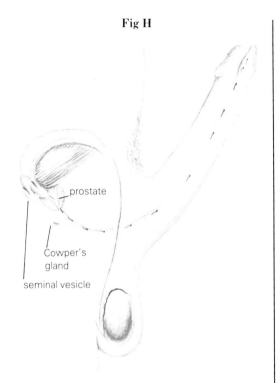

prostate

Cowper's gland

seminal vesicle

The male 'plumbing': the prostate, seminal vesicles and Cowper's gland all contribute to this sex fluid.

that the majority of men do usually manage to achieve and maintain an erection. The physiology of erection is very complicated—and still very poorly understood.

The actual 'stiffening' of the penis is caused by a dramatic increase in blood flow into the three hollow chambers of the organ (which I described in Chapter 2). So in effect, it becomes erect by becoming engorged with blood. (The same thing happens—albeit on a much smaller scale—with other 'erectile' tissues of the body, like those of the clitoris, the female and male nipples, the labia, and possibly the tongue.)

But what on earth makes this engorge-ment of the penis take place? It seems to be a complicated interaction between three different sub-divisions of the human nervous system—one of which has only recently been discovered by Professor Julia Polak at London's Hammersmith Hospital. Her researches have led in 1990 to the development of a new drug which is going to help a lot of impotent men.

Anyway, whatever the mechanism, the fact is that two different factors will give a man an erection:

thinking about sex

direct rubbing or stroking of his penis.

It's absolutely vital for any woman to realize that—contrary to what you might think from popular fiction—quite a few men *don't* immediately get an erection as soon as their beloved takes her clothes off.

Particularly in the older age groups, they may need quite a bit of the above-mentioned rubbing or stroking before they can get a good enough erection for intercourse. Wider knowledge of this fact among women would mean that there would be far fewer complaints of impotence in my postbag!

Two final points: firstly, it doesn't matter greatly what *angle* the erection reaches, as so many men think. Sex researchers have found that a large percentage of the male population come up to the angle shown in Figure I. But another large proportion come up to the angle shown in Figure J. Both of these (and any angle in between) are perfectly normal.

Finally, there is the question of morning erections and why they occur: some men get a bit worried about these too. They're perfectly natural and are believed to happen because of

Fig I

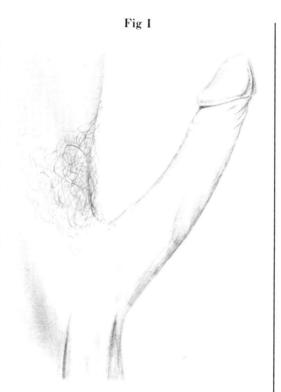

Male erection. An erection at this angle is just as normal as ...

Fig J

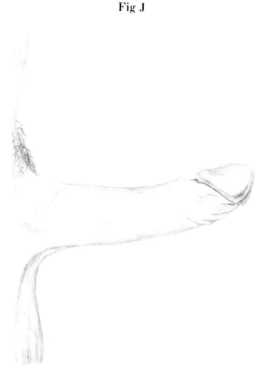

... an erection at this angle.

stimulation of the penis by the bedclothes, coupled with the fact that during sleep—and especially during dreaming—the 'respectable' centres of the brain aren't doing anything to prevent the penis reacting in the way that is natural to it.

Men also worry if their morning erections get a bit less frequent as they get older, but this too is normal, as you can see from the graph in Figure K. Indeed, if a man is getting any morning erection *at all*, it is a good sign that his sexual nervous system and his male hormones are working properly.

Many men who *think* they have become totally impotent can be reassured by their doctors as long as they are getting morning erections. In these cases, the doctor will often advise the wife to 'use' the morning erection to restore her partner's confidence in his own virility.

The man's climax

Now while women can reach a climax in all sorts of ways a man's climax is nearly always due to direct stimulation of his penis.

That stimulation can of course be by the hand, by the lips, by the tongue, or by almost anything else—but perhaps best of all, by the vagina of the woman he loves. I say 'perhaps'

The urethra (urinary pipe)—leads from the prostate to the tip of the penis.

only because the amazing and charming US sex researcher Ms Shere Hite told me that her massive US surveys have shown that a majority of men actually report a more intense climax with the hand.

But of course, both psychologically and romantically, it is usually far more satisfying to enjoy that climax inside your loved one's warm, pulsating body. In practice, statistics show that the great majority of climaxes reached by married males (or by those in a steady relationship) are during intercourse itself.

But what actually happens at that climax? Well, it begins with the moment—called by US sexologists 'the moment of ejaculatory

Average number of morning erections a week. Note that there's a slight decline as a man gets older.

Fig L

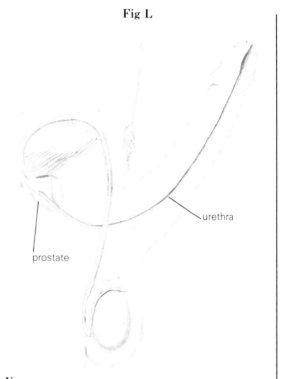

urethra

prostate

Fig K

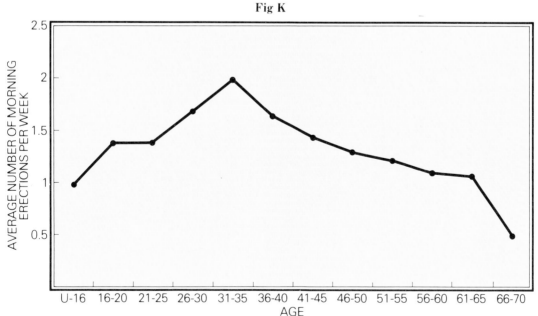

AVERAGE NUMBER OF MORNING ERECTIONS PER WEEK

AGE

U-16 16-20 21-25 26-30 31-35 36-40 41-45 46-50 51-55 56-60 61-65 66-70

Fig M

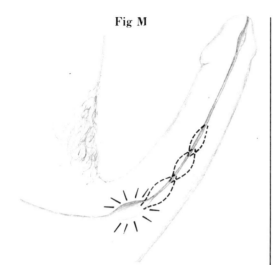

The sudden flooding of fluid into the base of the penis—producing 'waves' of sexual pleasure.

inevitability'—when the man realizes *it's got to happen now and nothing will stop it.* (This follows a short 'warning phase'—during which a man can stop it if he really tries.)

The feeling of 'ejaculatory inevitablity' actually seems to occur when the seminal fluid floods into the lower part of the urethra. As you can see from Figure L, that is the pipe which leads upwards from the region of the prostate gland to the tip of the penis.

Now as you can see from Figure M, it seems to be the sudden flooding of fluid into this lower part of the urinary pipe which produces such intense waves of sexual pleasure. These waves seem to be caused by violent contractions of the tube (one every 0.8 seconds)—which drives the sperm-filled fluid out in powerful squirts.

Fitting it all together

How does it all work together in an ideal scenario? Let's imagine a woman who wants to have a baby very much indeed. During the early afternoon of the day in question, one of her ovaries releases a ripe egg—which starts to find its way into her Fallopian tube . . . That night, she has a romantic dinner *à deux* with the man she loves. Under the influence of the candlelight, the food and the wine, the hormones in both their bodies start flowing. In response, her vagina is already becoming moist, while he feels that pleasurable sensation in his genitals that Ovid once called *notus calor* – 'familiar heat'.

After dinner, they take each other to bed. Soft murmurings and gentle caresses make her vulva even more moist and welcoming. Within a few minutes, he is able to bring her to her first climax of the evening through skilled stroking of her clitoris.

More love-play (*mutual* love-play, of course) heightens the excitement and enjoyment for both of them. By gentle 'tonguing' of her vagina, he brings her to two or three more climaxes.

Soon, with her love juices, flowing freely, she is ready to be penetrated. She takes his penis firmly between her fingers, and guides it into her. For 10 or maybe 15 minutes, they make passionate love. Finally, she lets him know that she is ready. In a splendid crescendo, they reach the height of their passion together: she achieves the most deeply-satisfying climax of the evening, just at the moment that he too reaches his orgasm.

Five hundred million sperm surge out of him as his sex fluid splashes across her cervix. Moments later, they are swimming lustily toward the aperture in that cervix, making for the womb. With luck, a few hours later the very strongest and the very best of them will have traversed that womb, entered the Fallopian tube—and found that ripe egg to fertilize. Some 266 days later, a baby will be born.

4

Sex and Your Emotions

The need for a cuddle—The need for romance—
Romance, emotion and sexuality in WOMEN—Romantic tips for men—
Romance, emotion and sexuality in MEN—Romantic tips for women—
A lifetime of romance

The need for a cuddle

Just as I was completing this book, the world-famous American 'agony aunt' Ms Ann Landers published the results of a survey into the desires of tens of thousands of US women. What, asked Ms Landers rhetorically, did all these women want most from their men?

The answer wasn't multiple orgasms or better orgasms or deeper penetration or any of the things that many men think women want. Definitely not: what they wanted, said Ms Landers firmly, is more *cuddles and romance*. Absolutely right, Ann Landers: my own modest problem page postbag has revealed just the same.

Let's look first at cuddling. Again and

again, certain phrases recur in my readers' letters:

- 'he doesn't cuddle me any more'
- 'we never seem to cuddle together in bed as we used to'
- 'I wish we could cuddle up in front of a warm fire, the way we did long ago'.

So it's as well to remember that good, old-fashioned cuddling is a very important part of almost any relationship. And not just for women: it's important for men too.

Personally, I'm a firm believer in 'cuddle therapy'. I'd recommend that any couple whose relationship is running into trouble should give first priority to finding more time to giving each other a nice, warm cuddle. It'll pay far richer dividends than worrying (as far too many people do) about whether their sexual technique is up to Olympic championship standard.

The need for romance

Similarly with romance: men in particular are all too likely these days to forget the importance of romance in a relationship. Regrettably, books, films and TV often picture sex as an emotionless business, in which people meet, leap into bed together, have intercourse, smoke a cigarette—and move on!

But real life can't be conducted at that level. We're not machines but deeply complex, emotional creatures who need to be cherished and loved. The man or woman who forgets that fact does so at his or her peril.

Romance, emotion and sexuality in women.

As Lord Byron remarked:
'Man's love is of man's life a thing apart,
'Tis woman's whole existence.'

As he implied, men would do well to remember that for a woman, love is usually a far more all-embracing, emotional and even spiritual business than it is for a man. Unfortunately, a man may regard sexual intercourse as far and away the most important aspect of a love relationship with a woman. But it's vital for him to realize that most women see life and love quite differently. A woman is *most* unlikely to view her relationship with a man in crude terms of a penis entering her vagina.

Instead, her view of the love relationship is likely to be bound up with such things as:

- the warm glow she feels when he's around
- the sense of being valued and wanted as a person by him
- the feeling of rightness and completeness that comes from being one half of a loving couple.

If a man doesn't appreciate that his partner has this strongly romantic perception of the love relationship, then he may well be heading for trouble. Certainly, a vast number of marriages founder these days simply because the man fails to satisfy the woman's need for romance—which is a very different thing from mere sex!

Romantic tips for men

What amazes me after so many years in the advice business is that again and again men go wrong because they fail to follow a few very simple 'dos and don'ts'.

Do:

- take the trouble to smarten yourself up before you meet her
- hold her hand
- catch her eye and smile at her when you're in a crowd.
- compliment her on her appearance
- tell her she smells nice
- buy her flowers (they're very inexpensive when you consider what rich dividends they pay!)
- take her for candlelit suppers (in all surveys of 'what women consider romantic', dinner by candlelight scores very high).

58

Don't:

- Ignore her all evening when you're out at a party together

- fall in the door after work in the evening and forget to kiss her

- flop down in front of the television and forget to talk to her all evening

- wander around the bedroom in smelly socks

- get into bed unshaven or unwashed

- assume that once in bed, you can simply leap on her without any preliminaries

- fall asleep the moment you've reached your climax (you could at least say 'Goodnight'!).

> *In the last years of the twentieth century there's an increasing trend towards the idea of the new man*

Romance, emotion and sexuality in men

The outstanding US expert on sex, Dr Bernie Zilbergeld, neatly encapsulated an all-too-common male view of male sexuality and what man is supposed to contribute to the sex relationship in his famous phrase which describes a man's fantasy-view of his penis: 'two foot long, and hard as steel, and it goes all night...'

Of course, this phallic-orientated, male chauvinistic attitude is quite ridiculous! But most men will find echoes of it in the back of their own minds. And it's as well for women to bear in mind that this attitude exists—because it explains many of the stranger aspects of male sexual behaviour!

In particular, it explains why men are so often worried about their phalluses. Most males have worries such as:

- is it big enough?

- will I be able to get it erect?

- how long will I be able to keep it up?

- will I be able to get it up *again?*

So if you're a woman, keep in mind the fact that a man's attitude to sex and love is likely to be very genitally orientated.

And if you're a man, just consider whether it wouldn't be better to move away from these old macho ideas. Thank heavens, as we move into the last years of the twentieth century, there's an increasing trend towards the idea of what's been called 'the new man'—the man who's more concerned with being gentle and caring and sharing with his partner than with being obsessed with his own phallus.

But whether he's a 'new man' or the most ghastly of old-style 'macho men', the fact is that he, too, *probably needs a spot of romance in his love-life.* So I'll conclude this chapter with a few hints to help women make their partners feel romantic—and loved.

Romantic tips for women

Do:

- tell him he's handsome—even if he isn't

take the trouble to see to your make-up and hair before you meet him (aggrieved feminists please note: I have given similar advice to *men* earlier in this chapter)

consider turning off the TV and giving him a cuddle instead.

Don't:

(as the song says) 'send him off with your hair all in curlers'

welcome him home with curlers in

wear terrible 'passion-killing' underwear in bed

heave a sigh of resignation as soon as you realize he has love-making in mind

say awful, unromantic things after love-making, like 'Would you please pass me a tissue to clear up this mess?'

A lifetime of romance

Alas, today's fast-increasing trend is for marriages to go on the rocks. It seems to me that the best chance of reversing this alarming drift towards divorce is simply to *bring back romance.*

As I was compiling this book, a nurse who works at a small hospital for the elderly told me about an old lady whom she had been nursing. This woman was 87 and had been married for about 60 years—yet before every visiting time she took enormous care to put on an elegant lace gown, make herself up beautifully, and dab a spot of perfume behind her ears.

Why? 'Well,' she told the nurse, 'my husband is a *very* romantic man, you know...'

It gives you fresh hope, doesn't it?

5

Sex and Good Health

Taking care of your body—Intimate hygiene—Diet—Exercise—
WOMEN: care of your breasts, and protecting yourself against cancer—
Protecting yourself against cervical cancer—Protecting yourself against
other female cancers—Vaginal and pelvic infections—Herpes—
Cystitis—Pelvic floor problems—Hysterectomy—Menopausal problems—
Pregnancy and sex—MEN: hygiene—Sexual infections—AIDS—
Circumcision—The prostate and prostate cancer—
Finally, don't take risks with your health!

Taking care of your body

Whether you're female or male, for heaven's sake take care of your body: it's the only one you've got! Doctors are all too well aware that in all western countries, a very high proportion of all illness is due to the foolish personal habits that many of us indulge in. The main ones are:

- poor diet
- smoking
- drinking
- lack of exercise
- getting overweight
- failing to relax enough.

These crazy patterns of behaviour cause cancer, heart disease and other major killers. *They also tend to screw up your sex life.*

For example, it's been known for centuries that alcohol is bad for men's sexual 'performance'. Research now indicates that this may be true of women too.

Similarly, it has been known for about 15 years that *obesity* has a bad effect on sexual function, and may actually make a man impotent. And research published just as I was finishing this book indicates that *smoking* must now be recognized as a likely factor in many cases of impotence.

Finally, there is the important point that if you let yourself get out of shape and take insufficient care of your body and your looks, *you'll rapidly lose your sexual attraction*. It sounds laughably obvious, yet countless men and women forget the truth of that statement—and are astonished when their partners are attracted to somebody else.

Intimate hygiene

First things first. How do you keep the intimate, sexual places of your body in the best possible trim?

Whether you are a man or a woman, a daily wash of the genital organs in hand-hot water with mild soap is a must. You don't actually need to have a bath every day of your life, though of course many people find it invigorating and refreshing.

Too *many* baths can in fact be bad for the sex organs. Many women, and some men, find that they keep getting irritating attacks of thrush (see later in this chapter) if they have too many hot baths. If *you* have any tendency to thrush or to those trying fungal infections of the skin between the thighs, you would almost certainly do better to have cool showers than hot tubs.

Whether you are female or male, *avoid* applying chemical agents to your genital area.

Be especially wary if you have sensitive skin or are prone to allergic reactions. Even bubble baths can sometimes be harmful to those delicate tissues!

> *If you let yourself get out of shape and take insufficient care of your body and your looks, you will rapidly lose your sexual attraction*

Diet

Yes—diet and your sex life are linked! This is partly for the reasons I've mentioned above: if you let your body become obese and out of shape, you'll probably damage your sex life.

But also, good nutrition does seem to have a beneficial effect on most human activities—and it seems highly probable that it's good for sexual activity too. At present, the best medical opinion is that if you want a good all-round diet, you should eat plenty of the following:

- green vegetables (including peas, beans, lettuce, cabbage, cauliflower and spinach)

- root vegetables (carrots, turnips, swede and potatoes—yes, potatoes!)

- fish

- wholemeal bread
- fruit

Despite what their manufacturers say, you should try and steer clear of too much:

- salt
- butter
- cheese
- fried food
- fatty meats
- cream
- *anything* that contains saturated (mainly animal) fats—including pastry and cookies
- alcohol—especially spirits.

It's a bit hard to say whether *sugar* should be added to this list. Certainly, sugar is nowhere near as fattening as most people imagine—but it does provide 'empty' calories (which seem to be of no real nutritional value).

Also—despite the understandable efforts of the sugar industry to convince us other-wise—it does rot your teeth! (And you may need your teeth for making love—see Chapter 8.)

Of course, nearly all of us enjoy a good meal of 'forbidden' foods now and again. And there's no doubt that a thoroughly wicked meal—with all the things you're not really supposed to eat—can be the prelude to a highly successful evening in bed.

Perhaps I should add that if you believe in *aphrodisiac* foods, then there's no harm at all in adding them to your diet. I have to say, however, that there's no medical evidence that champagne, oysters, *coquilles St. Jac-ques* or octopus actually work.

But the good thing about allegedly aphrodisiac foods is that if a person *believes* in them, then they'll do her or him some good. Also, if your dinner partner orders oysters and champagne, you do at least have some idea of what she or he has in mind!

Exercise

There's no doubt that sensible exercise benefits your general health. For that reason, a sensible amount of exercise is likely to benefit your sex life too—simply by toning up your body and keeping it fit.

The widespread belief that exercise—and, in particular, jogging—will reduce your libido is nonsense! I keep encountering athletes who assure me that 'medical research' has proved that running makes you less sexy.

Well, the 'medical research' in question was an April Fool's Day joke published several years ago by my own medical journal, *General Practitioner*! On April Fool's Day, we ran a completely bogus story—made up by a Buckinghamshire GP, Dr Bev Daily—about how a completely fictional American univer-sity had shown that exercise makes people lose their interest in sex because it raises the temperature in their running shorts!

This wonderfully daft story was swallowed hook, line and sinker by the London *Daily Mail*, and was duly published and flashed round the world during the first few days of April. All our subsequent efforts to convince people that the story was just a hoax have failed, and it's still quoted by runners round the globe. If they were to look at the original article, they'd find that the give away was a small paragraph near the end in which Dr Daily claimed that scientists were even now working on a device to combat 'exercise-induced loss of libido'—a pocket refrigerator to be worn inside the running shorts!

In all this, however, there is one faint echo of truth. It's this: really *intensive* exercise over a long spell of time (the sort of thing that serious Olympic contenders engage in) does have an effect on women's sex glands—it takes their periods away. Indeed, I am reliably informed that the highly-trained women's athletics squads of most western nations have almost all of them lost their periods (temporarily).

I'm also reliably informed that they have exactly the same healthy instincts towards the opposite sex as anybody else.

Women: care of your breasts, and protecting yourself against cancer

General care of the breasts isn't difficult: a straightforward wash with mild soap and water once a day is sufficient, followed by careful drying with a soft towel.

In late pregnancy and more especially early lactation, breasts and nipples need special care—mainly because cracks are liable to develop in the nipple. In the event of any cracking or soreness, apply a reliable antiseptic cream (your local pharmacist will advise you). If pain or even appreciable soreness develop, always consult your doctor or midwife.

Breast cancer

It's a tragic and, to most people, unpalatable fact that breast cancer attacks roughly 1 out of every 17 women in western countries. (I can't help feeling that if cancer of the penis were as common in men, something would have been done about it by now!)

Many of these cases of breast cancer can be cured if caught early enough (see Chapter 2), and in the near-total absence of adequate screening procedures throughout the world at the moment, the fact is that for most women the best hope of catching the disease early is to detect it themselves.

Possible warning symptoms are:

- a *lump* (this may well not be cancerous, but should *aways* be checked by a doctor)

- much less commonly, unexplained *bleeding* from the nipple

- occasionally, a *raw ulcer-like patch* of skin on the nipple

- sometimes, an unexplained *inturning of the nipple*

- unexplained *puckering of the skin* of the breast.

I should add that although many teenage girls and young women not unreasonably fear that they have breast cancer, it's primarily a disease of the over-30's. Cases occurring before the age of 25 do occur, but are very rare indeed.

I've already explained in Chapter 2 how vitally important the process of monthly self-examination for breast lumps is. (I'm not joking when I say that husbands and lovers can help here too, by looking out for lumps when they handle their loved ones' breasts.)

Look at the illustrations on the right which show you exactly how to make this breast check, which should be a regular self-examination. This procedure is based on the splendid and underfunded work of the Women's National Cancer Control Campaign in Britain. Follow it: it could save your life.

How to check your own breasts. Remember: you're looking for lumps, skin puckering or inturning of the nipple.

Fig A

1 Stand in front of a mirror and inspect your breasts.

2 Lift your hands and inspect again.

3 Stretch your arms above your head and check again.

4 Final visual check: put your hands on your hips, press down hard—and inspect again.

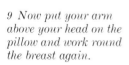

5 Now lie flat on the bed, with your head on a pillow. Use your outstretched middle three fingers to feel your breast for lumps.

6, 7 and 8 Work round the breast, searching for lumps.

10 Still with the arm on the pillow, check the upper, outer part of the breast, and your armpit. Then repeat for the other breast.

9 Now put your arm above your head on the pillow and work round the breast again.

Protecting yourself against cervical cancer

Cancer of the cervix—the neck of the womb—is also common. (If you're not sure where the cervix is, look at the illustrations in Chapter 2.)

In most western countries, it causes about one-fifth or one-sixth as many deaths as breast cancer. But in many poorer countries, the death rate is much higher.

I cannot emphasize too strongly that:

- all women (except virgins) are at risk

- the disease is *preventable*.

We still don't really know why cancer of the cervix occurs. It certainly has a link with sex—and this is the aspect that the newspapers usually stress!

It's true that it only occurs in women who have had sex—and that it seems to be a bit more common in women who have had several lovers.

On the other hand, the newspapers rarely mention that this appalling killer is also more common in:

- smokers

- less well-off women

- women who've had children

- women over 35

- women living in certain geographical areas.

But as I've said, *all* women who've ever had sex (even if it's only with their husbands) are liable to it. So unless you've led a totally celibate life (in which case, you're unlikely to be reading this book), *you owe it to yourself to take precautions against it.*

What precautions? Well first of all there's now considerable evidence that *barrier* methods of contraception (the cap or diaphragm, and the sheath) help protect a woman against cancer of the cervix.

Secondly, almost all doctors now agree that *all* adult women who have ever had sex should make sure they have regular 'Pap' smear tests. The process of having a 'Pap' smear (or 'cyto-test') is shown in Figure B, steps 1 to 3.

As you can see, all that happens is that the doctor uses a wooden spatula to scrape some cells off the cervix (the neck of the womb). The doctor puts these on a glass slide, and sends it to the laboratory for microscopic examination.

Fig B

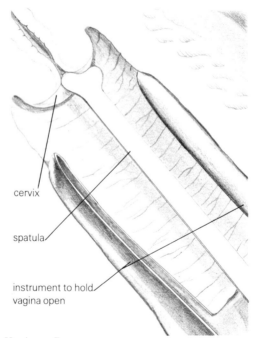

cervix

spatula

instrument to hold vagina open

Having a Pap smear:

1 The doctor inserts an instrument to hold the vagina open so she can see your cervix. She places the end of a spatula on the cervix.

The point of the whole thing is this: *if there are any abnormal cells present, this gives very, very early warning of the disease—long before it causes any symptoms.* And at that stage, it's nearly always curable by laser therapy or a small biopsy ('sampling') operation.

Cancer of the cervix does eventually produce symptoms—namely bleeding after intercourse and bleeding between periods. But by the time it produces these symptoms, it's awfully late in the day. It's far, far better to detect it 10 or 20 years beforehand by the simple and—in most cases—painless technique of a smear test.

Protecting yourself against other 'female' cancers

There are two other common cancers of the female sex organs. These are:

- cancer of the womb lining
- cancer of the ovary.

Unfortunately, both of these are difficult to protect yourself against—though the Pill is thought to offer some protection against both (see Chapter 7).

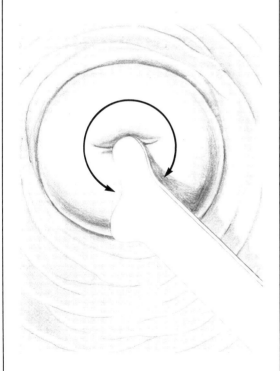

2 She rotates the spatula so as to scrape some cells off the cervix.

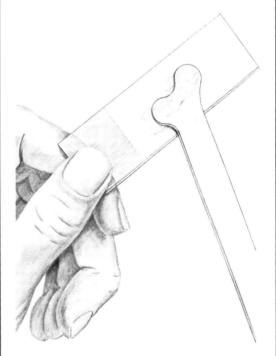

3 She transfers the cells to a glass slide, which will be examined at the lab.

Cancer of the womb lining (the endometrium)

This is most common in women who have passed the menopause—and the giveaway symptom is *bleeding occurring after the menopause*. This must *always* be investigated. Unfortunately, there is *no* widely-available screen test. Contrary to what many people believe, 'Pap' smear tests do *not* detect this type of cancer—they only detect cervical cancer.

The common operation called a 'D & C' (dilation and curettage, or 'scraping' the womb lining) *will* detect this cancer. But obviously, it's impossible for every middle-aged woman to keep on having this operation merely as a screening procedure.

There is now an outpatient or 'office' form of screening—usually called 'Vabra curettage'. But it's expensive, and at present can only be offered to very limited groups of women.

Cancer of the ovary

Unfortunately, this too is very difficult to diagnose early—which is a pity, as it's a common condition. It's most frequent after the age of 35. Symptoms may include *bleeding after the menopause*.

There is an 'early diagnosis' test: namely, ultrasound scan of the ovary. But unfortunately, because of high costs, only a very limited number of clinics can as yet offer this as a routine service to the over-35s. If you're 35-plus and you have a local clinic which offers this screening service, for heaven's sake use it!

Otherwise, the best protection is the routine pelvic examination which is often done at the time of a smear test.

Vaginal and pelvic infections

These are so common that the great majority of young (and not so young) women these days get them at some time or other. These infections do seem to have become much more frequent since the advent of the permissive society.

That's hardly surprising, because it seems likely that all of them can be spread by sex—at least some of the time. Other factors which have made vaginal infections so much more common in the last 25 years are:

- wearing tights (some organisms—specially thrush—*love* the warm conditions under a pair of tights)

- wearing nylon underwear (same effect)

- the fashion for frequent hot baths and jacuzzis (which also promote hot, moist conditions)

- the widespread use of the Pill (which makes you more liable to thrush)

- the widespread use of antibiotics (which also promote thrush).

Fortunately, most vaginal infections aren't serious—though they can be an irritating nuisance and badly mess up your sex life!

However, *deeper* pelvic infections—which attack the tubes—can be very serious, and can even make you infertile. This is in fact a common cause of infertility today (see Chapter 6).

Let's look at the various infections one by one.

Thrush

This is by far the most common vaginal infection in most countries. It's a fungus which causes:

- considerable soreness of the vagina

- itching

- an annoying discharge which is usually creamy white.

In men, thrush usually produces no symptoms, but some men become red and sore. However, the sex partner of a woman with thrush is very possibly *carrying* it. So *both partners* may need treatment, with an anti-fungal cream.

If you think you have thrush, you should go to a doctor and have a vaginal swab taken, to confirm the diagnosis. The doctor will usually give you both anti-fungus cream for your exterior surfaces, and anti-fungus pessaries (vaginal tablets) to clear things up inside.

If you've read what I said above about hygiene, you'll appreciate that you should also avoid: tights, nylon pants, hot baths, *men*—at least until the condition is cured!

In recurrent cases, Pill-users may have to consider switching to another contraceptive. If you're really desperate, try the remedy favoured by some feminist groups in the USA: apply yoghurt to the affected part!

Note: if you develop thrush, this does *not* mean that your partner—or indeed you— have been unfaithful.

Trichomonas vaginalis (TV)

This little bug is also very common. It's often mistaken for thrush, but doesn't respond to anti-thrush treatment.

Although there's some dispute about its method of transmission, it does seem to be passed on by sexual intercourse in nearly all cases. Catching it from the splash of a lavatory bowl, however, does seem to be a distinct possibility.

Male partners of women with TV don't often get symptoms—though they *might* experience some pain in passing water. But they are very likely to be carriers—so they must be treated at the same time as the woman. Failure to treat the partner is the most common reason for the failure in treatment of TV.

Symptoms of trichomonas are intense vaginal soreness, redness of the vagina and vulva, and a discharge which is usually bubbly and yellow-green in colour. Treatment—usually with an oral drug called metronidazole—is, as a rule, highly effective.

Chlamydia

This is a 'new' infection, in the sense that it wasn't discovered all that long ago, and many people have never heard of it.

Yet millions of women world-wide have it—and in many cases it has affected their tubes and made them infertile. Regrettably, inexpensive tests for chlamydia aren't yet widely available (it doesn't show up on ordinary swabs). The result is that the condition often goes undiagnosed.

Chlamydia should be suspected if a woman has persistent vaginal/pelvic pain, with or without a fever and a discharge. Salpingitis (see below) may be present. It's vitally important to get treatment with the right antibiotic—penicillin is useless, but erythromycin or tetracycline usually work.

Salpingitis

This means an inflammation of the tubes and is quite common in young women, especially if they've slept around. But even the most virtuous of women can get it, particularly if they use an IUD (see Chapter 7), because this increases the risk of tube infection.

Some cases are due to chlamydia (see above), some to gonorrhoea, and some to other germs. Symptoms of salpingitis are pain low down on one side of your abdomen, a similar pain during intercourse, fever, and generally feeling awful.

A swab should be taken, and antibiotic treatment started at once. Unfortunately, many health professionals don't yet realize that a lot of these cases are due to chlamydia (see above). If your tubes are to be protected, it's important to get onto the right antibiotics as fast as possible. So if you ever suspect that you may have salpingitis, get a doctor to give you an internal check-up *at once*.

Gardnerella

This too is a relatively newly-discovered infection, but one which is increasingly commonly diagnosed, especially in the USA. The chief symptom is a greyish vaginal discharge. Response to the drug metronidazole is good.

Gonorrhoea

This is a form of venereal disease, and unfortunately is quite common in all western countries.

The tragic thing about gonorrhoea is that *in most women it produces no symptoms*. In some instances, there may be an episode of pain, fever or vaginal discharge. But in most cases, what happens is that the woman makes love with somebody (perhaps someone she has a holiday romance with), becomes infected, but *doesn't realize*.

For months or even years thereafter, the gonorrhoea germ may be damaging her health—and specifically the health of her pelvic organs. It may make her sterile, or give her salpingitis (see above).

> *If you feel you've taken a risk, consider the possibility of getting a full confidential check-up*

Fortunately, many women *do* have their cases diagnosed—because the infection is detected in their partner and he tells them that they need treatment. But the sad fact is that in almost every country in the world, there's a very large number of women who are wandering around, quite unaware that they have gonorrhoea.

So, if you ever feel that you have 'taken a risk' (or if you suspect that your husband or boyfriend has taken a risk by being unfaithful to you), consider the possibility of getting a full confidential check-up—preferably at a specialist genito-urinary clinic of the type available in Britain and some other countries.

Once gonorrhoea has been successfully diagnosed, it can be treated—usually very successfully, if it's caught early enough. Treatment is usually with penicillin.

Unfortunately, since the Vietnam war, strains of penicillin-resistant gonorrhoea have spread from the Far East to the US and most parts of the world. At the present time, they can usually be defeated by other drugs, such as spectinomycin.

Finally, here are a few tips for avoiding gonorrhoea and other types of VD:

- avoid casual sex and one-night stands

- consider using a barrier method of contraception (see Chapter 7)

- be wary of dates with men who are air travellers—international travellers have been shown to be particularly liable to acquire and spread VD (often the resistant kind)

- if in doubt after a sexual contact, always have an internal check-up.

Syphilis

This is the most terrible of the venereal diseases. In Britain and certain other countries, it's now very rare except in highly promiscuous male gays—so the chance of a woman getting it is very remote. It is, however, more common in America (hence those pre-marriage blood tests for syphilis) and in a few more exotic parts of the world.

The chief symptom is a *painless ulcer* (raw patch) anywhere on the sex organs. This soon clears up and goes away—but the hideous disease persists internally. Blood tests (and tests on the ulcer, if it's still present) make the diagnosis clear. Treatment with adequate doses of penicillin is usually curative if given reasonably early.

Herpes

Herpes is still nowhere near as common as people may imagine from reading the newspapers. But the fear of it is certainly playing a part in reducing the amount of casual and promiscuous sex which has been going on since the permissive society arrived!

Herpes is *not* as awful a condition as most people think. It's caused by a virus, and is very like the recurrent cold sores which you see on many people's lips. In this case, however, the recurrent cold sore is on the vulva, in the vagina, or on the cervix (or, in the man's case, on the penis). In women, the blisters may sometimes cause a total inability to pass urine.

Unfortunately, as with cold sores on the lip, herpes isn't as yet curable—though drugs like immunovir and acyclovir do help. However, contrary to what so many people believe, the condition does often seem to burn itself out—so that the recurrences of painful blisters may eventually stop.

If you suspect you might have herpes, always seek specialist advice and treatment. You should *not* have sex until the doctor in charge of your case gives you the go-ahead.

Cystitis

Cystitis is one of the most common of all illnesses, and most doctors who are in general practice see several cases a week. It's often linked with sex—hence the name 'honeymoon cystitis'. Women are more likely to develop it after they've first started making love—or re-started after a spell without sex.

The word 'cystitis' actually means 'inflammation of the bladder', but in fact, a diagnosis of cystitis really implies that there's a group of symptoms which could be due to inflammation of either the bladder or the urethra (the tube leading out of the bladder—see Figure E in Chapter 3).

The symptoms of cystitis are: pain on passing urine; having to pass urine very frequently; and sometimes, blood in the urine.

The orthodox medical view of this misery-making and very painful infection is that it's usually due to *infection* of the urine with germs which have crossed the short distance between the bowel opening (rectal opening) and the urinary opening. This infection can normally be treated successfully with antibiotics.

However, the world-famous 'Kilmartin self-help régime' says that you should also:

- avoid bubble baths and all other possible chemical irritants

- wash your genital area daily with a clean cloth which you boil after use—and keep for no other purpose

- in the event of an attack of cystitis, take a painkiller

- then drink plenty of water with a level teaspoon of bicarbonate of soda

- finally, apply one hot-water bottle to your lower abdomen, and place another one between your thighs.

Remember too that as cystitis is so very often started off by love-play or love-making (and especially by *inept* efforts at love-play), it's a good idea to insist that your partner is gentle, careful and clean when he handles this delicate area of your body. You'd do well to get him to study Chapter 8 on love-play.

Pelvic floor problems

Countless women have weakened pelvic floor muscles as a result of child-bearing. This can lead to:

- involuntary loss of urine (incontinence) when you laugh, cough or sneeze

- unsatisfactory love-making

- prolapse (descent) of the womb.

In severe cases, a repair operation—in which the gynaecologist tightens up the lax tissues—is necessary. But as I said in Chapter 3 while discussing the function of the pelvic floor muscles, they *can* be toned up and made much firmer by determinedly following a course of pelvic floor exercises over a period of at least six months.

Hysterectomy

An incredible one in five of all women have this operation at some stage in their lives, so it's well worth your while knowing exactly what it involves. Hysterectomy just means removal of the womb or uterus (see Figure I in Chapter 1), and nothing else.

Because few people understand anatomy, they tend to get confused about hysterectomy in two ways. Firstly, they often think that the operation involves taking away all or part of the vagina and will therefore make it impossible for the woman to have intercourse ever again. This is nonsense.

If you look at the illustration again, you'll see that no part of the vagina is removed. When the womb has been taken out, this leaves a little gap at the very top of the vagina, and that gap is sewn up by the surgeon.

Some gynaecologists say that this actually makes the vagina a bit longer than it was before. Anyway, it certainly isn't any smaller, so it'll be just as effective a love-making organ as ever it was. Once the stitches at the very top of the vagina have healed, you'll be able to resume love-making just as before.

Some women find that their climaxes feel a little different because the womb has gone. Many women enjoy sex more than they did before for two reasons: whatever womb condition they were suffering from has been cured, and now that the womb has been removed, the fear of unwanted pregnancy is gone forever.

A second source of confusion is the muddle in people's minds over the womb and the ovaries. Many women (and men) think that if you have a hysterectomy this will stop your output of female hormones: they believe that you will therefore get hot flushes, put on weight, become neurotic and goodness only knows what else besides. Once again, this is utter nonsense. Look again at the diagram: it is the ovaries, not the womb, which produce female hormones. As long as the ovaries aren't removed at the same time, your hysterectomy won't produce any of the distressing symptoms of hormone deficiency.

Regrettably, it is sometimes necessary to remove the ovaries at the same time as a hysterectomy is done, though this only happens in a minority of cases. The ovaries may have to be taken out because they contain cysts or because they're diseased.

If the surgeon removes them while you're still young (indeed, at any stage before the change of life), then I'm afraid that there's every chance that the resulting sharp drop in hormones will give you quite severe menopausal symptoms in the days after the operation—mainly in the form of hot flushes

and sweating attacks. There may also be vaginal dryness later on.

Fortunately, however, these distressing symptoms can be prevented with carefully-prescribed doses of female hormones over the next few months or even years. But make sure you get the treatment: a disquieting number of younger women complain that they were never offered it. (See also below.)

Menopausal problems

Menopausal problems affect hundreds of thousands of women—and can mess up their sex lives. However, the outlook for your love-life is generally good—mainly because this is in some ways the very sexiest time of your life. (It's widely reckoned that women reach the peak of their sexual performance when they're over 40.)

Common menopausal problems are:

- hot flushes (referred to in the USA as 'hot flashes')

- sweating attacks

- dryness of the vagina.

All of these are in some way due to a relatively sudden drop in hormone levels. *And all of them can be successfully treated by hormone replacement therapy (HRT) using female hormones.*

The hormones can be given by mouth or by implant under the skin. However, where the main problem is a dry, sore vagina which is making intercourse difficult, it's a widespread practice to give the woman a tube of vaginal hormone cream.

A few weeks of nightly application of this will usually restore her vagina to its previous healthy state—and love-making to normal.

There's a very slight danger that her partner will absorb some of the hormone through the skin of his penis. A few men have temporarily developed little breasts as a result of this unusual method of absorption, but the risk is minimal.

Oral female hormone dosage should be very carefully controlled by your own family doctor, gynaecologist or menopause clinic. It is believed that, in the past, overuse of unbalanced hormone preparations (particularly in the USA) has led to cases of cancer of the lining of the womb—see earlier in this chapter.

But, quite obviously, management of menopause symptoms is *not* simply a question of replacing a few hormones. All women who have menopausal problems need love and understanding from their husbands, families and friends.

Pregnancy and sex

It's quite common for women suddenly to lose interest in sex either during pregnancy or immediately after it.

This reaction may be partly due to hormone changes. It can also be linked to the stress and tiredness which affect so many women during pregnancy, childbirth, and the months afterwards.

There may also be a psychological element. A number of women do have a feeling deep down that sex is all right for young women—but that once you become a mother (or a mother-to-be) then you really shouldn't enjoy it any more!

In many cases, this loss of interest cures itself—especially if the couple talk about it together and the man adopts a sensible and sympathetic attitude. If the problem persists, it's wise for the couple to seek the sort of common-sense advice mentioned in Chapter 11.

Incidentally, the great weight of medical opinion nowadays is that there is no reason at all why you shouldn't make love during pregnancy. Provided there are no abnormalities in the course of the pregnancy (e.g. bleeding) there seems to be no harm in making love as late as you like. A recent study in the *New England Journal of Medicine* seems to indicate that babies of couples who made love late in pregnancy are just as healthy as those of couples who didn't.

However, when you get very big, sex in the orthodox positions can be uncomfortable. You may prefer to go in for the positions marked as suitable for pregnancy in Chapter 10.

Alternatively, you may prefer to restrict yourselves to love-play when pregnancy is far advanced.

Men: hygiene

Because men's genitals are less complicated, they have less to worry about where health and hygiene are concerned. However, a man *does* have to keep his genitals in reasonable hygienic trim, for three reasons:

- if you don't observe the simple rules of hygiene described below, you increase your chances of cancer of the penis

- men who aren't hygienic tend to give their sexual partners certain illnesses—including, possibly, cancer of the cervix

- unless you keep yourself clean 'down below', you're likely to discover that women find you, to say the least, unappealing, especially where oral sex is concerned!

Some readers may find it incredible that it's

necessary to tell the above facts to any man. But I do assure you that doctors find that a distressing proportion of the men whom they have to examine have simply *no* idea of personal genital hygiene at all. (Yuk!)

All males should wash their genitals at least once a day, paying special attention to the part of the male organ just below the 'head'—this is where the skin glands produce a material called 'smegma' which rapidly accumulates in unhygienic males.

If the man isn't circumcized, he should take care to draw his foreskin back before washing. If you *cannot* draw your foreskin back, see the section on circumcision below.

Sexual infections

Infections of the sex organs are very common in men, as they are in women. And (as with women) they're *not* all sexually acquired.

Thrush of the penis

This produces redness and soreness and is caused by an all-too-common little fungus. Both partners should use an anti-fungal cream, and she should also use anti-fungal pessaries (vaginal tablets).

If thrush keeps recurring, have your urine checked for diabetes. Thrush is more common in diabetics, and some diabetic males have to be circumcised if it keeps giving them trouble.

Other fungus infections of the skin

These are common, especially in men who take too many hot baths. The fungi usually affect the warm area behind and alongside the scrotum, and the scrotum itself. This can be very painful and/or irritating.

Treatment? Don't use the steroid (cor-tisone-like) creams which so many people have in their medicine cupboards. These only encourage the fungi to grow!

Instead, use an anti-fungus cream prescribed by a doctor. Wear cotton underwear and take showers rather than sit in hot baths. Don't have sex till you've been treated, as this is unfair to your partner.

Non-specific urethritis

Also known as NSU or non-gonococcal urethritis (NGU), this is by far the most common sexually transmitted infection in males today.

In most cases, NSU appears to be caused by the relatively 'new' organism chlamydia, which I have mentioned in the women's section of this chapter. Some cases may be due to other bugs, notably one called mycoplasma. But whatever the cause, the symptoms are:

- pain on passing water

- discharge from the penis.

As we'll see in a moment, those symptoms are very like these of gonorrhoea, though NSU is generally regarded as a milder infection. It can, however, have very serious complications (e.g. arthritis) in a small number of cases. Also—and very importantly—it now seems very likely that NSU in a man can make his female partner ill, or even sterile, by giving her chlamydia.

Fortunately, treatment of NSU with one of the tetracycline group of antibiotics is usually successful.

Gonorrhoea

This form of VD is regrettably still common in every country in the world. In men, gonorrhoea produces two dramatic symptoms, about two to five days after having sex with someone who is infected. These are:

severe pain on passing water ('like passing razor blades')

a copious discharge from the penis.

There can be other symptoms if you've taken part in oral or other forms of sex. And there can be very serious and painful complications later.

Fortunately, treatment with adequate doses of penicillin cures most people. The resistant strains mentioned earlier in this chapter can be killed by newer antibiotics at present.

At all costs, don't sleep with anyone till you're cured. This kind of behaviour is almost criminally stupid—yet some men are thoughtless enough to do it.

AIDS

The first thing you need to grasp about AIDS is this. It *could* affect you, or one of your family or friends.

Lots of people refuse to accept this. They kid themselves that the AIDS epidemic is nothing to do with *them*. They say daft things like 'Oh, it only affects pooftahs, doesn't it?' Like ostriches, they stick their heads in the sand, imagining that everything will be OK. (But remember that an ostrich, with its great bottom in the air, is an easy target for something—even if it isn't AIDS!)

The truth is that AIDS is spreading fast throughout the world. As we progress through what I've christened 'the Nervous Nineties', hundreds of thousands of people are going to die of it. It's inevitable that

you're going to meet people who are HIV-positive—indeed, you may well have done so already, without realizing it.

On the other hand, I have to admit that some of the *early* publicity about AIDS (back in the mid-1980s) was wildly misleading. For a brief period, heterosexual people were given the impression that they were at enormous risk of catching the HIV virus through straight sex.

Quite frankly, that belief was totally untrue at that time. But it now seems likely that heterosexuals *will* be at much greater risk as we progress through the 1990s. Despite this, if you look at the graph alongside (Figure C), you'll see that in Britain, for instance, the risk to most heterosexuals is still fairly low. In 1990, a casual affair in London is wildly unlikely to give you AIDS; but in 1999, who knows...?

Admittedly, the risks for heterosexuals are far, far higher in certain parts of the world—notably Central and East Africa, New York, San Francisco, and possibly Belgium. However, in Britain, Ireland, most of Europe and Australasia and rural (not urban) America, the situation at the beginning of the 1990s is that it is still hundreds to one against a 'straight' love affair giving you the virus.

I repeat that this situation is going to change. Heterosexual transmission of the HIV virus is already terrifyingly common in Africa and (for some reason) in the Low Countries. But that hasn't yet happened in most of the rest of the world.

Throughout most of the globe, there are only certain categories of adults who are really at *great* risk of getting AIDS. They are:

promiscuous male gays

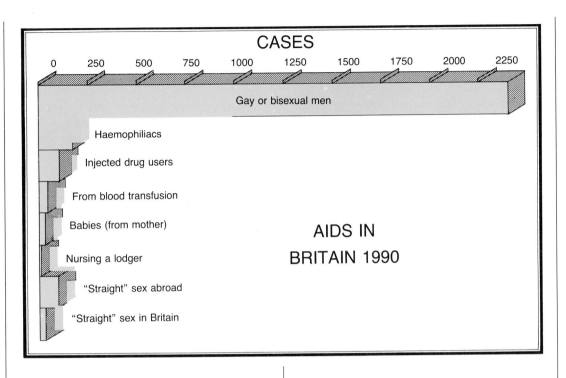

CASES

AIDS IN
BRITAIN 1990

Gay or bisexual men
Haemophiliacs
Injected drug users
From blood transfusion
Babies (from mother)
Nursing a lodger
"Straight" sex abroad
"Straight" sex in Britain

- promiscuous male bisexuals
- injectable drug users (if they share needles)
- haemophiliacs
- the sexual partners of people in the above groups.

Rather surprisingly, there's been something of an official reluctance to acknowledge these facts. And in the media, there have even been discreet attempts to censor them.

But the truth is that if you are a heterosexual who is faithful to your equally faithful partner (and if your partner is NOT in one of the above 'risk groups'), then the chances of either of you getting AIDS are just about nil.

Nevertheless, if you stray down the prim-

rose path of sexual dalliance—particularly in the later part of the 1990s—you may well come a very nasty cropper indeed.

Myths about AIDS

Now, before going any further, I'd like to get some daft myths out of the way.

Ever since the AIDS outbreak began, people have been starting silly rumours about the disease. These rumours are so widespread that they've caused a great deal of harm—and in particular, an awful lot of unpleasant and unfair prejudice against gays.

Let's try and dispel a few myths:

- 'You can tell if somebody's got the infection by looking at them.' No, you can't. Polls have shown that a lot of youngsters believe this one. They think that if somebody *looks* healthy, then it must be OK to sleep with them. Wrong, wrong, wrong. Most men and women who are HIV positive look perfectly fit, healthy and normal. But having sex with them could be your death warrant.

'You can catch it from touching somebody.' Wrong. Basically, you have to have really intimate contact with somebody in order to pick up the virus from him/her.

I've shaken hands with people who are HIV positive, and I can't say that it bothered me in the least. If I had to work with somebody who was HIV positive, it wouldn't worry me at all either.

Admittedly, there has been ONE case in Britain of a woman who allegedly caught the virus from physical contact without sex. She was a landlady who nursed her AIDS-stricken lodger through his final illness.

She claimed—and we have no way of knowing whether this was the truth—that they had never had sex together. But it seems that in the course of giving him intimate bodily care, certain raw patches on her skin were regularly exposed to his bodily secretions. The poor lady caught the virus, and subsequently developed AIDS.

But, in the ordinary day-to-day physical contact of human beings, there is no risk whatever.

'You can get it from giving blood.' What a load of old rhubarb! Of course you can't.

'You can catch it from cups and glasses.' No such event has *ever* been described. I would happily buy drinks from a gay barman (in fact, I'm sure I often do,

without realizing it!). And I'd cheerfully take drinks poured by an HIV-positive barman too.

'You can catch it from lavatory seats.' Again, there is no record in medical literature of such a thing having happened. I suppose that there is a million to one chance that if you had a raw ulcer on your bottom and you plonked it on a loo seat where somebody else had just deposited some sexual secretion, the virus might get in that way. But, honestly, is it remotely likely? You stand more chance of being hit on the head by a falling pig.

'All gays have it.' Of course they don't! The ordinary decent gay who is faithful to his partner is wildly unlikely to have the virus.

'Lesbians spread AIDS around.' Rubbish! Because of the gentle and largely non-penetrative nature of lesbian sex, these ladies are one group in the population who are astronomically unlikely to get AIDS.

Yet, incredibly, there have been reports of lesbians being turned away from Blood Transfusion Centres on the grounds that it would be 'unsafe' to accept blood from them.

'You can get it from swimming pools.' Well, nobody has so far! Although I don't believe that anyone has yet done any scientific tests on swimming pool water and the HIV virus, I think it is very unlikely that the germ could survive in a properly chlorinated pool. Furthermore, you'd probably have to drink about 50 gallons of the water in order to get any significant amount of virus into you.

On the other hand, there is a chance that a murky and ill-maintained pool could contain all sorts of different bugs (after all, it's thought that polio was often spread through swimming baths in the old days). So don't swim in a dirty pool, for general hygiene reasons.

What is AIDS, anyway?

The initials 'AIDS' stand for 'Acquired Immune Deficiency Syndrome'. (In some countries, it is referred to as 'SIDA'—because the words come the other way round in French and certain other languages.)

Now, what that mouthful of a name means is that the disease attacks your *immune system*—the system of your body which protects you against infection. Once your immune system has been damaged, you're fairly easy prey for all sorts of germs which would have no effect on a healthy person.

The virus which causes AIDS is now known as 'HIV'—meaning 'Human Immunodeficiency Virus'. If tests show that a person has the virus, then he or she is referred to as being 'HIV-positive'.

As far as we know, people who catch the HIV virus aren't *necessarily* going to get AIDS. But I stress the words 'as far as we know...'.

When the AIDS scare first got under way in the early 1980s, experts were saying that it was probable that only about 10% of HIV-positive people would go on to develop AIDS.

It soon became apparent that these statements were hopelessly over-optimistic. By the late 1980s, it was being said that 40% of HIV-positive people would get AIDS.

Then it became 50%....

I don't want to be gloomy, but we have to face the possibility that it might turn out to be 100%—let's hope not. One encouraging thing is that drugs such as AZT do appear to be having some effect in slowing down the progression to full-blown AIDS.

When you first catch the HIV virus, you're likely to notice no symptoms whatever. But it's believed that a small number of people experience a mild and brief illness, with a raised temperature and swollen glands, occurring about two or three weeks after infection.

However, as you can probably imagine, this is awfully difficult to distinguish from the symptoms of any old virus infection.

Unfortunately, blood tests for the HIV virus do not become positive until some months after the original infection (the period is very variable). So for that reason, there's absolutely no point in having a blood test the morning after you've taken a risk!

If you have a test at all (and you shouldn't do so without adequate counselling), it would be reasonable to have it, say, two or three months after the possible exposure to infection.

Incidentally, the fact that the blood test doesn't usually become positive for several months is the reason why (alas!) having a blood transfusion will never again be *totally* safe. There will always be a very tiny risk that someone with the HIV virus has donated blood during the period when his or her test was still negative. Perhaps understandably, some authorities aren't all that keen to publicize this risk—which is admittedly quite miniscule. (Personally, I would have no hesitation about having a blood transfusion in Britain or most of Europe.)

The course of HIV infection

What happens next? After an incubation period of anything between a couple of months and ten years, most HIV-positive people will develop one or more of the following syndromes:

Persistent generalized lymphadenopathy (PGL). This is a condition in which you remain reasonably well, but have swollen lymph glands in various parts of your body. The outlook in PGL is still thought to be reasonably good, though it's known that some patients do go on to develop AIDS.

AIDS-related complex (ARC). This is a rather more serious condition, in which the person usually suffers from diarrhoea, loss of weight, persistent thrush infection and fever. Unfortunately, there is quite a high risk that the condition will progress to AIDS.

Purpura. A bleeding disorder, caused by lack of clotting cells called 'platelets' in the blood.

Brain problems. Sadly, it is now clear that HIV does attack the brain in a significant number of people. This is why some newspapers have claimed that HIV-positive doctors should not be allowed to work—in case their judgement is impaired.

AIDS itself. The features of full-blown AIDS are described below.

So, I've pulled no punches. You can see that if you are unlucky enough to catch the HIV virus, the outlook is very uncertain. However, it's important not to give up hope —because after all, there are many people who have been HIV-positive for years, and who are still fit and well.

The best hope for them is that a drug which actually kills the virus (as opposed to delaying its progress) will one day be found. Until that time, they have (unfortunately) to regard themselves as potentially infectious for the rest of their lives.

The symptoms of AIDS

In describing the symptoms of AIDS, once again I'm going to pull no punches. But a word of warning: *please* don't read this account of the symptoms and then go and decide (off your own bat) that you've got it.

I quite often encounter people who think that they (or their children) have got AIDS —and in the vast majority of cases they're wrong, thank heavens.

But if you have got reasonable grounds for thinking that you might have the disease —or just the HIV virus—then your best move is to go to a specialist (in Britain and Ireland, that would be at a Genito-Urinary or 'Special' Clinic), and have proper counselling—plus, if *really* necessary, a blood test.

The common symptoms of AIDS depend mainly on the fact that the virus knocks out the body's defences against infection. It mainly does this by attacking some white blood cells called 'helper T lymphocytes'.

This makes the victim very liable to invasion by viruses, bacteria and fungi. Common symptoms include:

severe pneumonia—caused by a germ which is normally too 'weak' to attack human lungs overwhelming bowel infections

distressing skin and mouth infections—particularly with fungi such as thrush.

Also, the virus may cause two other serious symptoms:

Kaposi's sarcoma—a form of skin cancer, in which bluish lumps appear on the skin (other cancers may develop too)

dementia—due to the fact that the virus often attacks the brain.

This is a most terrible disease, and one for which the world desperately needs a cure.

How did AIDS arrive?

It's astonishing, isn't it, that AIDS just seems to have sprung up suddenly, to torment and threaten the human race? No wonder that certain moralists have decided that it's God's vengeance on sinful humanity!

In fact, the change in sexual morality which took place in the 1960s and 1970s—on a worldwide scale—opened the way for certain opportunistic sexual infections, including herpes as well as AIDS. Bacteriologists are well aware that if the behaviour of humanity alters in any way, there may be germs that will exploit that change. That is exactly what happened with the HIV virus.

So, how did it all begin? There's a wonderful and fanciful theory that the virus started its life in a CIA laboratory, and then 'escaped'. But few people believe that one! In fact, the HIV virus almost certainly started attacking human beings in Central and East Africa, back in the 1970s.

Why it did this, no one knows. One theory is that it may have come from animals—some tropical monkeys carry a virus which is similar to HIV. Alternatively, it may have been a relatively harmless human virus that suddenly changed its nature.

Anyway, the disease is now on the rampage in Central, East and West Africa. (So if you go there, do not have sex with people who live there, and avoid blood transfusions.)

It seems quite likely that the virus then spread to the island of Haiti, in the West Indies. This is the sad, poor and primitive little republic (quite near Cuba and Jamaica), which used to be famous as the land of Papa Doc, the voodoo dictator.

In the late 1970s and early 1980s, it was common for gay men from America to vacation in Haiti, buying themselves the favours of local young men.

So, from Haiti the virus seems to have been taken to the gay 'bath-houses' of New York and San Francisco—places where it was possible for a gay guy to have sexual contact with as many as 50 different men in a couple of hours. Without moralizing, anybody can see that this was a recipe for bacteriological disaster.

In 1981, US doctors were surprised to find that they were suddenly seeing a lot of young men who were suffering from the unusual type of pneumonia which I've mentioned above.

Soon after, large numbers of men began to develop Kaposi's sarcoma on their skins. Some people had both pneumonia *and* the skin cancer.

Before long, the penny dropped. Nearly all the sufferers were gay.

By 1983, the virus which was causing such havoc in Greenwich Village and other gay centres had been identified—in both French and US laboratories. Yes, the virus had spread to France and Britain, and also to Holland (whose gay brothels were popular with American tourists), Australasia and the Far East.

For a while, the press labelled AIDS 'the Gay Plague', and it was easy for us heterosexuals—including us medically qualified heterosexuals—to think that it couldn't possibly affect any of us.

Then it became clear that heterosexuals *were* catching the HIV virus, in one of three ways:

through sharing needles used for injecting drugs

through infected blood transfusions (and infected blood products)

through the 'AC/DC' lifestyle of infected bisexual men.

Taking *needle-sharing* first: this is an unfortunate habit employed worldwide by users of injectable drugs (such as heroin) who have no access to sterile needles. It soon became clear that female (and male) drug addicts were picking up HIV—and, in many cases, subsequently developing AIDS.

An additional nasty twist to the saga was provided by the fact that in most countries, many drug users go in for prostitution (female or male) to pay for their habit.

So, in no time, there were HIV-positive women and men on the streets of New York, Los Angeles, London, Edinburgh, Amsterdam and Sydney, offering their poor, infected bodies for sale.

What about *blood transfusions and blood products*?

In the mid-1980s, it was noticed that men and women who had had blood transfusions were developing AIDS. This was specially common in the US, where (I'm afraid) they have never been very choosy about who donates blood. Inevitably, many of the donors at that time were drug addicts who were selling their blood for cash; and equally inevitably, some of them were HIV-positive.

It was quite some time before HIV-screening for blood donors was introduced in the US and, indeed, all western countries. (But for the reason explained above, there will always be a *very* small risk of AIDS from a blood transfusion.)

Soon after this, a further disaster became apparent. Blood *products* are used to treat various diseases; in particular, a blood product called 'Factor Eight' is given to people with haemophilia. Many batches of Factor Eight soon turned out to be contaminated with HIV, but this was not discovered till it was too late.

In Britain, for instance, there are about 5,000 haemophiliacs. Because the authorities persisted in using Factor Eight imported from America, over a quarter of those people caught HIV. So did some of their wives and girl friends. Many now have AIDS—and quite a few are dead.

The other way in which HIV started reaching heterosexual people during the mid- to late 1980s was through *bisexuality*. There really are a lot of bisexual men around —far more than most people realize. Soon it was becoming clear that bisexual men were being infected with the virus by their male lovers and they were then passing it on to women.

Although there weren't *many* women who had AIDS at this stage, the implications of the 'bisexual transfer route' were very serious. Up until now, it had been assumed that the only form of sex which could transmit the virus was *rectal* sex which, of course, is favoured by many gays.

But the fact that women were now catching the HIV virus from their bisexual lovers strongly suggested that *vaginal* intercourse could also pass it on.

This has turned out to be true, though it does still seem that vaginal sex is much less 'efficient' than rectal sex in passing on the virus. That may possibly be because the vaginal wall is much tougher than the wall of the rectum which often splits or tears a little during anal intercourse, providing an easy opportunity for germs to get in.

Nonetheless, heterosexual transmission of HIV remained low in most countries throughout the 1980s. By 1990, however, it was clear that an enormous amount of heterosexual transmission was taking place in Africa, and also (for some reason) in Belgium.

To begin with, scientists theorized that this might be because people in poor areas of Africa could be using rectal intercourse as a form of contraception. This now appears to be untrue: many cases of HIV infection have occurred in Africa as a result of 'straight' vaginal intercourse.

The reason *why* vaginal intercourse should transmit the disease so efficiently in Africa is not clear, but it has been suggested that it may be connected with the fact that quite a few people—particularly prostitutes —do have minor tropical sores in the genital areas. These might provide a way in for the virus.

Certainly, the latest research in Africa seems to indicate that *men* with genital ulcers are much more likely to contract AIDS than men who haven't got any sores or ulcers on the penis. The researchers studied a large group of men who had gone with prostitutes in Nairobi. (Incidentally, a terrifying 85% of the prostitutes were HIV-positive.)

Blood tests carried out over a period of months showed that men who had some form of genital sore or ulcer were *five times* more likely than other men to pick up HIV.

A further finding of the Kenyan researchers was that if you already have *another* sexually transmitted disease, then you're more vulnerable to catching HIV. This might be because resistance has already been weakened by the infection.

Another astonishing finding of the Kenyan research team is that uncircumcized men *appear* to be much more likely than circumcized men to contract HIV from vaginal intercourse. Another group of researchers has made the same finding. But I don't think that all men should dash out and get circumcized—at least, not until this work has been confirmed!

At the beginning of the 1990s, then, it is clear that one of the most frightening things about AIDS is the fact that transmission by the vaginal route appears to be increasing fast.

If what is happening in Africa (and what seems to be happening in Belgium) becomes common in the rest of the world, then I'm afraid that AIDS is, sooner or later, going to explode into the Earth's heterosexual population with the same viciousness and fury which it has already visited on the gay population.

And since no drugs are available to cure it, and no vaccine is in sight, the only hope of keeping it in some sort of check is for us to do what so many gays have done: cut down on the number of partners (preferably to ONE), and practise safe sex. More about this toward the end of the chapter.

Should we panic?

No, I don't think there's any need for panic —provided we keep our heads, and start running our sex lives a bit more sensibly than we have during the last 30 years or so!

The first thing to do is to understand what the risks are. Let's look at them separately for women and for men.

Women. Let's analyze the latest figures for AIDS cases among women, taking Britain as an example of a fairly typical western country.

You may be surprised to hear that at the start of the 1990s, only about 130 British women had developed AIDS. Very few of these poor ladies actually caught the virus through having 'straight' sex with a man in their own country.

This table shows you exactly how they caught it:

So, from Table 1, you can see that at the beginning of the 'Nervous Nineties', the risk of acquiring AIDS through intercourse with a 'non-risk group' man still *appears* to be fairly low.

You can also see that the risk is very much higher if you have intercourse abroad; or if you have intercourse in Britain with a 'risk group' man.

It's also clear that drug abuse is already an important factor in causing AIDS among British women. As you can see, 25 female users have contracted AIDS.

At first sight, Table 1 might seem to be a licence to go out and make love. After all, only about four British women seem to have got AIDS through sex with a 'non-risk group' guy. But the trouble is that the table

Table 1

HOW BRITISH WOMEN ACQUIRED AIDS
(1990 figures)

Intercourse abroad with 'non-risk group' man	30 women
Injected drug abuse	25 women
Intercourse in Britain with 'risk group' man	20 women
Infected blood transfusion abroad	20 women
Unknown	8 women
Infected blood transfusion in Britain	6 women
Intercourse in Britain with 'non-risk group' man	4 women
Female haemophiliac	2 women
Nursing infected lodger	1 woman
Female baby of infected mother	15 baby girls

Note: 'risk group' man means gay, bisexual, a drug user or a haemophiliac.

shows *only AIDS cases*. It does NOT show the figures for people who are HIV-positive. And there are thousands and thousands of them; we just don't know how many. My guess is that at least 4,000 British women may be carrying the virus.

However, Table 1 does show us something about the relative risks of various categories of men. I think that the message for women in this table is pretty clear:

be very wary about intercourse abroad—particularly in heavily infected areas like Africa, New York and San Francisco

don't have intercourse with a 'risk group' man—that is, a bisexual, a drug injector or a haemophiliac (always assuming, of course, that you can recognize him as such)

avoid casual affairs

if you *must* have sex outside of a mutually faithful relationship, then use a condom (male or female).

There's one other 'self-protection' point which you *won't* find in the table:

don't have rectal sex, particularly with casual contacts. If the man has HIV, this is the most efficient way of giving it to you. They don't call AIDS 'Anally Injected Death Sentence' for nothing.

Men. So that's the situation for women at the start of the 1990s. Now, should *men* panic?

Well, a glance at the figures makes it clear that men have far more reason to be worried than have women.

Table 2

HOW BRITISH MEN ACQUIRED AIDS
(1990 figures)

Gay/bisexual	2,430 men
Haemophiliac	175 men
Intercourse abroad with 'non-risk group' woman	75 men
Injected drug abuse	70 men
Unknown	35 men
Infected blood transfusion abroad	15 men
Intercourse in Britain with 'non-risk group' woman	10 men
Infected blood transfusion in Britain	12 men
Intercourse in Britain with 'risk group' woman	8 men
Male baby of infected mother	11 baby boys

Note: 'risk group' woman in this table means a user of injectable drugs.

Again, let's take Britain as a fairly typical example of a western country. At the moment, there are 24 male cases of AIDS for every female one. The breakdown of Britain's male AIDS cases is shown in Table 2.

Again, let me stress that these are figures for CASES of AIDS. The number of men who are HIV-positive (and therefore infectious) in Britain is much, much higher—though unfortunately we don't know exactly what those figures are.

But the table does give us some guidelines. It makes it clear that, so far, only a handful of men have developed AIDS through having 'straight' sex in Britain. It shows that, at the moment, 'straight' sex *abroad* is far more risky.

It also shows that, at present, the number of men who've got AIDS through going with a 'risk group' woman (i.e. a drug user) in the UK is surprisingly low. But this number is expected to increase rapidly because of the tragic fact that many prostitutes (especially in Edinburgh) are becoming HIV-positive.

And one of the most striking things on the table is the clear indication that the three groups of men who are far and away at most risk of AIDS are:

drug users

haemophiliacs

gays and bisexuals.

What lessons can we learn from the table? Well, this book was basically written for heterosexual people, so I'm not going to presume to offer any advice to gay or bisexual men here. (They've now established their own excellent sources of advice through organizations like the Terrence Higgins Trust.)

For haemophiliac men, too, there is specialized advice about sex available from the Haemophilia Society, 123 Westminster Bridge Road, London SE1.

But for the average heterosexual chap, I think that the messages to be drawn from Table 2 are these:

think very carefully before you go in for intercourse abroad—especially in high-HIV places like Milan, Central and East Africa, Amsterdam, San Francisco and New York

don't have sex with a drug-using woman, and remember that many prostitutes *are* drug users

avoid casual affairs

don't be tempted into gay sex

if you DO have an affair with somebody other than your regular partner, try always to use a condom.

Sex in Europe

Up to now, we've been looking at Britain as a fairly typical western country.

But what actually is the AIDS situation in the rest of Europe? Not very good, I'm afraid. The World Health Organization estimates that up to ten million European people will be infected with HIV by 1991.

Table 3 shows the number of people who have AIDS, and the number of people who are *thought* to be HIV-positive, in western European nations.

But do bear in mind that the figure for the number of HIV-positive people is just guesswork on the authorities' part. Really, no one has much of a clue.

Table 3

AIDS AND HIV IN EUROPE (1990 figures)

Country	AIDS cases	Estimate of number of HIV-positive people
Belgium	500	12,000–15,000
France	7,000	300,000
Ireland	100	900
Italy	3,700	200,000
Netherlands	800	15,000–30,000
Portugal	250	not available
Spain	2,900	not available
West Germany	3,250	80,000–300,000
United Kingdom	3,000	11,000 known 50,000–100,000 estimated

The figures for AIDS *cases* are reasonably reliable, however, and they show that things are already very bad in France, with 7,000 people affected. In West Germany and Italy (where Milan is a particular hotbed of HIV), the number of cases is about the same as in the UK.

An unusual feature of the Italian situation is that a staggering 70% of AIDS sufferers are allegedly drug abusers. I wonder whether this is really true—or whether the fact is that Italian gays prefer to *pretend* that they are drug users.

Look specially at Belgium, because it may have significance for the rest of us. Although the number of cases is small, the Belgian authorities believe that *in over a quarter of all instances HIV is being transmitted heterosexually.*

Although the total AIDS figures for Europe (over 20,000 cases in 1990) may seem bad, they almost pale into insignificance compared with the Americas. About 75% of all the world's known AIDS cases have occurred in the Americas. And in New York, it's estimated that half a million people—that's one in fourteen of the population—are HIV-positive.

Will we all be wiped out by AIDS?

There were fears about this when AIDS first appeared. But the situation now is that, although the spread of HIV has been pretty devastating (particularly in Africa), the human race should survive!

The major threat to us would occur if the virus changed its nature so that it became more easily spread *in other ways.*

But at the moment, the number of ways in which it can be spread is very limited. We've mentioned most of them:

by rectal sex

by vaginal sex—though not as easily

by injection of infected blood or blood products (*e.g.* from a contaminated transfusion)

by injection, using a contaminated needle.

There are, however, one or two other ways:

from an infected mother to her unborn child

by Artificial Insemination of sperm from an infected male donor (that's why all sperm donors should now be regularly HIV-tested)

by blood splashes. Unfortunately a very small number of health workers have become HIV-positive after being heavily splashed with infected blood

very rarely, by close and intimate non-sexual contact, as in the case of the lady I've mentioned above who allegedly caught the virus while nursing her infected lodger. There has also been a case in America of a mother who appears to have caught HIV from her young son, who is haemophiliac (you'll probably remember that, in the 1980s, experts tended to pooh-pooh the idea that transmission could take place by physical contact)

by oral sex. As recently as 1989, an official British Government health publication was saying that HIV could not be transmitted in this way. But in fact, one near-certain case has already occurred: in an American man who was incapable of ordinary sex, but who apparently acquired the virus through engaging in cunnilingus with an HIV-positive prostitute. You have been warned.

Finally... protecting yourself

So, summing up: you CAN avoid AIDS. But the threat is so great that I believe that every sexually active person should make a real effort to protect himself or herself over the next, worrying decade.

The risk of heterosexual transmission is slowly increasing, so:

don't sleep around

try to make sure you pick a sexual partner who isn't in a high-risk group

try to make sure your partner isn't promiscuous

if you're a woman, don't go with a man who sleeps with prostitutes

if you're a woman, avoid rectal sex if you have an affair

whatever sex you are, stay away from injectable drugs

if you must be unfaithful to your partner —use that condom!

Circumcision

Circumcision remains popular in America, and in Jewish and Moslem cultures—but it's not very popular elsewhere. In Britain, less than 7% of all male babies are now circumcised—partly because of worries about the horrendous damage which can be done by a badly-performed circumcision (e.g. partial amputation of the penis).

However, circumcision does make it easier to keep the male organ clean, and so greatly cuts down on the risk of cancer of the penis in later life (see Hygiene above).

Most adults will have had the decision about circumcision taken for them by their parents. So the only point I want to make here is this: Dr Kinsey discovered that in many adult males, the foreskin will not 'go back' (or 'unpeel') when the penis is erect. That isn't a good state of affairs—either sexually or hygienically!

So if *your* foreskin is too tight to go back properly, then you owe it to yourself and your partner to see a doctor and have a circumcision done. Provided you consult an experienced surgeon, you should find this a relatively trivial operation.

The prostate and prostate cancer

I've described the anatomy of the prostate gland in Chapter 2. Alas, in nearly all men it starts to enlarge a bit as they get older.

Because the urinary pipe goes straight through the prostate, this can lead to certain problems with passing water. In particular, men may notice that:

- they have more trouble in 'starting' than they used to

- the 'stream' may not be very good

- they may have to keep on passing water— this can be difficult and embarrassing on long journeys.

Rather surprisingly, prostate gland enlargement doesn't seem to interfere with *sexual* functions.

So why does this practically universal enlargement occur? The answer is that we don't know. I once read an impressively-argued book by a 'natural' therapist who claimed that it was all because today's man delays his climax far too long during love-making! His dubious theory was that if all males 'came' right away at the start of inter-course, none of them would get enlarged prostates!

Anyway, *mild* prostate enlargement can be treated by simple common-sense measures— like avoiding too much alcohol, coffee and tea. If prostate enlargement gets very trouble-some, however, the answer has to be surgery. Basically, there are two types of operation, as explained in Chapter 2.

Sex may well be possible after either type of operation, but as a rule the man will not be able to ejaculate any fluid, and this will alter the sensations he feels.

Cancer of the prostate gland produces simi-lar symptoms to those of benign enlargement, but is much less common. Treatment is by removal of the gland, or by hormone therapy.

The cause of prostate cancer isn't known, but some research in America and Japan has suggested a possible link with too much *fat* in the diet. Prevention of prostate cancer is obviously very difficult. In the USA, some surgeons think that all men over the age of 45 or 50 should have a yearly rectal examination to try and detect this form of cancer, but this kind of screening isn't really practical on a wide scale.

Finally, don't take risks with your health!

In this chapter, I've summed up the various health risks which can affect your sex organs.

You'll see that some, though not all, of these dangers are self-inflicted. Others—particu-larly cancer of the cervix—can be prevented through a sensible use of screening tests.

Without wishing to sound too puritanical, I have to say that the wilder excesses of today's permissive society have greatly increased the incidence of some of these health hazards.

In order to protect your own health and that of your partner, it's really only common sense to avoid some of the more extreme manifestations of permissiveness—particu-larly such activities as orgies and one-night stands, which are open invitations to germs.

It's your body—so treat it with care!

6

Fertility and Its Problems

Sex and fertility—How to start a baby—Infertility is nobody's fault—
Getting help—Are you doing it right?—WOMEN: failure to ovulate—
Blocked tubes—Emotional problems—Sex positions and conception—
MEN: a low sperm count—Other causes—Artificial insemination—
Test-tube babies—Surrogate motherhood—Surrogate fatherhood—
Adoption

Sex and fertility

It's often forgotten that sex—quite apart from being great fun—is intended to produce babies!

If a couple make love without any attempt at contraception, there's roughly a one in 25 chance that the woman will conceive. However, there are many cases where conception takes place the very first time, and equally, there are many other cases where a couple have to make love 50 or 100 times before a child is conceived.

Whether conception occurs or not depends on various factors, but chiefly on:

- whether they are doing it at the right time of the month

- whether both of them are fully fertile.

The surprising thing is that in many cases one or other (or both) of them is not fully fertile. In a staggering *one in seven* of all couples there are significant fertility problems.

So if you have trouble conceiving, you're very far from being alone. The good news is that there's a reasonable chance these days that the problem can be successfully treated.

How to start a baby

It may sound obvious, but if you want to conceive a child, the best thing to do is to make love as frequently as you reasonably can, at the right time of the menstrual cycle. Although it is theoretically possible to get pregnant at almost any time of the month, conception is as a rule likeliest *about 14 days before a period starts.*

Obviously, it's a bit difficult to pinpoint this time if your periods are irregular. But the temperature chart method of determining ovulation—described later in this chapter—can help you. Some women get a mid-month backache or abdominal pain which gives more than a hint that they're ovulating.

In additon, if you've used the Billings method of natural family planning—described in Chapter 7—you'll know that by studying your own vaginal secretions, you can get some idea of your likely ovulation day.

In any case, you don't have to pinpoint the ovulation day with absolute precision. Just as this book was being completed, news came from the University of California that a man's sperm can live for considerably longer in a woman's body than was previously recognized—perhaps for as many as five days.

So as long as you make love somewhere *near* the day of ovulation, there's a reasonable chance that a sperm will find its way to an egg—and conception will result.

However, if you haven't been successful in conceiving a baby within a year (or less for an older couple for whom time is shorter) read on...

Infertility is nobody's fault

The first thing to get clear in both your minds is that it's nobody's fault.

Either or both partners may turn out to have some *difficulty* or *disorder*—but that doesn't mean it's their 'fault'. We need to get rid of this ridiculous idea that infertility is something for which somebody has to be blamed—and feel guilty!

The other thing to get clear in both your minds is that there's no truth in the widespread belief that the difficulty almost always lies with the woman. This legend has persisted for thousands of years—mainly because many men can't bring themselves to believe they are infertile. In fact, in about one in three of all couples with fertility problems, it's the man who has the difficulty.

Let me stress that this doesn't mean that he's not very virile or that he's 'not a real man'.

Again and again doctors see big, beefy he-men, many of whom are extremely able and enthusiastic lovers, who just happen by some quirk of fate to be of low fertility.

The same is true of women. Some of the sexiest and most attractive women on earth have had serious fertility problems. Indeed it has to be admitted that, as we'll see in a moment, a woman who has had a pretty sexy past may, alas, find that it's precisely *because* of her previous torrid love-life that she has become infertile.

Now let's look at ways of getting assistance if you're having trouble in conceiving a baby.

Getting help

The first thing to say is that you should seek medical help reasonably *soon*. After 30, time is beginning to run out for a woman (though not for a man), and after 35 it runs out very fast indeed!

In many countries (and especially in Britain) infertility clinic waiting lists are very long—simply because of the many infertile marriages. So get your name down promptly.

The investigations done at an Infertility Clinic are *very* expensive and time-consuming. If it's at all possible, there's much to be said for having the initial, simple and inexpensive tests—described later in the chapter—done by your local GP, Family Planning Clinic or Well Woman Clinic.

Are you doing it right?

Oddly enough, this is one of the first areas that the doctor will need to explore—though I hope fairly diplomatically!

Why? Because every doctor who works in the field of infertility is used to seeing women who can't understand why they're not pregnant—and who then turn out to be virgins! In most of these cases, a little common-sense advice about what you're actually supposed to *do* when you make love will work wonders. Sometimes though, the reason for the wife's virginity is an emotional problem (discussed later).

The probable day of ovulation is shown by the 'kick' in the temperature graph. The woman is likely to be fertile for several days on each side of this.

The other point on which the doctor will want to satisfy him- or herself is this: are you doing it *often enough?* This may sound absurd, but if the husband or wife is away on business a lot and the couple simply aren't together at the right time of the month, then clearly it's no wonder she hasn't conceived.

Women: failure to ovulate

For a variety of reasons, an awful lot of women do not ovulate (produce an ovum). This can be the case even though they may be having periods. So one of the first things to do in most cases of failure to conceive is to try to check whether the woman is ovulating.

A simple and cheap way of doing this is for her to take her temperature every morning over a spell of several months. If she is ovulating, her chart should register a 'kick' like the one shown in the monthly temperature graph in Figure A.

Admittedly, temperature charts can be difficult for even the most experienced doctors to interpret. In some cases, it's necessary to check whether ovulation is occurring (and—most important—*when*) by one of these methods:

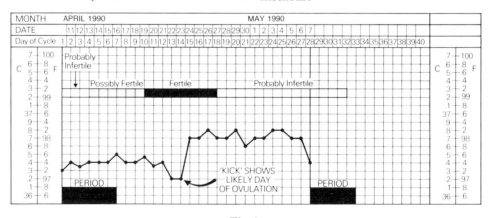

Fig A

- hormone tests

- ultrasound scan of the ovary

- biopsy (sampling) of the womb lining

- laparoscopy (inspecting the ovary with a telescope-like device pushed through a small cut in the abdomen).

Obviously, these methods are much more expensive (and, in most parts of the world, more difficult to obtain) than the simple temperature chart procedure.

Once a woman knows that she's ovulating—and *when*—then obviously she should make love around that day in order to conceive. But

Fig B

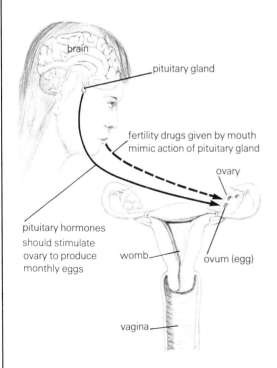

pituitary hormones should stimulate ovary to produce monthly eggs

How fertility drugs work.

if the tests show that she's *not* ovulating, then these days there's still hope for her.

Failure to ovulate can very often be successfully treated with the famous 'fertility drugs'—which stimulate the ovary to produce eggs. As you can see from Figure B, most of these drugs mimic the action of the natural hormones which are produced by a woman's pituitary gland, and which should make her ovary produce an ovum each month.

Unfortunately, as you probably know from the newspapers, use of certain fertility drugs does often over-stimulate the ovaries, so that they produce *too many* eggs. The result is a multiple pregnancy; indeed in a few cases, the fertility drugs have had the startling effect of giving the woman seven or eight babies.

I'm afraid that the survival rate of the babies in these extreme cases of multiple pregnancy is low.

Obviously, infertility specialists try to control the dose of fertility drug very carefully so that if possible only one, two or at most three babies are produced at a single pregnancy.

Naturally, a woman who has been desperately trying for a baby over a period of many years is usually only too delighted if she ends up with twins or even triplets!

Blocked tubes

Another tremendously common cause of infertility in women is blocked tubes. You can see the problem in Figure C. If the Fallopian tubes are blocked for any reason, the man's sperm can't get through to the woman's ova.

The causes of this difficulty are:

- a previous sterilization operation (some women undergo sterilization, then get divorced and remarried and want their tubes unblocked) inflammatory disorders in the lower abdomen—for instance, reaction to a past burst appendix, or endometriosis;

previous infection of the tubes.

I have to say that tube blockage due to this last cause (previous infection of the tubes) is far more common than most people realize, and that these infections are often—though very far from always—sexually transmitted.

Indeed, one of the unfortunate after-effects of the so-called permissive society is that literally hundreds of thousands of women in western countries have had their tubes blocked by infections which they acquired

Fig C

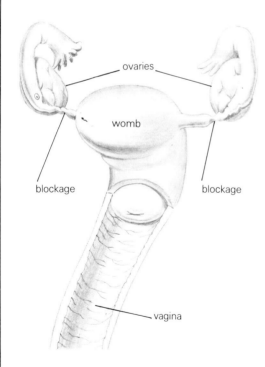

Blocked Fallopian tubes.

during a sexual contact—but which they were usually quite unaware of at the time.

Let me stress, however, that your tubes *can* become infected in other ways (for instance, as a result of using an IUD—see Chapter 7). And in any case, I'm not suggesting that if you have blocked tubes, you should feel guilty about some affair of long ago. The important questions are these:

how do you find out your tubes are blocked?

how can you get treated?

How do you find out your tubes are blocked?

If you have had serious difficulties in conceiving, then the infertility experts will usually want to investigate you for possible tube blockage. This *can't* be diagnosed by a simple vaginal examination. It has to be done by means of one of these investigations:

special X-rays of the tubes

injecting gas through the tubes to see if it goes through freely

laparoscopy.

How can you get treated?

Until not too long ago, there used to be virtually *no* treatment for most cases of blocked tubes. But great advances have been made.

Firstly, it may sometimes be possible to treat the underlying disease—for instance, if an infection is still present, to treat it with antibiotics. The common cause of tube blockage, endometriosis, can often be successfully treated with hormones.

Secondly, a totally blocked tube can sometimes be repaired by delicate surgery, working with an operating microscope (micro-surgery).

Thirdly, the 'test-tube baby' technique may be used to bypass the blockage altogether. This brilliant advance is described later in this chapter.

I have to say that the treatment of blocked tubes by micro-surgery or the test-tube baby technique is still very expensive—and, in most parts of the world, very difficult to obtain. But it does at last offer some hope to the vast number of women who are unable to have a baby because of this extremely common problem.

Emotional problems

In a minority of cases, infertility is due to emotional problems in the woman (for emotional problems in *men*, see later in this chapter).

The main emotional difficulty which causes infertility is called vaginismus—a common disorder in which the woman automatically tightens up whenever an approach is made to her vagina. This may make intercourse very difficult—or downright impossible.

A few women with severe vaginismus manage to persuade clinics to impregnate them with their husband's sperm, using the AIH technique (see below). But in general, it is better to try and *cure* the vaginismus problem, using the psychological methods outlined in Chapter 11. The couple can then make love, and so conceive children in the normal way.

I should also mention that it's generally believed that when a woman is under any kind of stress, this may impair her fertility. Certainly stress and worry can stop her from ovulating some months (that's why women often temporarily lose their periods when they're under some strain). So obviously, trying to iron out any stresses in your life may help you to conceive.

Sex positions and conception

A lot of nonsense is talked about love-making positions and contraception. The most ludicrous myth of all (still believed by a lot of younger adults) is that it's not possible to get pregnant if you do it in a standing position. This is rubbish: you can become pregnant in *any* love-making position.

However, there are two important points concerning sex positions and fertility. The first of these is that most women stand the best possible chance of conceiving if they make love flat on their backs, with knees raised, in the position often described as the 'missionary' position—see Chapter 10.

Indeed, the sperm stand an even greater chance of entering the womb if the woman puts a pillow under her bottom *before* love-making, so as to tilt her pelvis up slightly. Also, she should stay in the same position for a few minutes after the man has reached his climax.

The second point to make is that a very large minority of women have what's called a 'retroverted' womb. This isn't a disease, but is just like being tall, short, or left-handed. All it means is that the womb points *backward* instead of *forward*. You can see this from Figure D.

Roughly 10 to 20% of women in most western countries have retroverted wombs. And the crunch is this: if you're retroverted, then you stand a slightly better chance of conceiving if you make love in one of the 'face-down' positions shown in Chapter 10.

So if your doctor or fertility clinic tells you

Fig D

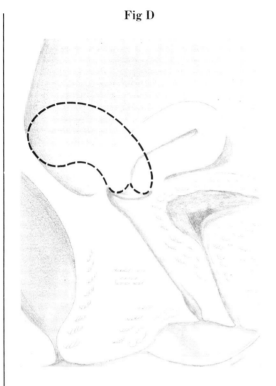

*Retroversion: a retroverted womb (dotted line)
points backwards instead of forwards.*

that your womb is retroverted, you will improve your prospects of conceiving by making love, say, kneeling forwards. Again, you should remain in this position for a few minutes afterwards to give the sperm the best possible chance of getting into the womb.

Men: a low sperm count

Unfortunately, vast numbers of men do have a low sperm count (or no sperm at all) even though they're perfectly capable, virile lovers.

That's why the simple, inexpensive test of doing a sperm count should be carried out very, very early in the investigation of a couple with infertility problems (and certainly long before the woman is subjected to any uncomfortable, expensive or time-consuming tests).

All the man has to do is to provide a sample of his seminal fluid in a hospital specimen jar. He should climax directly into the container and not, as many men do, in a condom—because the rubber may harm the sperm.

The specimen jar should be taken within an hour or two to the hospital laboratory, where it will be examined under a microscope and a count made of the number of sperm in it. Repeat tests are often necessary, mainly to exclude technical errors.

Why is the sperm count so often found to be low? The sad answer is that in most cases we simply don't know.

Sometimes a man's sperm output is low (or even zero) because of past infection of the testicles—particularly by mumps. Sometimes it's low because of injury to the testicles, or because of a recent spell of ill-health. Also, certain drugs can depress sperm production, as can some hormone disorders (discussed later). However, very often the cause remains a mystery.

Treatment

If the sperm count is repeatedly *nil*, then I am afraid that there is usually little that can be done. The couple should consider AID (see below) or adoption.

However, if the sperm count is merely on the low side, then there *is* hope. You'll get detailed advice from your infertility clinic, but possible ways of improving the sperm count include:

● wearing loose, cotton underwear instead of tight, synthetic-material briefs (the latter increase the temperature of the testicles, and this depresses sperm production)

- having surgical treatment for any *varicose veins* which may be present just above the testicle (a common condition)

- having hormone treatment to stimulate the testicle—though this method is of very limited success at the moment

- 'saving up' love-making—in other words, abstaining from sex for a week or so before the woman's ovulation day, in order to build up the sperm count.

Other causes of male infertility

Among other causes of male infertility are two main ones. The first of these is *emotional problems*—in cases of impotence and severe premature ejaculation (which is often so bad that the man can't help reaching a climax *before* he enters his partner). The treatment of these disorders is discussed in Chapter 11. In the rare cases where premature ejaculation doesn't respond to treatment, the couple can conceive by AIH—artificial insemination by the husband.

Another less common cause is a *hormone problem*. There's a relatively small number of men who do have a hormonal problem which can be treated.

In particular, some males have too high a level of a hormone called prolactin. Treatment with a drug called bromocriptine lowers its level and may help the couple to conceive.

Artificial insemination

Artificial insemination is technically very easy to carry out, and has helped many couples to have much-wanted children. There are two types: AIH and AID. In both cases the doctor simply takes some seminal fluid and injects it into the upper part of the woman's vagina at about the time of ovulation.

AIH

This means 'artificial insemination by the husband'. It's done in a few cases of premature ejaculation, and also when the husband has some sort of anatomical abnormality which makes effective intercourse impossible.

AID

This means 'artificial insemination by donor'. It's used when the husband is completely infertile. Naturally, both husband and wife have to be completely happy that they will be able to accept a baby which was really fathered by another man.

It's also important to realize that AID is far more contentious than AIH. It's illegal in some countries, and in *all* countries there may be legal problems about registering the parents' names on the child's birth certificate. Relatives and friends may not be too understanding, so most AID couples keep quiet about it.

In general, what happens is that the doctors or clinic who are providing the AID service have a list of donors—who are frequently medical students. Obviously, the chosen donor should roughly match the husband in general colouring, race and physical size. You will have to rely on the doctor or clinic for this—because it's almost unknown for the donor to be introduced to the couple. In most countries, the doctor will attempt to keep the man's identity a complete secret, though it has been suggested that proper registers of donors should be set up, so that the name of a donor could, if necessary, be checked at a later date.

Some doctors working in the AID field have allowed individual donors to father many children through AID. But it's now increasingly felt that a young man who is a sperm donor should make only a few 'donations', *not* in order to save his strength for his medical studies but to cut down on the risk of inter-marriage among the children he has sired by AID.

There's now increasing emphasis on screening potential sperm donors to make sure that they're healthy. But you have to bear in mind that in the unlikely event of the AID baby being born with some abnormality, there's no question of your having any legal redress, unless there has been some form of negligence.

As with AIH, the procedure for carrying out AID is very simple. The selected young man arrives at the clinic, and makes his 'donation' into a sterile container. It may be immediately frozen for use later. But it's quite likely that the doctor will have arranged for the donor to donate on the day that you're due to ovulate. You will come to the clinic a little later in the day, and the doctor will use a syringe to inject the sperm into the upper part of your vagina (the area of the cervix).

Test-tube babies

The test-tube baby technique is one of the most brilliant medical advances of recent years. It has now enabled well over 1,000 childless women to have the babies they so much wanted.

Invented by two determined and clever men, British researchers Dr Robert Edwards and Mr Patrick Steptoe, the technique is basically an ingenious way of getting round the all-too-common problem of blocked tubes.

It's important to realize that it isn't usually of help with other causes of infertility, as people often think. (Would-be parents sometimes walk into an infertility clinic and say 'We would like the test-tube baby technique'—as if that were the answer to everything!)

But as you can see from Figure E, the Steptoe technique is really a method of bypassing the blocked tube. The surgeon removes a ripe ovum from the woman's ovary, using a telescope-like device known as the laparoscope.

Then the ovum is incubated in a glass dish, along with sperm provided by the husband. One of the sperm fertilizes the ovum—and not

Fig E

②surgeon uses laparoscope to remove her egg

③egg is placed in glass dish in lab and

④fertilised with sperm from husband

①woman's tubes are hopelessly blocked

⑤fertilised egg is grown in lab for a short time

⑥it's then inserted into the mother's womb via her vagina

The test tube baby technique: how the Steptoe-Edwards method by-passes the blocked tube.

long after, the fertilized ovum is inserted into the woman's womb, via a slim tube passed up through her vagina.

Remember, however, that at present the technique is very expensive. Furthermore, at the moment only a minority of attempts succeed. If you're paying for each attempt, you could ruin yourself financially before you become pregnant.

Still, it's undoubtedly a great step forward in combating infertility. (By the way, the 'test-tube baby technique' is something of a misnomer, since at no stage is a test-tube involved in any way.)

Surrogate motherhood

This technique is far more controversial. And in some parts of the world, it would actually be illegal—especially if done on a commercial basis.

So what is it? Well, if a woman is infertile but her husband *is* fertile, then it is of course possible for another woman to bear a child for them. She carries the baby for nine months—but after it's born, she hands it over to the couple.

I'm certain that arrangements like this have been going on discreetly for many years, using the 'traditional' method of fertilization. In other words, the infertile wife tells her husband that he can sleep with the other woman.

But since the early 1980s, there's been a movement towards a more 'clinical' form of surrogate motherhood, in which a clinic arranges for the other woman to become pregnant by the husband through artificial insemination of his sperm. Hefty sums of money are often involved.

Personally, I don't find it possible to criticize a couple who want a baby so desperately that they go in for this kind of thing. But they should bear in mind the possible drawbacks, which include the following:

- the surrogate mother may become so attached to the child that she refuses to part with it

- all sorts of difficulties can arise with the surrogate mother's husband, if she has one

- if she has a husband—or indeed, a lover—confusion can arise as to who really *is* the father of the child

- if the child is born handicapped, there may be a temptation for the infertile woman to reject it.

Surrogate fatherhood

I use this term to describe an age-old practice which doesn't hit the headlines as surrogate motherhood does.

It's this: for centuries, women whose marriages are infertile have quietly got themselves pregnant by men other than their own partners. In Britain, this is sometimes lightheartedly known as 'the milkman syndrome'.

Quite seriously, this procedure is very widespread. Some years ago, a doctor did a study on blood groups in a very respectable provincial English town. The families whom she was investigating had one thing in common: at one stage in their lives, all of the parents had attended an infertility clinic—apparently with successful results, because they now all had children.

However, what the doctor found from her study of these families' blood groups was almost unbelievable. *Nearly 40% of the children couldn't have been sired by the men who were supposed to be their fathers.*

The conclusion is obvious. Many of the women had decided that their husbands were unlikely to give them a child—and had discreetly 'gone elsewhere'.

> *Many of the women had decided that their husbands were unlikely to give them a child and had discreetly gone elsewhere*

When I say that this tradition is 'centuries old', I'm not exaggerating. I recently visited an Italian spa town which has been famous since the Middle Ages as a centre for treating infertility. For about 500 years, women have gone there to have warm vaginal irrigations with the spa water. This treatment is alleged to have helped countless marriages to overcome fertility problems.

However, a few conversations with local doctors rapidly gave me another perspective on this so-called cure. They cheerfully acknowledge that over the centuries, many of these women have actually become pregnant as a result of a rather more effective intravaginal therapy provided by the local shepherds...

Obviously, I can't say that I would recommend this time-honoured method of surrogate fatherhood to women whose husbands are infertile. AID or adoption would seem to be preferable, and less likely to cause disruption in the family. If you *are* driven by desperation to do it, then for heaven's sake pick somebody who both looks like your partner and can be depended upon to be discreet!

Adoption

If you're having fertility problems, you may at first find it difficult to reconcile yourself to the fact that, in the long run, adoption may possibly be the only answer.

But when it's beginning to look as though your fertility problem may not be overcome, you should start thinking very hard about adoption—before it's too late. (Adoption societies are notoriously reluctant to allot children to couples whom they regard as 'too old'.)

In many western countries these days, there's a terrible shortage of babies for adoption. This is due to various factors: the availablility of efficient contraceptives, the prevalence of abortion; and the fairly recent trend for single women to keep their babies rather than have them adopted.

But if you try hard enough and early enough, there are children available for adoption—especially if you're willing to accept one who is handicapped, or perhaps of a different race from yourselves.

Certainly, adoption can bring wonderful benefits to a childless couple. Again and again, I've seen a transformation in the lives of people who were miserable and even embittered because they hadn't succeeded in having children—and who have found a new purpose in living thanks to the arrival of an adopted child.

7

Sex and Contraception

Down with James Bond!

Yes, down with James Bond and his naughty ways! What am I talking about? Well, for some time now, I've been campaigning in the media about the very bad contraceptive example set by James Bond (and by various other fictional heroes of today).

What I'm complaining about is the lunatic way in which Bond leaps into bed with girls—and *never bothers to take any contraceptive precautions!* I'm glad to say that organizations as diverse as the Family Planning Association and the Salvation Army agree with me that this is no example to set the public.

It's no wonder that so many young adults (and, indeed, many quite mature or even middle-aged adults) are stupid enough to go round making love without using contraception. And no wonder too that so many unwanted pregnancies result from this irresponsible approach to sex.

Seriously, unless you're actually *trying* for a baby, it's absurd to have sex without using some sort of efficient contraceptive. Use one of the available methods detailed in this chapter, and your love-making shouldn't only be fun—but *safe* as well.

P.S. Actually I have to admit that I really love the James Bond stories. But I wish to heaven that M would order the fellow to go and get himself a vasectomy.

Making your choice

There's a wide range of contraceptive measures available these days—so many that unwanted pregnancies (and abortions) really should be more or less a thing of the past. So look through the list here, and make your choice—*preferably together*. Because contraception isn't—as so many men seem to think—just the woman's responsibility: it's the man's as well.

Regrettably, male-dominated medical science has tended to invent contraceptives which have to be used by women—*and whose side-effects women must suffer* (the pill— invented by men—being a case in point). But the few male methods (particularly vasectomy) are slowly gaining ground. And it's not generally realized that in most western countries, the sheath is now only fractionally less widely used than the Pill—partly as a result of the Pill scares of recent years.

In making your choice, you need to ask yourselves two questions:

- which methods are *aesthetically* acceptable to you as a couple?

- how *effective* is each method?

Your aesthetic reaction to an individual method is a subjective matter. When you've read the description of each method in this chapter, you'll be able to assess whether the thought of a particular method makes you shudder, or strikes you as a decidedly good idea.

What about the *effectiveness* of the various methods? To help you assess this, I have included something which you won't often see: it's a simple table of effectiveness of the various commonly-used types of contraception.

Such tables are usually expressed in percentages, and I've found that these confuse people hopelessly. For instance, they think that '90% effective' means that you'll get pregnant one out of every 10 times you make love.

What my table does is this. *It tells you what would happen if 100 couples used the method for a year. The figure shown against each method indicates the number of women who would be likely to get pregnant during that time.*

Method	Number out of 100 women who would get pregnant by the end of a year
Vasectomy	Nil
Sterilization	Nil
Pill	Nil
IUD	2
Mini-pill	2
Diaphragm (Cap)	3 or 4
Sheath	3 or 4
Rhythm	15 approx.
Withdrawal	20 approx.
Nothing	30 plus

I have to stress that there's much argument about the effectiveness figures. Also, they depend a great deal on such factors as age and motivation, and are therefore approximate.

So, a couple aged 45, for example, who were

tremendously well motivated to use the rhythm method properly could very likely assume that its failure rate for them would be very low indeed. A highly-fertile couple of 20-year-olds, on the other hand, whose main idea in life was to make love to each other as often as they could get near each other, would almost certainly find the rhythm method about as successful as the maiden voyage of the *Titanic*.

Women: the choices

I'm very reluctant to divide the various contraceptive techniques into 'women's methods' and 'men's methods'; as I say, the choice should ideally be made *together*.

However, we have to be practical. Women do often make the choice for themselves— sometimes because it's forced on them by a male lack of interest in contraception! But also, in today's world, it often happens that a woman with *no* regular partner makes a conscious decision in favour of a particular form of contraception which will protect her, if and when she takes a lover (or lovers).

So, what are the choices available to a woman? From the list of commonly-used methods in the table above, you'll see that she has the option of:

- sterilization
- the Pill
- the IUD (loop, coil, etc)
- the mini-Pill
- the diaphragm (cap)
- rhythm

All these methods are discussed in full below, plus certain newer and/or less widely available methods of female contraception.

The Pill

The Pill remains fantastically popular in most western countries. For instance, in Britain there was a time quite recently when a startling *one in three* of all women of child-bearing age was taking it!

But although the Pill has been in widespread use for many years (it was invented in 1956), there are still worries about it—and new facts are constantly coming to light about it. So it's better not to go on it unless you've fully discussed any doubts you may have (and any recent alarming reports) with your doctor or clinic.

Having said that, I have to add that the Pill is probably the most outstandingly successful contraceptive of all time. Taken properly— which means for 21 days out of every 28—it will give you virtually 100% protection against pregnancy.

It does this because it contains two female-type hormones (an oestrogen and a progestogen). These affect the pituitary gland—at the base of the brain—so that it no longer sends out signals telling your ovaries to ovulate.

Side-effects

Most women who go on the Pill get no side-effects. But during the first few packs, a substantial number do experience headache, nausea, breast tenderness, weight gain or bleeding between periods.

Serious side-effects are rare. But cases of thrombosis (clots) can be *fatal*. The danger of this happening is much greater in smokers, in more mature (35-plus) women, and in those with certain other risk factors. In my view (and that of many other doctors), *heavy smokers should never take the Pill*. Even moderate smokers should try to give up this dangerous habit.

The relation of the Pill to cancer is very complex. At the time of writing, it *appears* (and I stress the word *appears*) that the Pill probably helps protect you against two types of cancer—of the ovary and the womb lining— but may increase the risk of other types, including cancer of the cervix.

The position should become clearer soon. Make sure you discuss any worrying reports with your doctor or clinic—and take advantage of regular smear tests for cancer of the cervix which all Pill-prescribing doctors or clinics can arrange. (For more details about gynaecological cancers, see Chapter 5.)

Finally, after all these warnings, do bear in mind that the Pill does have certain very *good* effects. In particular, a well-chosen brand should make your periods:

- painless
- shorter
- lighter.

The mini-Pill

The mini-Pill is used mainly by women who no longer wish to take the Pill (e.g. the over-35s) and by breast-feeding mothers (this is because, unlike the ordinary Pill, it doesn't suppress milk production).

It's not a low-dose version of the ordinary Pill, but is a quite different thing, containing only one hormone (a progestogen) instead of two. That's why it's often called 'the progestogen-only Pill' or 'POP'.

At the moment, it does appear to be much 'milder' than the ordinary Pill, and complaints of side-effects are much lower. Disruption of the periods is the chief possible side-effect: they may become too far apart, or irritatingly frequent!

The mini-Pill seems to work *mainly* by thickening the secretions in the cervix, making it difficult for sperm to get through. You must—repeat *must*—take it *every single day at about the same time, without any breaks at all.*

It's at maximum effectiveness about 6 to 8 hours after you take it. So if you usually make love in the late evening, you'll get the best protection by taking your mini-Pill each day at around 4 pm.

One word of warning: although the mini-Pill's reputation is as a very mild contraceptive, it *is* nonetheless a hormone. This means that its long-term effects will not be known for a long time to come. Pay attention to any health reports about it which appear and, if in doubt, do discuss any anxieties you may have with your doctor or clinic.

The IUD

'IUD' stands for 'intra-uterine device'. This description covers all of the many devices which are placed inside the womb, including the coil, the famous Lippes loop, and the various copper devices. You can see what the popular Copper Seven looks like inside the womb in Figure A.

Many millions of women worldwide rely on the IUD for protection against unwanted pregnancy. In the USA, however, its popularity has been limited by the sad occurrence of a number of disastrous infections in women who were using a brand called the Dalkon Shield.

That particular brand of IUD has long been taken off the market, but it must be admitted that there is a small danger of womb and tube infection with any type of IUD. Bear in mind that if the tube infection does occur and is left untreated, this could seriously affect your future fertility.

But the *common* side-effects of IUDs are:

- heavy periods
- prolonged periods
- expulsion of the device.

Despite these and other much rarer side-effects, IUDs suit four out of every five

Fig A

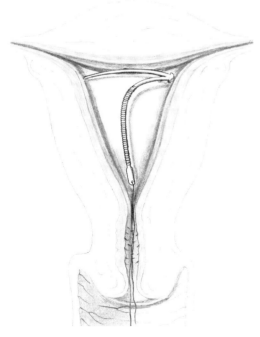

An I.U.D. in the womb—this is the Copper 7, the most popular type in the U.S.A.

women who try them. The insertion process takes only a few minutes; it's generally easier and less uncomfortable if the woman has had children.

The cap (diaphragm)

The cap or diaphragm has become more popular in recent years, probably as a result of various pill scares. The most widely-used contraceptive cap is a simple disc of rubber. As you can see from Figure B, the idea is that a woman slips it into her vagina *so that it covers her* cervix (the neck of her womb).

Before putting it in, she coats it with a contraceptive cream or gel. The combined effect of the barrier provided by the cap, plus the anti-sperm effect of the cream or gel, gives the woman a highly effective contraceptive device.

Rather surprisingly *neither she nor her partner should be able to feel the device once it's in position.* So a well-fitted cap shouldn't interfere with love-making in any way.

The important words here are 'well-fitted'. Women's vaginas vary substantially in size, so you must be fitted (by a doctor) with the size of cap which is right for you. Equally importantly, you have to be taught how to put the device in correctly before love-making, and how to take it out the following morning.

Many women don't find it that easy to put it in correctly. The cap *must* be inserted so that it covers the cervix—otherwise it will be quite useless.

When the cap fails to protect against pregnancy, the usual reason is that the woman has been putting it in the wrong place—usually in *front* of her cervix. So it's very important to be sure that you understand your own anatomy (and can feel your own cervix) before you rely on this method.

Fig B

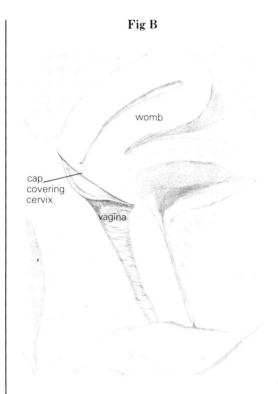

The woman puts the cap (diaphragm) into her vagina so that it covers her cervix, making a barrier to prevent sperms getting to her womb.

In recent years, some couples have gone in for putting the cap in together as part of love-play—but this isn't to everyone's taste.

Note: there are some rarer types of cap available in Britain and other countries (not widely in the USA) for women whose vaginal muscles are too lax for an ordinary diaphragm. Several new types of cap have also been invented recently.

The sponge

The Today Sponge (sold in some places under the name 'Prelude Sponge' or 'Collatex Sponge') came onto the market in various countries, including the UK and the USA, in the mid-1980s. It's a vaginal sponge, and the interesting thing about it is that it seems to be very acceptable aesthetically to many women who appreciate its non-messy qualities.

It's a soft disc of sponge, about 5 cm (2 in) across. You can see it in Figure C. The sponge comes already impregnated with spermicide, so you don't have to add any when you want to make love.

All you do, in fact, is to take the Today Sponge out of its pack, moisten it, and then gently tuck it into the topmost part of your vagina—using the tips of your index and middle fingers to ensure it fits tightly against the cervix. Neither you nor your partner should be able to feel it during intercourse.

The sponge has to be left in place for at least six hours after intercourse, though it can be left in for up to two days if necessary. When the time comes to remove it, you simply hook your finger round a polyester tape which is attached to the underside.

The Today Sponge is disposable, and you can buy it over the counter in a chemist's shop (without a doctor's prescription).

But how safe is the Today Sponge? There have been claims that it is 98% effective.

Fig C

The Today Sponge. The dimple is intended to enable the device to nestle over your cervix.

But recent trials have shown this to be a hopeless over-estimate! The International Planned Parenthood Federation now rates the sponge as being about as safe as a spermicide used alone—which is *not* very safe. My guess would be that if one hundred women used the Today Sponge for a year, at least ten of them would probably get pregnant.

Still, the sponge is a lot better than using nothing. And because it is also quite a nice sort of thing to pop into your vagina, many women feel that it's worth keeping a few in the house (or in the suitcase), just in case of a romantic encounter.

The spermicide which is contained in the sponge is now believed to give at least some protection against sexual infection—though I don't think it would be much insurance against AIDS.

When the device was first introduced, back in the mid-1980s, a US congressman raised fears that it might cause cancer. So far these fears have not been borne out. But, as with any contraceptive, you should keep an eye out for adverse reports. If in doubt, ask your doctor.

> *At the start of the 1990s, over half a million women had used the Capsule*

There have also been suggestions that the sponge could be a *theoretical* cause of the dangerous Toxic Shock Syndrome (the serious infection which is occasionally caused by using tampons). But any risk must be very small.

The Capsule

At the start of the 1990s, over half a million women had already used the Capsule.

'What on Earth is the Capsule?' I hear you cry! Well, it's a new system of delivering a hormone into a woman's bloodstream by implanting six little silastic capsules under the skin of her arm, as you can see from the drawing (Figure D) on the next page.

The idea is that these capsules will continuously release a contraceptive hormone, keeping you safe from pregnancy for a period of *five years*.

Obviously, the capsules have to be implanted under your skin by a doctor. It is a minor procedure, with virtually no pain. You are given a small jab of local anaesthetic, just above the elbow. Then the doctor inserts the six rods—each of which is about 3 cm (1⅓ in) long—in a sort of fan shape, as you can see overleaf.

There's no need for you to be stitched up; just a bit of gauze and a plaster will usually suffice.

The Capsule, known in most parts of the world by the trade-name Norplant, is certainly very effective. The makers claim that it is the second most efficient method of contraception (sterilization being the first). I'm not yet entirely convinced by that myself! But it certainly does seem to be about 99.5% effective—which means that if 200 women used it for a year, only one would get pregnant.

However, there is evidence that heavier women may *not* be so well protected by the Capsule—they may need a slightly bigger dose of hormone.

What about getting the six rods out again? This too must be done by a doctor. As with the insertion, a small nick in the skin has to be made after giving a local anaesthetic injection. But removal isn't usually painful or difficult.

How does the Capsule work? The hormone in it is called 'levonorgestrel', one of the two hormones contained in very well-known Pill brands such as Ovranette and Microgynon. Released day and night from

Fig. D

1.3 inches

Hormone
released

The Capsule

your arm over a period of five years, it does three things which help to keep you from getting pregnant:

- in about 50% of your cycles, it stops you ovulating

- it alters the lining of your womb so that it's not receptive to a pregnancy

- it thickens the secretions of your cervix, making it difficult for sperm to get through.

Well now, this all sounds very good, but there are drawbacks with everything—and that applies to the Capsule too.

The main side-effect of Norplant is that it disturbs the periods in a very high proportion of women. Periods tend to come at irregular intervals, and there may be bleeding (or just slight 'spotting') between them.

Some women *lose* their periods—and this may cause confusion over whether they're pregnant or not. (If you ARE pregnant, you must have the little rods removed at once.)

However, these menstrual problems do tend to settle down after several months of use. So it may be worth putting up with a moderate amount of irregular bleeding for a few months before asking for the tubes to be taken out.

Other possible side-effects include:

- nausea or vomiting

- dizziness

- headache

- weight gain

- spotty skin

- possibly depression

possibly loss of interest in sex.

Infection at the site of insertion of the rods is a faint possibility, but very unlikely if the doctor is good at her or his job.

The major question-mark which hangs over the Capsule and all other methods of hormonal contraception is this: *could it cause cancer?*

And the honest answer is that we don't know, and probably won't know for many years to come.

Note: other hormone implant devices are under development, and they mostly work in the same way as the Capsule.

The female condom

One of the most extraordinary developments of the last few years has been the female condom. It was, of course, invented as a response to the AIDS crisis—in the hope that it would give women a simple method of protecting themselves against the HIV virus. In fact, neither the male nor the female condom can give anything like *complete* protection against 'the big A', but they certainly *help*, and so are well worth using.

You can see the female condom in Figure E on this page. It's made of rubbery material, and is rather similar in shape to a male sheath, but a bit wider. The idea is that the lady places the larger (outer) ring over the opening of her vagina—and 'feeds' the rest inside her vagina. The man's penis should then stretch it out to its fullest extent.

In its early days, the female condom has run into certain technical problems over lack of lubrication, but these should soon be overcome. On the credit side, many women who've tried it out report that the outer ring does rub very pleasantly against the clitoris during love-making! I suppose that's what you'd call being 'user friendly'.

The Morning-after Pill

It's now very common to use 'morning-after' methods to prevent unwanted pregnancy. In Britain and most western countries, these methods are *not* regarded by the vast majority of doctors (or by the Law) as producing an abortion. So the Morning-

Fig. E

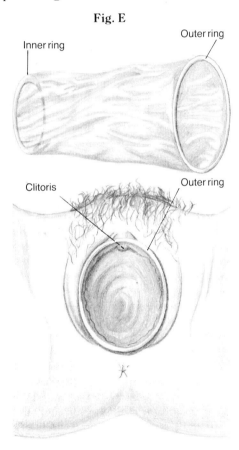

The Female Condom

after Pill is very widely prescribed by family doctors and Family Planning Clinics.

However, this definitely isn't a 'routine' method of contraception: it should only be used in emergency—say, after a rape, or after a condom has broken.

The Morning-after Pill (often known by the trade-name 'Schering PC4') must be taken as soon as possible after intercourse —72 hours is the limit. There's also a 'Morning-after Coil', which can be used slightly later.

The DIY termination agent

The 'do-it-yourself' termination agent is the highly controversial French drug called 'RU–468' or 'mifepristone'. Over 25,000 Frenchwomen have taken it in order to rid themselves of an unwanted pregnancy— and large numbers of women in other parts of the world have done the same.

Quite understandably, the very existence of this tablet has upset a great many people. They regard its use as immoral. In the late 1980s, pressure groups briefly forced the manufacturers to take the drug off the market. But on the orders of the French Government (!), the makers were forced to start producing it again.

In contrast, women's groups seem to be very much in favour of RU–468, taking the view that it will help women control their own fertility. It seems likely to me that in countries where it remains banned, women will smuggle it in.

In Britain, the drug is still only being used on a small scale, under strict medical control. It is given as soon as possible after a period is noted to be overdue. At present British Law requires its use to be legally notified as causing an abortion.

The drug has to be used in conjunction with vaginal pessaries containing prostaglandins. The combination produces an effectiveness rate of 95%.

Both mifepristone and the prostaglandins are fairly powerful drugs, and I must emphasize that long-term side-effects are still a bit of a mystery. You should most definitely NOT use these drugs without medical approval. Do bear in mind that if you used them off your own bat and did NOT bring the pregnancy to an end, the foetus would have been exposed at a critical time in its development to two very potent hormones.

The Shot (the Jab)

The Shot, also known as the Jab (or, in Scotland, the Jag), is a highly effective contraceptive, which is now used by over two million women worldwide.

It's an injection which gives you nearly (not quite) 100% protection against pregnancy—usually for a period of three months. (A larger dose gives longer protection.) The commonest brand-name is 'Depo-Provera'.

Early in its use, in the 1980s, feminist organizations, black women's groups and parliamentarians were quite rightly very indignant about the way in which certain doctors had bunged this drug into women without telling them about side-effects (and, in some cases, without even getting consent!).

These unethical practices seem to be much rarer now and, in fact, many women actually plead to be given the Shot when they feel that no other contraceptive will do.

But do bear in mind that the Shot has a lot of side-effects: nearly half of all users have disruption of their periods (either too frequent or none at all). Headaches and weight gain are quite common. And if you get side-effects when you've had a jab, there's no way of getting it out again!

Also, no one can yet say if the Shot might eventually cause cancer. So always ask your doctor about the latest research on this.

Rhythm—and other 'natural' methods

The last few years have seen some renewed interest in the rhythm method ('the safe period'). This is particularly true in the USA where strenuous attempts have been made to develop a really effective device which will pinpoint the 'danger time' of the month during which a woman is fertile.

Unfortunately, these attempts have not yet been very successful. A device which measures the electrical resistance of a woman's skin (which varies at different times of the month) hasn't yet given good enough results. Nor has a do-it-yourself technique for measuring ions in the mucus on the cervix.

Women's groups have popularized the new idea of *feeling your own cervix* to find out what stage of the month you've reached. The idea is that, each day, you pop a finger into your vagina and learn to recognize the 'soft' feeling which can be noted around the time of ovulation. Unfortunately, this technique is not easy, and (so far) not very successful.

More promising is the prospect of new *chemical tests* which will help a woman identify the start of her 'danger time'. Several excellent urine tests (such as the Unipath Clearplan One Step) are already on the market which will tell you when ovulation is about to commence.

Alas, by then it's a bit late, since you should have stopped intercourse several days previously!

I feel fairly optimistic that someone will soon develop a simple, inexpensive urine test system. Such a system would let a woman know *exactly* where she is in her monthly cycle so that she can plan her love-making accordingly. (It would be a good idea if the Vatican were to fund the research and development costs.)

Traditional rhythm method

For the moment, however, couples who want to use the 'safe period' have to rely on the 'traditional' variants of the rhythm method, which are:

● the temperature chart technique

● the Billings technique ('knicker gazing').

Both techniques aim to help you identify your most fertile time—which is likely to be *about* a fortnight or so before the start of a period.

The *temperature chart technique* involves plotting your body temperature on a special graph each morning (see Figure A, Chapter 6).

The *Billings technique* involves looking at your vaginal secretions each day, and recording the nature of them on a special chart (provided by Billings Clinics or Catholic Marriage Guidance Clinics). The secretions are usually thin, clear and slippery just before ovulation.

Frankly, my personal view is that neither the Billings nor the temperature chart technique is very safe. But if you do decide to try them, DON'T do it without medical help.

There are excellent clinics which are run under the auspices of Catholic Marriage Advisory Councils and similar organizations and which provide thorough and dedicated training.

Lactation methods

In recent years, it has been shown that really intensive breast-feeding does provide a good measure of protection against pregnancy. The !Kung tribe of central Africa, for instance, are able to space their families very successfully because of the fact that the !Kung women breast-feed intensively over a period of about two years after the birth of a baby.

The British Medical Research Council has shown in Edinburgh that some women from the tribes of central Scotland can also do this. You have to realize, however, that when I speak of 'intensive' breast-feeding, I really do mean *intensive*.

!Kung women put the baby to the breast every hour or two throughout the 24 hours, until the child is about two years old. (No wonder they have an exclamation mark in front of their names.)

Not many western women have the time, nor the inclination, for that kind of commitment to breast-feeding over such a long period of time. On the other hand, I have known a number of Irish medical couples who have quite deliberately decided to make the best possible use of lactation as a contraceptive method by continuing intensive breast-feeding for as long as possible—or at any rate, until the youngster has acquired a set of teeth!

Female sterilization

In contrast, the last female method that I am going to deal with is far more popular: sterilization, a most effective method.

In most western countries (and many developing ones) the use of sterilization, both female and male, has increased dramatically in recent years. A very large number of couples are choosing sterilization once they have completed their families.

Male sterilization (vasectomy) is dealt with later in this chapter. As for female sterilization, the first thing to understand is what it does. As you can see from Figure F, the point of the operation is to block the woman's Fallopian tubes in some way, so that the sperm cannot get to the ovum.

This can be done by cutting through the tubes and tying them off, or by clipping them with a device like a very firm plastic paperclip. The effectiveness of sterilization is very *nearly* 100%, but it's important to realize that, as with any operation, occasional failures do occur.

The two common methods of carrying out the procedure are:

traditional sterilization

laparoscopic sterilization.

'Traditional' sterilization requires a longer stay in hospital. It's done through an incision—perhaps 10 or 13 cm (4 or 5 ins) long—in the lower part of the abdomen, round about the top of the bikini line.

Laparoscopic sterilization is the newer and much more minor operation. It's done with the aid of the slim, telescope-like viewing device called the laparoscope. This is pushed through a very tiny incision near the navel, while a 'tube-clipping' instrument is pushed through another very small incision in the woman's side. The two cuts are so small that, in the USA, this is known as 'the Band-Aid operation'.

Fig. F

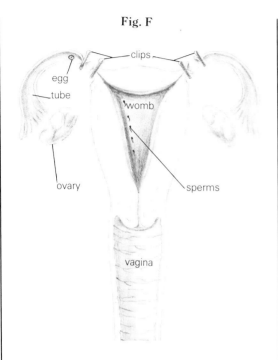

Female sterilization: the surgeon can block the Fallopian tubes by cutting, clipping or tying them. Whatever method is used, the egg should no longer be able to reach the sperm.

Quite obviously, most women would prefer to have this newer operation, but it's not available everywhere in the world; not all women are suitable for it; and there is a slightly higher failure rate (i.e. pregnancy rate) than with traditional sterilization.

MEN: their new role

So now we turn to male contraceptive methods. It will become immediately apparent to you that this part of the chapter is far shorter than the female part! The reason for this is quite simply that, so far, there are few effective male methods of contraception. Contraceptives have, on the whole, been invented by men—for women to be the guinea-pigs.

However, things are slowly changing. Although, as we shall see in a moment, there is no effective male pill on the near horizon, the fact is that vast numbers of men do now use the only really efficient male methods—the sheath and vasectomy.

Also, thank heavens, more and more thoughtful, caring males are starting to play a part in discussing what method the couple are going to use. You'll never believe this, but some men actually go along to the Family Planning Clinic with their partners in order to take part in the consultation and help choose which method is best. A few of them even offer to abstain from sex for a while, to give their partners a rest from the Pill—though that's pretty rare!

The sheath (condom)

Although a lot of people are put off by the idea of the sheath, there is no doubt that it's one of the most popular and effective methods of contraception in the world. In most western countries, it's only just behind the Pill in the popularity stakes—and if there are any more Pill scares, it will probably regain the Number One position that it had in pre-Pill days.

I believe that more women should insist on their partners wearing a sheath—especially as, unlike the Pill or the IUD, it has virtually no side-effects. (A very few people are allergic to rubber, or to chemicals used in the process of vulcanization of rubber—but they can use 'hypo-allergenic' sheaths.)

There's also the very important plus-point that a sheath (like a diaphragm) probably helps to protect a woman against cancer of the cervix. It also gives at least some protection against infection.

Indeed, sheaths are so useful that a small but increasing number of independent-minded women do carry them themselves for their own protection—and if they decide to go to bed with a lover, they make sure he uses one!

Some men who are having a bit of trouble with their potency do find it a little difficult to put a condom on—indeed, it's really quite common for women to say to a doctor, 'We can't use the sheath, because my husband can't get on with it. . .'

The answer to this problem is to make the putting on of the sheath *a part of love-play*. In other words, the woman can stimulate the man's penis with her hands—as described in Chapter 8—until it's really hard. Then she can gently unroll the condom onto it. *That* usually solves the problem.

Note that sheath manufacturers have at last cottoned on to the idea of making sheaths that will give women pleasure. They now make condoms with gentle 'ribbing' on the sides, so as to increase vaginal stimulation. Some women also appreciate the new coloured condoms, which look a lot better than the rather unattractive khaki shades of yesteryear.

Finally, it has to be admitted that sheaths do sometimes break. For that reason, many family planning specialists do recommend that you use a spermicide as an added precaution.

Some sheaths are now supplied with a pre-added spermicide. Alternatively, you can buy and use a *separate* spermicidal preparation. In Britain, it is common for a couple to insert a spermicidal pessary (vaginal tablet) about 10 minutes before intercourse: in America and some other countries, a spermicidal aerosol foam is more common.

Vasectomy

While I was preparing this book, I was a bit disturbed to read that vasectomy had just been declared a crime in Italy. Yes—it's now a criminal offence, for both surgeon *and* patient! Presumably tourists with vasectomies will still be allowed in: at least, I hope so—because I happen to have had one.

In Spain too, the governing body of the medical profession regards vasectomy as a crime. In most civilized countries, however (especially those where the *machismo* tradition is dying) vasectomy has become fantastically popular in recent years. Surgeons find it hard to keep up with the demand, and it has almost become a matter of routine for the younger middle-aged man to consider getting himself vasectomized, to spare his wife the health risks of more years on the Pill or the IUD.

Indeed, among medical families in Britain, a recent study showed that about a quarter now rely on either vasectomy or female sterilization as their method of contraception (with a 50/50 split between the two methods).

As you can see from Figure G, a vasectomy is really a very simple business indeed—and far less complex and traumatic than female sterilization because the 'plumbing' is all external. The operation is often done under local anaesthetic—and indeed, I watched my own being done (though I wouldn't recommend this to the faint-hearted).

In the few days after the operation, the man can expect a fair amount of bruising and swelling. He should wear a support, and may need to take some painkillers. He should definitely *not* undertake any heavy work (lifting, etc.) for several days.

There are a few complications, such as the occasional stitch slipping, leading to bleeding or a large but temporary swelling. Inevitably, this happened to *me*—and I had to spend about three weeks in bed. For full horrendous details, see Dr Richard Gordon's best-seller *Great Medical Disasters* (London: Heinemann Books).

But I've never known anybody come to any long-term harm from a vasectomy. Unusually for surgical operations, no deaths have *ever* been reported—except for two tragic cases of lockjaw which occurred in two men who were operated on in insanitary conditions in India.

Happily, a couple can resume love-making as soon as they like after the operation (some have been known to manage it about 2½ hours afterwards!). The man will not be 'safe', how-ever, until he has had—on average—about a dozen climaxes, to clear out all the sperm in the upper part of his piping.

Surgeons recommend a simple sperm test, usually carried out two or three months after the operation, to make sure that no sperm is left in the fluid. Until then, the couple should use another method of contraception.

Yes, there *is* fluid produced—effectively the same volume as before. And yes—sex is just as good afterwards as it was previously.

However, men with psychosexual problems should be screened out by the counselling sessions provided before a vasectomy—partly because a man who has deep fears of castration may mistakenly get the idea that the operation has lessened his potency, or affected him in other ways. (As I was completing this book, a notorious British rapist was being convicted; he had the nerve to claim in court that his crimes were due to his vasectomy!)

Finally, if as a couple you decide on this method, there is one other thing you should bear in mind. It is this: *do not go in for it if you think you might change your mind.*

In general, it is best to regard vasectomy as an irreversible step. There *is* an operation to reverse it, but the results are not very good. So both of you should be very sure that vasectomy is the right *permanent solution to the question of contraception in your relationship.*

Note: No operation has a 100% success rate, and there are very rare cases in which a man fathers a child long after an apparently successful vasectomy.

The male pill

There *isn't* an effective and widely available male pill at the moment, although couples

Fig G

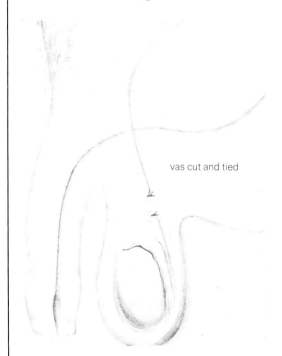

vas cut and tied

Vasectomy (see also figure P in Chapter 2).

often go to the doctors asking for it! Regrettably, most efforts at developing a successful male pill have foundered—mainly because the female hormones which are used have had disastrous effects on a man's virility.

The French have tried to get round this by giving a special ointment to men who had volunteered to take the male pill. The ointment contained *male* hormones, and the idea was that a man should spread it on his skin to counteract the dreaded *impuissance*.

I need hardly tell you what happened: the wives and/or mistresses of these intrepid Frenchmen accidentally absorbed the male hormone ointment through the contact of skin against skin. The poor women promptly started growing moustaches!

So the development of a male pill hasn't exactly been a riotous success so far. The most hopeful development comes from China, where it has been discovered that male fertility is low in a region of the country where people cook with cottonseed oil.

Chinese doctors have found that the fall in sperm count is due to an ingredient called 'gossypoll'. A gossypol pill does remove all sperm from the seminal fluid—a discovery which lends an entirely new meaning to the phrase 'Chinese take-away'.

However, gossypol does also take away dangerous amounts of the body's vital potassium reserves. Until this and other side-effects can be beaten, gossypol is unlikely to be widely used as a male pill.

But the Chinese research has directed scientists' attention to the fact that non-hormonal chemicals of this sort can lower the sperm count. Already, researchers are looking at various non-hormone drugs which have a similar effect.

Choosing together

I hope that by now you have got the message that the main point of this chapter is that contraception is something which a couple should, if possible, choose *together*.

Of course, a woman who is on her own but having occasional relationships must make the choice for herself. But for the stable couple, the choice of contraceptive should, whenever possible, be a joint one.

A footnote about abortion

I have said nothing about abortion in this chapter—because, of course, abortion is *not* a form of contraception. To many people, abortion is a repugnant business, but it's a fact of life that it occurs in every country in the world. Indeed, in many western countries, at least one pregnancy in five ends in abortion. This is really rather tragic—particularly when effective contraception is so readily available.

This book takes no sides in the debate about abortion. But if you do find yourself in the situation where you feel you have to try and obtain one, I'd just like to make two points.

First, if it has to be done, then it's better done as *early* as possible—because the risks to the woman increase drastically as the pregnancy becomes more advanced. And second, if you decide to have it done, then do not for heaven's sake go to an amateur or 'back street' abortionist—or risk the terrible dangers of attempting it yourself. *You may well end up dead.* A termination is never a pleasant experience—but at least if it's done by a qualified and experienced gynaecologist early in the pregnancy, the risks to your life and your health are minimal.

8

Love-play

Why love-play?

Yes, why have love-play? What's the point of it all?

Quite a few bewildered people (mostly of the male persuasion) ask that question. They can't quite see why sex needs to be more than a question of a man putting his penis inside a woman and thrusting away like mad—just like they do in the men's magazines.

But in the real world, things aren't like that at all! For a start, one thing that every young lad needs to know is that most women will *not* have a climax unless they are given a little love-play—certainly before intercourse, perhaps during it, and possibly afterwards too.

Strange as it may seem, this comes as shattering news to many males. But it's true. The majority of women don't usually reach a climax during intercourse itself—only during love-play. So for them, no love-play usually means no climax (and, almost certainly, no *multiple* climaxes).

Furthermore, every man needs to know that nearly all women find intercourse uncomfortable or even downright painful *if there hasn't been preliminary love-play.*

Why? Firstly because love-play makes the woman's vagina start secreting those famous 'love juices' which are so absolutely vital to lubricate the process of intercourse. Without them, the vagina would be so dry that intercourse would be very unpleasant indeed for

117

the woman (and not a lot of fun for most men).

Secondly, preliminary love-play makes the vaginal muscles—which guard the opening of the the vagina—open up in preparation to receive the penis. If a man tries to enter before that initial opening up process is completed, she will feel discomfort and even pain. And in the case of some couples, he won't be able to get in at all—this is a common cause of non-consummation of a marriage!

Thirdly, love-play makes the woman's vagina lengthen as she gets more sexually excited— so that there is much more room inside.

Those are the purely mechanical reasons why love-play is so important to women. But it's also tremendously important from a *romantic* point of view, as we shall see in a moment.

First, however, we shall deal with the question of love-play *as something women can do to men too*. Yes, it's true, dear female readers: you aren't the only ones who need love-play. Your partner will benefit greatly from it too.

Why? Well, once again let's look at the purely mechanical aspect of sex for a moment. Vast numbers of men have difficulties and worries over their erections. 'Will I be able to get it hard?'. . . 'Will it *stay* hard?'. . . 'Will it collapse on me?'

That's one reason why so many of them do stupid things like leap inside a woman the moment they've achieved an erection—they're terrified it might collapse!

But if a man's in bed with a woman who is skilled at love-play, he need have no anxieties whatever. For with deft fingers and lips, she will assuredly bring him to an erection—perhaps many times in an evening, depending how matters develop.

Indeed, I'm convinced that a woman who is really adept at love-play could cure most cases of impotence single-handed (so to speak). Would that there were more such women around! In fact, some sex therapy programmes—particularly in the USA—have deliberately recruited women who *are* outstandingly good at love-play, so as to help men who have sexual difficulties and anxieties.

Actually, even the most active and 'virile' of males who has no doubts or anxieties about his 'performance' will nonetheless benefit from being on the receiving end of skilled love-play techniques. This is partly because love-play plays such an important role in romance but the other point to make about love-play is this. *It's so very nice!*

After all, where else can you find an activity which can give such intense pleasure to two people? Love-play is really enormously agreeable and pleasant—and it's a great pity that more men and women don't know how to do it properly. Read on . . .

Romance and love-play

One of the main reasons that love-play is so good is that it is awfully romantic! Yes, romantic. Love-play is of course the natural progression of, say, a candlelit dinner, with soft lights, sweet music and the gentle touch of the hands across the dining table. Without love-play, there can be no romance.

Consider the sort of awful situations in which there is a complete *absence* of love-play, and you will see that they represent the exact opposite of romance. Here are a few such situations:

- a man going with a prostitute for a five-minute encounter

- a man coming home drunk and forcing himself on his wife

- a woman being raped.

In all of these unpleasant situations, the contact between man and woman is basic, squalid and brutish. There's no romance—and, of course, there's no love-play.

How very different when two people love each other and want to make each other happy! Right from the start, they do everything they can to 'pleasure' one another—and to make each other feel good and warm and wanted. In short, they use love-play—which is an essential ingredient of any romantic relationship between a man and a woman.

General caressing

How does love-play begin? Well, as you can see from the title of this section, it usually begins with General Caressing. And a fine old soldier he was too. . . .

I use the word 'general' because it is very important that the man—in particular—should always take care to avoid starting with any kind of *direct* approach to the woman's genitals.

Many males don't realize that most females are very definitely turned off by sudden, premature, unsubtle approaches to the vaginal region. Some men hold the touching belief that if you make a quick lunge towards a woman's vagina, she will promptly melt into your arms—but that is, of course, nonsense.

No: what nearly all women prefer is an indirect (and—yes!—romantic) approach in which the man:

- says nice things and tells her he loves her

- strokes her hair

- holds her hand

- strokes her shoulders

- strokes her arms

- strokes her back.

All of these actions, you'll notice, are pleasant and arousing—but sexually non-demanding. If a man does them to a woman, she can enjoy them without feeling pressurized. (This was really one of the great discoveries that the old firm of Masters and Johnson made in their researches at their sex clinic in St Louis, Missouri: they found that non-sexual caressing was a great way of building up somebody's confidence and making them feel relaxed and happy.)

From this stage, the experienced lover will move on to rather more specifically sexual caresses—but, if he's wise, without yet making a direct approach to the woman's vagina.

For example, he can:

- caress her buttocks

- stroke her legs

- fondle her breasts

- and, of course, kiss these parts of her body too.

Research with the amazing vaginal probe at London's Institute of Psychiatry shows very clearly that while this sort of pleasant caressing is going on, a woman's vagina does start preparing itself for love-making as she becomes more and more aroused.

Much the same principles of gradually increasing stimulation apply if you are a woman caressing your man. However, I have to admit that most men do prefer a rather more direct approach than is favoured by most women. So very few males will complain if a female fairly rapidly starts transferring her attention to his penis. Now read on . . .

Love-play with the fingers

So let's now move on to actual love-play with the fingers—what many people call 'petting'.

A lot of people get very embarrassed about this subject, and think that there is something terribly 'rude' about using your fingers to give your loved one sexual pleasure. But in actual fact, it's very hard to see how a couple could have a really good and satisfying sexual relationship if they didn't go in for 'finger-play'. Certainly, very few women would reach orgasm without it. (And still fewer would reach multiple orgasms.)

However, love-play with the fingers is *not* just an instinctive thing: you have to know what to do. If you do *not* know what to do, you will hurt your partner!

This is actually very common—especially among newly-weds. The couple leap into bed and, before very long, she makes a lunge for his penis and gives it a rather violent tweak. Result: he doubles up in temporary agony!

More seriously, a man can do a woman quite a lot of harm with clumsy, unskilled attempts at finger petting. What often happens is that he cuts her—externally or internally—with his fingernails. This can cause pain, and quite a lot of bleeding. And, most importantly, the pain may put her off sex for a very long time— and indeed help to cause the common sex difficulty called 'vaginismus' (see Chapter 11).

So, when using finger-play:

- be sure your nails aren't jagged

- be gentle

- if necesary, use a lubricant

- make sure you know what you're doing— and

- practise!

Now, what exactly do you do? Let us look first at the nice things a man can do for a woman—and then at the equally nice things she can do to him.

Things men can do for women

OK, so you're going to use your fingertips to give your partner pleasure. Begin by *gently* brushing your fingertips past the opening of her vagina. *Don't* rush things, and don't do anything silly like trying to ram a finger straight in immediately.

Instead, lovingly stroke the outside of her vagina. If you've wooed her carefully, lovingly and romantically, you'll find that she's already beginning to become moist with love juices.

Next, use the pads of your fingers to caress the area of her clitoris—as shown in Figure A. Rub gently on either side of it—or, if she prefers it, rub directly on it (though not all women like this). *Ask her what she likes.* There's no point in lying there doing something that simply doesn't turn her on!

If things are very dry round her clitoris, it may be worthwhile scooping up a little of her love juice on your fingertips. But if there's not much of it around, then there is no reason why you shouldn't lick your fingertips.

Alternatively, some couples use a lubricant, such as baby oil—or one of the lubricants sold in sex shops (see Chapter 9).

Learning how to stimulate a woman's clitoris properly is one of the great loving arts, which every man should master—though remarkably few do. If in doubt, remember: keep it gentle, but *fast*. And do what she likes—not what *you* think is best!

Once she is really moist, you may well wish to move on to the next stage of finger-play, which is slipping a finger *inside* her vagina. That is a very good preparation for inter-

Fig A

Love play: caressing her clitoris.

course; if more bridegrooms knew how to do it, there'ld be fewer unconsummated marriages.

You can use any of your fingers, but the middle one is usually the most effective. Slide it in gently as shown in Figure B.

Then move it softly but rapidly in and out. Do *not* make the movements too vigorous, or you may catch her delicate tissues with your fingernail. If you follow this finger technique properly, you'll find that your thumb or forefinger will, at the same time, rub gently against the region of her clitoris—so giving her added stimulation.

I'm not exaggerating when I say that really *mastering* this technique may take you years. Yet mastering it will pay rich dividends, in terms of the pleasure and satisfaction you'll give to your loved one.

But once you are reasonably adept at the 'middle finger method', then you can try some of the following:

- put your thumb inside instead, and gently rotate it

- put your middle *and* index fingers in, and use the pads of the two fingertips gently to stimulate her G-spot (if you don't know where that is, look back at Figure K in Chapter 2)

- use your index finger to stimulate the sensitive *sides* of her vagina

- use a finger pad to stimulate the back wall of her vagina (though not all women like this, so be guided by what the lady tells you)

- use the tips of two fingers to stimulate her cervix gently.

At all times, be gentle and sensitive. Take

Love play: caressing her vagina with your finger.

your lead from the speed and intensity of her breathing, from any little moans of pleasure she makes—and, above all, from what she asks you to do!

Things women can do for men

Now what can a woman do with her fingers to please a man?

Well, we men don't have as many (or as interesting) sex organs as you do. But we do have several areas which are very sensitive to soft female fingertips.

First of all, you can stroke your partner's nipples—most men like this. You will find that

122

his nipple gets a little erection, though not on the same scale as yours.

Next, you can stroke his testicles. This will not bring a man to a climax, but it's an agreeable and sometimes rather comforting sensation for him.

And finally, of course, there's his penis. There are various ways of stimulating this with your fingers. In practice, you need to find out what the man you love likes having done to his organ.

So for heaven's sake, ask him! Half the mixups and confusions in people's beds are caused by the fact that so many couples are too embarrassed to speak while they're trying to get each other excited.

Figure C shows in graphic—nay, explicit—detail the most common, and probably most effective, way in which a woman can stimulate her partner's penis. The arrows indicate the directions of movement, and the usual idea is to make each movement very fast (perhaps four times a second), but fairly gently.

Alternatively, you can go in for long, slow, languorous movements. Or you can hold his organ between your hands, and just squeeze and release it repeatedly, doing it lovingly and fairly firmly.

It's not generally known that you may well find it easier to do this sort of love-play if you actually anoint his penis with a little baby oil, or other bland lubricant. I gather that some men prefer talcum powder.

You may also find it helpful to hold his testicles with your other hand while you are gently rubbing his penis. Girls in massage parlours (who, I assume, probably know more about this than most people) have a technique in which they increase pleasurable tension in the penis by holding the testicles downwards with one hand while they rub the male organ with the other.

Love play: caressing his penis.

Fig C

All these finger techniques are useful in adding fun and fulfilment to a loving relationship. Don't worry—as some women do—that you will damage your partner's penis by handling it. (You're far more likely to damage his ego by *not* handling it.)

However, in a vigorous session of love-play, you should take care not to do two things when it's erect:

- don't twist it violently to one side—this is an occasional cause of quite serious injury (it's also quite a good thing to do to a would-be rapist!)

- don't 'twang' it back violently towards his feet—when it's erect, it's *not* meant to go that way.

Love-play with the lips and tongue

Naturally, the mouth plays a very important part in love-play. Kissing your partner all over is immensely agreeable—as is being kissed all over in return.

When you are doing this, you can of course combine caressing with your tongue. And don't forget those little nibbles and 'love-bites', which most people like being on the receiving end of.

But . . . it's best not to go in for love-bites around the sexual parts of the body, where they may cause damage and excessive pain.

What about love-biting the breasts? Some women like this, others don't—and may even by frightened by it. It's probably best not to love-bite the nipples (which are very sensitive in both sexes) but just to confine yourself to gentle sucking.

Now to the controversial subject of kissing the 'naughty bits'. I don't know why people still get so het up about this subject, but a lot of them are deeply offended by it, even today.

In fact, kissing someone in their most intimate part is the most natural and delightful way of showing your love—and of giving him or her great pleasure. It's certainly not to everybody's taste, but research does indicate that the majority of younger couples now go in for it.

Mouth-play for a man to use on a woman

So how can a man pleasure the woman he loves by using his lips and tongue? It's really quite simple. If you're a man who isn't used to this sort of thing, then just begin by giving long, lingering kisses to the upper part of your partner's pubic hair.

From there, you can move down and gently kiss the region of her clitoris. This gives most women tremendous pleasure and satisfaction—and it's a very useful way of helping the woman who has difficulty in reaching a climax.

Next, as shown in Figure D, you can gently titillate her clitoris with the tip of your tongue. This isn't easy to begin with, but after a little practice you'll find it tremendously effective in pleasing her.

Finally, there's a technique which gives many women great pleasure, but which not all men are keen on trying. It involves actually putting the tongue inside her vagina.

It's certainly well worth having a go at, though it's like oysters—a bit of an acquired taste! All you do is gently insert your tongue into your partner's vagina, and gently move it in and out. This is very effective—though if the lady gets very enthusiastic, you may find it a trifle difficult to draw breath!

This method of love-play is often used as part of the '69' manoeuvre.

Fig D

Love play: caressing her clitoris with your lips and tongue.

Mouth-play for a woman to use on a man

Now, what nice things can a woman do for her partner with her mouth? Basically it's just a question of using your lips and tongue to give him pleasure. You can, if you wish, take one of his testicles in your mouth—be very gentle since they are rather sensitive!

You can also kiss the area of skin just *behind* his testicles—an area which is very sexually receptive in most males.

But the thing which men appreciate most is direct stimulation of the penis. You can do this in three ways:

- simply kissing it (a nice, loving thing to do)

- licking it with your tongue (this is very sexually stimulating—and naturally, a great help to the man who has a bit of difficulty getting an erection) putting it in your mouth and sucking (you have to be careful not to give him a painful jab with your teeth!).

Once again, oral love-play techniques on the penis (termed 'fellatio') aren't to *everybody's* taste. But research shows that a very high proportion of couples do now enjoy it.

It's a great way for a woman to help her partner who's having a little difficulty in getting an erection. Learning how to do it properly takes a certain amount of time—but will pay rich dividends. If you aren't quite sure what to do, have a look at Figure E, which makes very clear just how lips and tongue can

Love play: caressing his penis with your lips and tongue.

Fig F

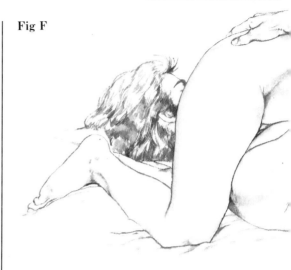

The soixante-neuf *position: so called because if you try really hard, you can imagine that your bodies are making the figures '69'.*

Fig E

126

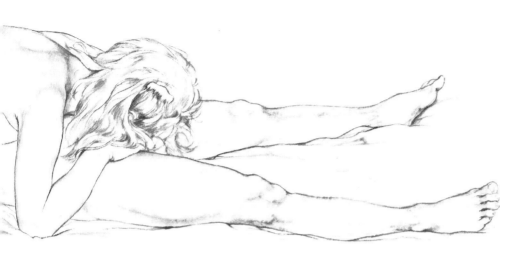

be used to help a man to reach an erection and to give him great pleasure in a very loving way.

Incidentally, you'll find that these oral love-play techniques on your partner are often best performed while he's doing much the same thing to you. This involves taking up the famous '69' or '*soixante-neuf*' position. As I still get letters from puzzled readers demanding '*Qu'est-ce que c'est, cette position soixante-neuf?*' we've illustrated it alongside for you in Figure F.

A warning about possible dangerous techniques

Finally, I'm all for people being as inventive and original as possible in their love-play, if it improves and enriches their relationship. But I ought to warn you that there are cetain love-play techniques which are widely practised and often mentioned in books—but which could be a bit dangerous.

It's obviously foolish to do anything which could be hazardous to your health or that of your partner. So I advise you to cast a wary eye over the list which follows.

Putting things in the vagina

Be very cautious about putting anything in the vagina except what nature intended for it! Unfortunately, some of those frightful and tacky men's magazines at the cheaper end of the market have given a lot of young males the notion that it's a good idea to play silly games with cucumbers, bananas and whatnot. This is no way to get your vitamin C!

Seriously, foreign bodies might possibly carry infection. *Hard* foreign bodies can damage the vagina—I have certainly encountered one case in which terrible damage was done to a woman because her husband was stupid enough to put a wooden rod inside.

And most hospital casualty officers are familiar with those incredible cases in which a woman arrives in an ambulance with a bottle or a jar jammed inside her. It's all right to put a clean vibrator in the vagina if you want to do so (see Chapter 9), but no other objects.

127

Incidentally, words fail me at the idea—given world-wide prominence in Shirley Conran's novel *Lace*—that a man can give a woman pleasure by putting a *goldfish* inside her vagina. If I heard of anybody doing such a stupid thing, I'd report them to the RSPCA (and that isn't a joke!).

Rectal love-play or 'bottom-play'

This seems to be almost universal among sophisticated couples these days (partly as a result of the influence of Marlon Brando's film *Last Tango in Paris*). I suppose it's not altogether surprising, since nature for some reason has equipped the bottom with a lot of sexually excitable nerve endings.

Rather astonishingly, there's no doubt that many women can reach a climax simply through having the rectal opening gently stimulated with a fingertip. This activity is called 'postillionage'.

Also, as readers of Harold Robbins novels will know, it's quite easy for a woman to slip a well-lubricated finger up a man's bottom and massage his prostate gland. This definitely helps some men get aroused, and gives an intense and rather unusual climax.

But...what the films and novels don't make clear is that the back passage is, of course, a germ-laden area of the body. To be blunt, a finger placed there will come away with germs on it. As you probably know, HIV, the germ of AIDS, is often transmitted by the rectal activities of homosexual males. I'm not suggesting that tickling your loved one's backside will give you AIDS. But if you decide to go in for that, then at the very least you ought to wash your hand afterwards. On no account put it near her/his genitals (or your own) till this has been done.

Incidentally, bottom-play without a lubricant is likely to be *very* uncomfortable, and may cause bleeding. This is why sales of butter are alleged to have gone up so dramatically after the afore-mentioned Marlon Brando film.

Using drugs to heighten love-play

This is widespread—and absolutely mad. I cannot over-emphasize the fact that drugs like heroin, cocaine and the various substances that people 'sniff' are likely to take away your sex drive, ruin your health, and very possibly kill you.

Some experts appear to think that *small* amounts of alcohol and 'pot' (which is, of course, illegal in most countries) can safely be used to relax people and so make love-play more agreeable. However, any doctor will tell you that *larger* amounts of alcohol have a serious adverse effect on people's love-lives—hence the well-known euphemism for impotence: 'brewer's droop'.

To sum up, don't spoil your love-play with drugs. They aren't a passport to instant happiness—in fact, they're more likely to be a passport to the grave.

9

Sex Aids

Are sex aids any good?

Today, the sex aid business is a multi-million dollar one. Vast quantities of alleged 'marital aids' are manufactured—and vast numbers of men and women (yes, women too!) buy them.

But are they any good? Are all these people wasting their money? And would sex aids help *you*?

Like most doctors, I was extremely suspicious when the first sex aids appeared on the market. I just couldn't see how mechanical or manufactured objects could play a part in a human activity—namely sex—which is so natural and spontaneous.

However, I have to say that there's now no doubt that a small number of sex aids really are helpful to some people—especially women who have trouble reaching orgasm.

In fact, I'd say that you can divide sex aids into three groups:

those which are genuinely helpful to some couples

those which are really just a bit of fun, if you happen to like that sort of thing

those which are *useless*—and possibly even dangerous.

So in this chapter, I'll try to help you distinguish between these three groups.

The seedy side of the sex aid business

One problem about trying to assess the merits (or dangers) of the various sex aids is that the whole sex aid industry has a very seedy image.

Why is this? It's partly because sex aid shops have sometimes been associated with people who have criminal connections. Many such shops are located in sleezy and insalubrious areas, and some are next door to prostitutes' premises.

Also, I have to be quite frank and say that some of the equipment sold by certain sex shops is quite alarming, and has decidedly unpleasant overtones of sadism and cruelty. I'm talking about whips, gags, masks, vicious-looking spiky belts, and so on.

On the other hand, one can't get away from the fact that, as I've said, a lot of couples are actually helped by some of the simple aids sold in sex shops. And an interesting development of recent years has been the fact that the sex aid industry has tried to improve its image by employing personable lady representatives to travel round the country, organizing women-only 'parties' or 'showers' (just like Tupperware parties) where people can buy items from the ... er ... demonstrator. Very sensibly, the saleswomen have tended to concentrate on relatively 'non-offensive' items, such as naughty lingerie.

Fig A

Naughty lingerie—enthusiastically promoted by sex goods manufacturers.

Naughty underwear

In Figure A, you can see the sort of lingerie which is sold as a sex aid. I think it's perfectly reasonable to say that these could put a bit of extra fun into a couple's relationship—and perhaps get their love-life going if things are flagging a bit.

The common items are see-through and 'baby-doll' nighties, G-strings, peek-a-boo bras, and open-crotch knickers. For males, there are also *very* abbreviated briefs and 'posing pouches' which some women like buying for their men.

I need hardly say that you don't have to go to a sex shop to get naughty undies. A lot of these items can now be bought quite easily (and possibly considerably cheaper) in high street stores.

Vibrators

Vibrators have been the one really big success of the sex aid industry. Much to my initial surprise, I've had many letters from women who have found them useful in overcoming lack of libido and failure to reach a climax.

The very idea of a vibrator puts many people off to begin with. But a considerable number of patients actually discover that they like them. They seem to be particularly helpful to three groups of females:

- women who are on their own (either temporarily or permanently)

- women whose husbands are unable to stimulate them properly because of disability (e.g. arthritis)

- women whose partners are—to be blunt— not all that skilled at, or enthusiastic about, love-play.

In addition, quite a lot of couples just use vibrators for sheer fun—or perhaps to spare them a lot of effort when they're tired. (One

Fig B

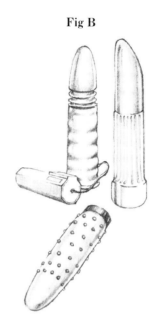

Common types of vibrator—mostly used to help women, but can be used on a man too.

woman told me quite frankly that when her husband was exhausted, they were both more than happy for her to 'finish herself off' with a vibrator.)

You can see several common types of vibrator in Figure B. The usual thing is for one or other partner just to hold them gently near or on the woman's clitoris, and let the gentle 'buzzing' motion have its effect.

As you'll observe, some vibrators are actually penis-shaped, and can be placed in the vagina. I suspect that these were invented by men; they certainly don't seem to be as popular with women as the clitoral vibrators.

If you do decide to put a vibrator inside the vagina, you should:

- make absolutely sure that the device is clean

- make certain that there are no rough or jagged bits which could hurt

- insert it *very* gently, perhaps using a lubricant.

All the vibrators shown in Figure B are battery-powered, but there are also mains-powered vibrators, and Figure F in Chapter 3 shows how a woman can use one. Interestingly these devices are now sold on a massive scale all over the western world in pharmacies and electrical goods shops (rather than sex shops) as 'massagers'.

Ostensibly, they are supposed to be either for 'beauty' or for 'rheumatism'—take your pick!—but it's well known that a vast number of women use the mains-powered massagers for sexual pleasure or relief.

This recent trend among women is discussed further in Chapter 17, which is about women's new attitudes to sex.

Finally, two words of warning about vibrators—one serious and one not so serious. Firstly, there's a disturbing tendency nowadays to use vibrators rectally, for added sensual stimulation. Indeed, some brands are actually *sold* as 'rectal vibrators' (they're a lot thinner than the ordinary kind).

Using rectal vibrators is absolute madness. Quite apart from the hygiene problem mentioned in earlier chapters, there's the all-important fact that a vibrator can disappear up your bottom, never to be seen again! Or—to be more precise—it *will* be seen again, after a surgeon has operated on you to remove it.

The less serious point is this. Before you buy a vibrator, you should appreciate that virtually all these devices are very noisy! If you live with your in-laws or in an apartment with thin walls, then most probably a vibrator is *not* for you.

Pelvic floor developers

I've explained the importance of the pelvic floor muscles in Chapters 2 and 3. Simple 'Kegel' exercises will help most women who have slack pelvic muscles to tone up their pelvic floors.

However, there are also various devices which will assist the exercise process. They aren't usually sold in sex shops, but may perhaps be recommended by an individual gynaecologist.

They include the 'perineometer', a US device in which the woman places a small bulb in her vagina, and then practises squeezing it

Fig C

Pelvic exerciser—the woman with lax pelvic muscles puts it in her vagina and practises contracting the muscles.

with her pelvic muscles—meanwhile reading off her 'power rating' on an attached dial!

In Britain, pelvic exercisers tend to be shaped blocks of material—like the one in Figure C—on which the woman can flex her muscles. There would also be no harm in exercising with the 'geisha balls' mentioned later.

Jokey bits and pieces

As I've said, quite a lot of the items sold in sex aid shops are really just a bit of a joke. They may not do anything for your sex life, but they can make quite an amusing birthday or Christmas present.

Obviously, however, you have to be a little careful about buying these items—since many people wouldn't find them funny at all. I have to be subjective for a moment and say that personally, I find *some* of the objects found in sex shop catalogues rather crude. On the other hand, these jokey items do seem to appeal to a lot of people, and sell in large numbers.

Here are a few of the things which are on sale:

- willie-warmers—in cold climates, these are quite a common present for a man

- yes/no pillows—'yes' on one side, and 'no' on the other: a fairly blunt way of saying whether or not you're interested

- phallic soap—could give someone quite a surprise in the bath.

As you can see, the humour of these items is decidely more Chaucer than Oscar Wilde . . .

Clitoral stimulators

A clitoral stimulator is a device which the man wears on the base of his penis, and which carries some sort of projection which is supposed to rub against the woman's clitoris during intercourse. You can see what I mean from Figure D.

The idea of this is the entirely laudable one of giving her more pleasure and helping her to reach an orgasm. Unfortunately, although a great many clitoral stimulators are sold, there doesn't seem to be much evidence that they work. Some people say that they are uncomfortable rather than pleasurable, and have a tendency to rotate sideways on the man's penis, and then poke one or other party in the groin!

Fig D

Clitoral stimulators: these fit over the penis, with the knobbly bit uppermost.

Ribbed and tickly condoms

I feel it's vaguely encouraging these days that quite a lot of people are beginning to realize that *women* are entitled to sexual satisfaction too! The manufacturers of condoms have recently cottoned on to the idea that they ought to do something to give women pleasure—so they have started marketing *ribbed* (or slightly bumpy) sheaths under brand names like Excita. I wouldn't exactly call these condoms a 'major breakthrough', but some women do seem to find the sensation which they produce quite agreeable.

These carefully tested condoms (made by large and reputable manufacturers) have to

Fig E

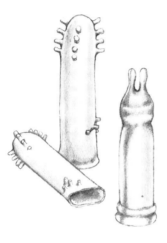

Sheaths with projections—it's claimed that they stimulate the vagina.

be distinguished from the '*tickly* condoms' sold in sex shops. As you can see from Figure E, these are sheaths which have all sorts of projections, in the shape of extraordinary things like rabbit's ears. The long projections are supposed to rub up and down inside the woman's vagina during intercourse, and so give her extra pleasure.

The important point to bear in mind is that these tickly condoms are *not* effective as

contraceptives. They're only intended for bedtime fun.

Whether they will help your sex life is debatable. A woman certainly needs a sense of humour to cope with a man who approaches her looking like a rampant sea anemone!

Rubbing oils

By contrast, these *are* known to be quite effective and pleasant to use. The great US sex researchers Masters and Johnson found that the use of a massage oil was very helpful to couples with sexual difficulties. And of course, masseurs (and masseuses) have known for thousands of years that a body massage is improved by the use of an oil.

In our own time, I understand that the ladies in massage parlours find lubricant oils of great assistance in their difficult and demanding work. You too may find a body oil helpful—to rub on the sexual or non-sexual parts of your partner's body, as you choose.

Important considerations are that the oil shouldn't be harmful or irritant to the skin or genitals; that it shouldn't stain the sheets!

Sex shops sell preparations with names like Love Oil, Love Cream, Joy Jelly, and Emotion Lotion! These usually contain perfumes, so there is a small risk of a sensitivity reaction if they are applied to delicate tissues.

In fact, vast numbers of couples in Britain, America and other countries have discovered that equally good results can be achieved by gently anointing each other's bodies with simple products such as baby oil or body lotion. For best results, warm the oil in your hands before rubbing it onto your loved one's shoulders, arms or wherever.

Alleged aphrodisiacs

Steer clear of these! They don't work—and they could be dangerous.

Sex shops sell all sorts of tablets and potions which are supposed to boost virility or increase desire. Any effect they have must be purely psychological, because they mainly contain nothing more than sugar!

However, in some parts of the world it's possible to obtain a drug called Spanish Fly (cantharides). It's claimed that this will drive women wild with desire.

In fact, it'll do nothing of the kind—*and it may well kill them*. I remember a case in Britain in which a stupid young man surreptitiously administered Spanish Fly to two young women whom he fancied at his office. They died in agony—and he, quite rightly, finished up in jail.

Some British sex shops sell pills labelled 'Spanish Fly'. If these really *do* contain the drug (which I doubt) then it would be absolute insanity to take them.

In doing research for this book, I also noticed that some sex shops sell pills which are claimed to 'cure sterility'. This is of course utter nonsense. If you are having problems with your fertility, read Chapter 6, and then go and consult a doctor.

Alleged erection boosters

To be frank, I *cannot* guarantee that any of these devices work. They're mostly rings which go round the base of the penis, and I suppose it's possible that the feeling of support and perhaps confidence which they may give some men could help them a bit. Also, the constriction they provide may reduce the blood flow returning from the penis to the rest of the body—and so help it to become erect.

Fig F

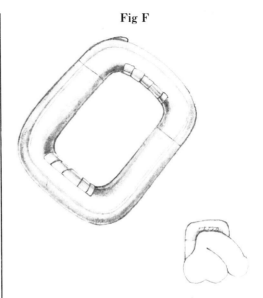

The Blakoe energising ring.

So what are these devices? The best-researched one that I know of is called the 'Blakoe energizing ring' (Figure F). It has little metal plates, which are supposed to generate some sort of electrical current around the base of the man's penis. This curious invention has at least had a moderately favourable mention in the British *Journal of Psychiatry*.

Other devices of similar type include the electrical penis circlet, the Arab Strap, and the intriguingly-named Dr Richards' Ring. Probably worth a try if you're desperate—but if you have impotence problems, read Chapter 11.

Splints and penile extensions

Nearly all men think that their penises are just a bit too small, so there's a ready market for 'penile extensions'. These are devices which are shaped and coloured to look like the end of a penis, and which the man fits onto his organ like a sheath. Heaven knows what a woman is supposed to think when a man approaches her with one of these things on! Personally, I reckon the whole idea is quite mad—except, perhaps, for the one man in half a million who really does have a 'micro-penis'.

Penile splints are a slightly different matter. They are designed to help the man who is totally impotent—either for physical or psychological reasons. In many cases, I'm afraid that all they can provide is a sort of 'replica penis' which fits over the real thing.

Note: it is now possible to obtain an *internal* splint which will stiffen a totally impotent penis. This has, of course, to be implanted by a urological surgeon. The most sophisticated such device is an American invention which can be pumped up at will when the couple want to make love. But the operation to insert it is very expensive, and not without risk.

Dildos

Dildos are objects which are shaped—and often coloured—to resemble a penis. Like the penile splints mentioned above, they are often used by couples whose sex life together has been spoiled by impotence. Obviously, they are very far from being everybody's *tasse de thé*, but if a hand-held dildo can help a loving couple to continue to enjoy a sex life together, then good luck to them.

Incidentally, contrary to what so many people believe, dildos are mostly bought by heterosexual couples—*not* by lesbians. Lesbians aren't much interested in phallic objects and are much keener on caresses with fingers and mouth, of the type described in Chapter 8.

Goat's eyes, and other vaginal stimulators

These are mostly small rings, which fit just below the head of the penis. Unfortunately, this makes them rather liable to fall off—and get lost (temporarily) inside the woman!

Best known of these devices is the 'goat's eye'—illustrated in Figure G. It's so called because it's allegedly an Oriental invention, made out of the eyelashes of goats. This

Fig G

The 'Goat's Eye'—it fits on the man's penis and is alleged to add to the woman's pleasure.

wasn't too nice for the poor old goat. I'm glad to report that present-day goat's eyes appear to be made from synthetic materials.

Other types of vaginal stimulator which work on the same principle are known by such names as Joy Ring, Happy Hat, and Frilled Collar.

Geisha balls

Geisha balls, or Duo-Balls—which are shown in Figure H—are really quite disarmingly ridiculous. As you can see, the pair of balls are connected by a fine thread. The interior of them is so designed that even if they are moved very slightly, they tend to roll about and clonk together.

You may find this hard to believe, but the idea is that women who are in need of sexual stimulation put them in their vaginas. I am told that in New York it's particularly common for women to wander around all day with these things rolling about inside. I can only say that this must make it very hard to concentrate on one's work. Also, the constant clonking noise of the Duo-Balls must be a little difficult to explain!

Fig H

Duo-Balls or Geisha Balls.

More seriously, geisha balls can be used to exercise the pelvic floor muscles (slackness of these muscles is very common, and is discussed in Chapter 2). And if a woman has got a fairly lax vagina, she may actually find it helpful to make love *with the geisha balls inside.*

However, do warn your partner that they are there. Otherwise, he may be startled by the unusual feeling, or alarmed by the characteristic clonking noise!

And he may be a bit taken aback if you say to him: 'Don't worry, Charles—it's just my balls knocking together.'

Thai beads

While we're in an Oriental mood, I ought to mention Thai beads—though I am afraid it's only to say 'Don't use them!' They are very widely sold in most western countries now, and unfortunately men quite often buy them for their partners.

They consist of a series of small beads, held together by a string. Unbelievably, the instructions tell you to stick them up your partner's bottom before intercourse—and then whip them out just at the moment of climax.

This is doubltless a very unusual sensation, but as I have already indicated, any sort of rectal game of this kind is rather unhygienic. Furthermore, there is the distinct possiblity that, if you don't hang on to the string firmly enough, the Thai beads might vanish completely up your partner's rear end: not a pleasant prospect, I think you'll agree.

Penile developers

These are vacuum suction devices, which are supposed to give a man a bigger penis—in effect by sucking out his organ to a larger size. Vast numbers of them are sold to gullible men, but in my view they're a complete waste of time and money. In any case, I wish that men would realize that they don't actually *need* bigger penises.

Incidentally, many years ago I advised a couple who couldn't consummate their marriage to buy a vibrator for love-play. For some extraordinary reason, they decided to buy one of these penile developers instead. They then rang me up to complain that the instructions were in Danish!

Delay creams

So-called delay creams and sprays are advertized as being a help for men with premature ejaculation (see Chapter 11 for a discussion of this common disorder).

They usually contain a local anaesthetic, which is supposed to produce a certain amount of numbness in the man's penis, and so make him less likely to come too soon.

In practice, these preparations don't seem to work awfully well, and you can see the obvious pitfalls. For instance, numbness produced by a local anaesthetic could make it difficult for the man to get an erection—and might affect both partners!

Also, repeated application of local anaesthetics to the skin can sometimes produce very distressing allergic reactions. A man who has 'hairtrigger trouble' should read Chapter 11.

Videos

Nearly all sex aid shops seem to sell videos, which are supposed to be used as a sexual turn-on. There seems to be not the slightest doubt that watching rude videos *is* a turn-on to many people, including a high proportion of women.

Many females express disgust at the idea of viewing a sexy video—yet are amazed to find that it has a dramatically erotic effect on them. Therapists at clinics such as the one run by London's Institute of Psychiatry do use such videos very successfully to help women who complain of absent or lost libido.

But a glance at the catalogues of sex shops will show you that some of the videos they offer are very shocking indeed. What worries me is that the synopses often indicate that they glorify activities such as rape, gangbanging and violence toward women.

Other videos appear to stress the terrible old male-chauvinist, phallic-orientated attitude to sex which has been responsible for so much sexual unhappiness in the past. For example, I recently read this synopsis of a video advertized in a popular men's magazine: 'Three beautiful girls seduce Danny—they bend, stroke and suck his giant member till it overflows over their faces, then all three fight for the right to take his endless seed.'

I don't know about you, but I find that absolutely appalling! Still, if you can obtain a nice, romantic, sexy video (which—most important—isn't pornographic and doesn't break the law) and want to use it to help your love-making, then good luck to you. In fact, many people find the love scenes between, say, Julie Christie and Warren Beattie which you would see on a general-release film *far* more erotic than anything on a sex shop video.

Naughty games

Nearly all sex shops seem to sell naughty board games, in which the participants have to ask each other sexy questions, perform rude forfeits, and take their clothes off. If you and the person you love want to go in for this sort of lark together in front of the fire on a cold winter's evening, then that's fine.

But obviously, it's important that this kind of game shouldn't be used to pressure an unwilling person into an embarrassing position, or into answering embarrassing questions, or into group sex.

Boob Drops

They're a popular if slightly ludicrous new line in the sex aid industry. The general idea is that a woman buys a bottle of Boob Drops, and puts a little on each nipple just before love-play.

The drops—and I promise I'm not joking—come in strawberry, banana and chocolate flavours! The publicity for them claims that they will drive a man wild. I have to say that they will probably give him a good chuckle—and possibly a considerable surprise that his partner has banana-flavoured breasts!

10

Love-making Positions

How many positions are there?

One of the nice things about making love is the fact that there are lots and lots of different ways of doing it. You can make love in a wide variety of ways, and so give each other all sorts of differing pleasant sensations.

How many different ways are there? People are forever arguing about this; one person will say with absolute assurance that there are 71—while another will announce that the ancient Persians discovered no less than 423.

What's the truth? The fact is that there's no *exact* number of positions. It would be possible to make up a list of hundreds and hundreds, provided that you were willing to accept that there were only very minor differences between some of them.

It's also important to remember that some of the wilder antics described in certain books are either dangerous or quite impossible for anyone but a pair of Olympic gymnasts. To take an extreme instance, the oft-quoted example of making love 'swinging from a chandelier' is clearly utter nonsense. (One wonders how many aristocractic families have ruined their best light fixtures this way . . .)

On a more practical level, some of the 'man leaning back' positions mentioned in certain ancient texts are very likely to strain a man's spine—and possibly fracture his penis too! I jest not. Leaning back too far while making love can have disastrous consequences. But rest assured that all the positions mentioned in this chapter are quite safe.

I'm going to describe about 50 comfortable and interesting positions which you can try out with your loved one. And I'd suggest that you try and find little variations on those to suit yourselves. It's surprising and delightful how moving an arm here or a leg there can create a whole new range of sensations and pleasures.

You'll find about 30 of these basic positions fully illustrated. And just for fun, I have given each of them a rating—a bit like the *Guide Michelin*.

♥   means its 'romance rating'
S   means its 'sensuality rating'
P   means its 'pregnancy rating'—in other words, whether it's a good one to use when you're pregnant.

Three of any symbol means the top rating; zero is the lowest.

Why bother with all these different positions anyway?

That's a good question. And the fact is that if you're happy making love in just one single position, and both of you are perfectly satisfied, then that's fine! Carry on doing it the same way.

But the fact is that most people do like a reasonable amount of variety in their love-making. They find that trying out various positions prevents dullness creeping in. (And dullness is something that can cause a lot of problems in marriage.)

They also find that trying out something different gives them all sorts of pleasant new sensations. Indeed, sometimes these sensations can help a woman to respond far better than she did before. Sometimes too, they will even help her reach a climax—when previously she had difficulty in doing so.

Furthermore, some women find that sex in an 'ordinary' position is uncomfortable or even painful. (This is particularly common when the male partner is much heavier than the wife.) In these circumstances, a change to an alternative position may well solve the problem.

Incidentally, women who have a 'retroverted' womb—that is, one that points backwards—sometimes find that they have to try out all sorts of love-making positions before they discover one that's really comfortable.

But the main reason why people do like to try out different positions is that it just happens to be fun . . .

Love-making positions and fertility

Does the position in which you make love affect your chances of getting pregnant? There are two points to bear in mind here.

Firstly, a lot of people still have the idea that if you make love in a standing position, then pregnancy is impossible. This is nonsense—you can start a baby in any position.

But the second point is very important for couples who have some difficulty in conceiving. If your fertility is a bit below par and you're trying for a baby, you should take care to choose love-making positions which give the man's sperm the best possible chance of entering the womb.

For instance, a woman whose womb is retroverted stands the best chance of getting pregnant if she makes love in one of the 'face down' positions described later in this chapter.

This is because a 'face down' position will make the neck of her womb dip into the pool of sperm which forms at the top of her vagina after her partner has reached his climax.

Many infertility clinics advise women with retroverted wombs to have intercourse on all fours, with the man behind them—and to stay in this admittedly somewhat undignified posture for about 10 minutes afterwards.

In contrast, women whose wombs point in the normal direction are usually advised by infertility clinics to have sexual intercourse in one of the 'face up' positions—preferably with a couple of pillows under her bottom, so as to encourage the sperm to stay at the top of the vagina, in contact with the neck of the womb.

Love-making positions, arthritis and disability

From my problem page postbag. I have learned over the years that knowledge of a variety of love-making positions can be a surprising help to people with arthritis, as well as to people with certain other disabilities.

For instance, it's very common for a woman who has arthritis of the hips, but who is otherwise still fit and sexy, to find that the pain and stiffness in her hips make it impossible for her to lie back and make love in the traditional or 'missionary' position (see *Montferrand* illustration).

A lot of women who have this problem have written to me asking if there's any other posi-

tion which wouldn't give them pain. Very frequently, a simple change to, say, the 'Spoons' position (see *Dax* illustration)—described later in this chapter—is enough to solve the problem.

Similarly, men and women who are disabled by back problems, or even by paralysis of a limb, often find that they can still make love with their partners by choosing a position in which their disability is no longer a handicap. To take one light-hearted example, I can remember a woman who had broken both her legs, and who therefore had to spend several months with her two lower limbs immobile in plaster. She was, however, very keen on making love with her husband—and she managed to continue to do it regularly by going in for an energetic version of the 'cross-buttock' position described later in this chapter.

Love-making positions and pregnancy

The one time when vast numbers of women really do need to try out other positions is during pregnancy.

From about the middle of pregnancy onwards, it becomes increasingly difficult for a woman to bear the weight of a man on her tummy. These days, many couples make love far into the eighth or even ninth month of pregnancy. And at *that* stage, sex in the missionary position is getting perilously near to impossible.

Mothers-to-be are therefore well advised to try out some of the positions to which we have given a good pregnancy rating in this chapter—particularly the ones in which the man enters from the side or from behind.

The positions most likely to give happiness

In a moment we'll embark on the list of positions which I've chosen for this book. They are, in my view, the positions which are most likely to give a loving couple a good deal of pleasure and happiness.

But if you're repelled or appalled by a particular posture (for instance, some people have a deep aversion to all 'rear entry' positions because of their canine associations), then you shouldn't bother with it: move on to something else instead.

What you'll *not* find in this chapter are daft, dangerous or impossible positions—though I must admit that it's a bit of a temptation to include one or two of the more bizarre ones I have encountered in my researches.

For instance, before me as I write is a book of Regency prints. One of them shows a lady who's standing not just on her hands—but on her fingertips. Her legs are spread apart at an angle of about 130 degrees.

She's having intercourse with a gentleman who's balanced horizontally between her thighs in a posture which appears to defy the laws of Newtonian physics. His only visible connection with *terra firma* is with his left index finger, which is just touching the carpet. With his other hand, he's playing the trumpet.

After much reflection, I've decided not to include this slightly impractical position ... Incidentally, on the next page, I see that the Regency gentleman is in the same posture—but playing the violin. Words fail me.

Face to face, with man above

The first and most common position of lovemaking is of course the one shown in the *Montferrand* illustration. It's the so-called 'missionary' position—the one in which the woman lies flat on her back with her knees raised, while the man lies between her thighs.

This is a pleasant and comfortable position which suits most people very well. Most important is the obvious fact that the couple can kiss each other on the lips while making love. They can also talk to each other—something which isn't terribly easy with the more exotic postures!

Sex books always allege that the history of

the position's name is that the white missionaries of Victorian days recommended it to their native converts. I've no idea whether this is true—but if so, I think it says a great deal for the good sense of the missionaries! For this is a very nice, warm, snuggly position, with what sexologists like to call 'a good degree of penetration'.

There are, however, a couple of drawbacks to the missionary position. One is that it's a little difficult for the man to reach the woman's clitoris with his fingertips. (So if it's important to you to have your clitoris stimulated during love-making, you might like to try some of the 'rear entry' positions described later in this chapter.)

The other drawback is that if the man is much heavier than the woman, the missionary posture can be quite uncomfortable, or even painful, for her. The same may be true if she's pregnant. In these circumstances, a *cuissade* or rear entry position may be both more comfortable and more fun.

Finally, I ought to mention that a surprising number of men do have a bit of trouble with the missionary position because they lose their erections just as they try to get 'on top'.

A woman should bear in mind that a man who's a little uncertain about his erection may perform better if he's flat on his back.

MONTFERRAND (MISSIONARY)

♥♥♥   S   P

Variations on the missionary position

A very good idea is to put a couple of pillows under your bottom, so as to tilt it upwards. This decidedly alters the sensations which you and your partner will experience in the missionary position, mainly because you'll find that penetration is deeper. Putting a hot-water bottle under the woman's buttocks has a similar effect.

The next position is *Toulouse* (see illustration). As you can see, it's very similar to the missionary position—except that the man's legs are *outside* the woman's. This may seem a rather trivial point, but in fact, the sensations produced by this position are rather different. And—very important—the position is quite useful for the many women who find that child-bearing has made their vaginas lax. This is because the fact that the woman's thighs are *inside* the man's enables her to use her thigh muscles to hold him more snugly—which is nicer for both of them, as a rule.

A simple variation on this position is for the woman to entwine her legs with the man's by just putting her calves across his—and then hooking her feet round his and pushing her pelvis forward. This is a bit like the all-in wrestling hold known as the 'Indian death-lock'—but rather more fun.

A third position in this group is *Béziers* (see illustration). It's really very like the missionary position—except that the woman spreads her legs out as widely as possible. A lot of ladies find a great deal of sensuous pleasure from this cat-like, 'stretching' position.

As you can see, women who own four-poster beds may actually curl their feet around the bedposts. And couples who have a liking for mild forms of bondage may actually go in for tying the woman's ankles to the bedposts. (*Warning:* bondage is most certainly *not* everybody's cup of tea.)

♥ ♥ ♥   TOULOUSE   S   P

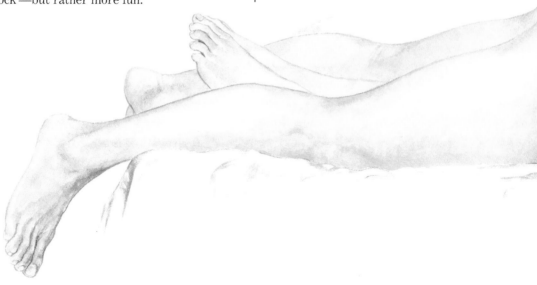

BÉZIERS
♥ ♥ ♥   SS   P

The next 'face to face with male above' position is *Bagnères* (see illustration). As you can see, this is a natural development of the missionary position—except that the lady missionary has brought her legs up and wrapped them round the man's waist.

The lady has to be fairly fit and supple to be able to do this, but the resulting position is good fun for both partners. The altered tilt of the woman's pelvis will usually produce interesting new sensations for both of them.

In a slight variation on this position, the woman can cross her legs tightly and do a sort of scissors lock round the man's waist.

And so on to *Avignon* (see illustration), where once again, the woman has her legs at the level of the man's waist—but here, as you can see, he's *kneeling* on the bed (or whatever). If the man is a trifle too enthusiastic there's a slight tendency for his repeated thrusts to keep banging the lady's skull against the headboard of the bed; however, this can be guarded against by skilful placing of the pillows.

BAGNÈRES
♥♥   SSS

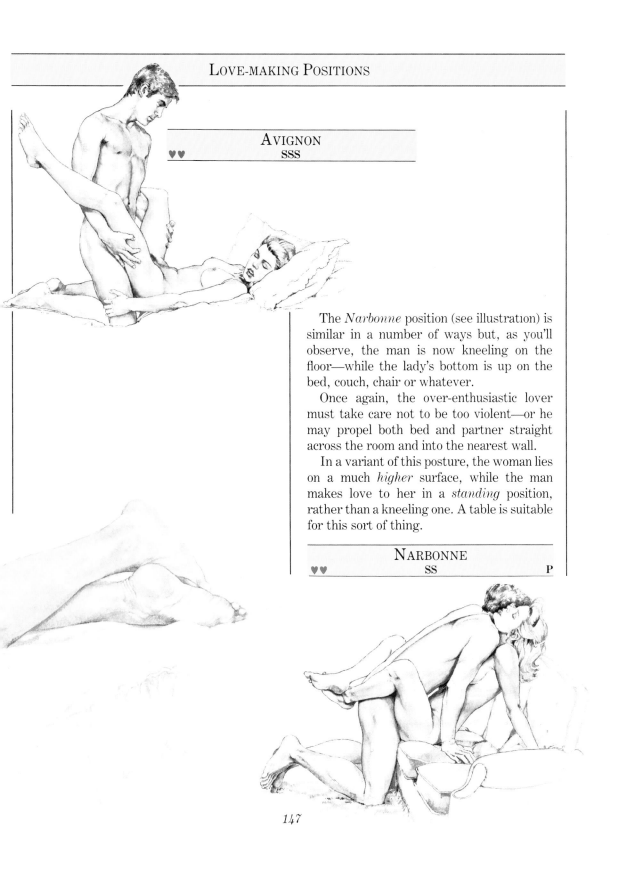

AVIGNON
♥♥
SSS

The *Narbonne* position (see illustration) is similar in a number of ways but, as you'll observe, the man is now kneeling on the floor—while the lady's bottom is up on the bed, couch, chair or whatever.

Once again, the over-enthusiastic lover must take care not to be too violent—or he may propel both bed and partner straight across the room and into the nearest wall.

In a variant of this posture, the woman lies on a much *higher* surface, while the man makes love to her in a *standing* position, rather than a kneeling one. A table is suitable for this sort of thing.

NARBONNE
♥♥
SS
P

147

The *Bordeaux* position (see illustration) is an interesting one, but only suitable for the woman with a really supple spine. Lying on her back on the bed, the lady has drawn her legs up really far, so that she's able to put them over the man's shoulders.

This somewhat exotic position will almost certainly give her all sorts of unusual and even bizarre sensations. The man will probably quite enjoy it too. He should take things very gently, because penetration is very deep indeed in this position.

This position is probably best avoided in late pregnancy, because of the depth of penetration achieved. And I certainly wouldn't recommend it for the sexually inexperienced woman, who might quite reasonably take fright at being asked to assume such an acrobatic pose.

However, if you really are a very acrobatic and gymnastically-inclined person, you could move on to even more extraordinary things from here. For instance, when you and your partner have taken up the *Bordeaux* position, you could then stand on your head (seriously!). To achieve this somewhat heroic pose, just ask him to stand upright gently, while lifting your bottom upwards with his hands.

BORDEAUX
♥♥   SSS

P.S. Are you insured for this kind of thing?

Last in this 'Face to face, male superior' group is the *Montois* position (see illustration). It's fairly self-explanatory, and is often entitled the 'cross-buttock'. In this position, the woman may achieve various interesting sensations, because the man's penis is pressing against the *side* of her vagina. In a variation on this position, the man only turns his body through 45 instead of 90 degrees. This is somewhat improbably known as the 'half cross-buttock'.

MONTOIS
♥   SSS   P

149

Face to face, with woman above

Now we come to the first group of 'female superior' positions. There are still a few men who think that these positions are somehow demeaning to the dignity of the male sex—but I'm sure that their opinions may be safely discounted.

Let's begin with the simple *La Voulte* position (see illustration). As you can see, the woman is lying on top of the man—in this case with her legs outside his.

This is really a most comfortable position, particularly if the woman is much lighter than her partner. Men appreciate it too—especially as there's a sort of suggestion that the female is seducing the male by making love to him in this way.

To get into this position, all you really need do is this. First, make sure your partner has an erection (sounds silly, but you'd be surprised at how often this elementary preliminary is neglected), then gently throw a leg across his thighs, and climb on top—if necessary, using your hand to guide him in.

In an obvious variation of this position, the woman has her legs *inside* the man's. This is *Carcassonne* (see illustration). As with the equivalent 'male superior' position which I described earlier in the chapter, this position gives a snug fit—which may be helpful to the couple if the woman's pelvic muscles are a little loose because of child-bearing.

LA VOULTE

♥♥♥   S   PPP

CARCASSONNE

♥ ♥ ♥   SS   PPP

Another useful 'female superior' position is *Brive* (see illustration). It's called the 'frog'—and I *think* I christened this myself in an earlier book of mine (though if somebody else thought of the name first, I apologize). I hasten to add that the expression 'frog position' has no Gallic overtones, and isn't meant to imply that this particular posture is favoured in the land of the can-can. It just means that you both spread your legs in a breast stroke-type way, so that your pubic regions are pushed together.

Anyway, as you can see by its high Sensuality Rating, this is another of those positions which isn't specially romantic, but does often give extremely good sexual sensations.

Another extremely useful female superior position is *Perpignan* (see illustration). You can see that it's quite easy for a woman to get into this position by starting in the posture shown in *La Voulte*. She just bends her knees until she's kneeling, and then sits up.

Now this position is very nice but why do I call it 'useful'? Simply because couples who have minor or even major sex difficulties are often advised to try it. The main reason for this is that the position puts no pressure on the woman: if (as is very common) she's a little frightened of intercourse, or tends to panic when the tip of a penis enters her body, then this position leaves her *in control*. She can withdraw a little whenever she wants to—and in effect take charge of the whole act of love if that's what she feels happiest with.

It's easy to develop other positions from this one: for instance, the woman can put one or indeed both legs out to the side (depending how supple she is), and so vary the sensations she feels.

Women who are good at yoga can cross their legs in front of them—across the man's chest. It's even possible to adopt the famed 'lotus position'—though it might be as well to support yourself with your hands while you do this, for fear of falling over and perhaps giving your man a badly sprained penis!

The *Lyon* position (see illustration) is really just one stage on from *Perpignan*. As is clear

PERPIGNAN
♥ ♥   SS   PPP

BRIVE
♥   SSS   PP

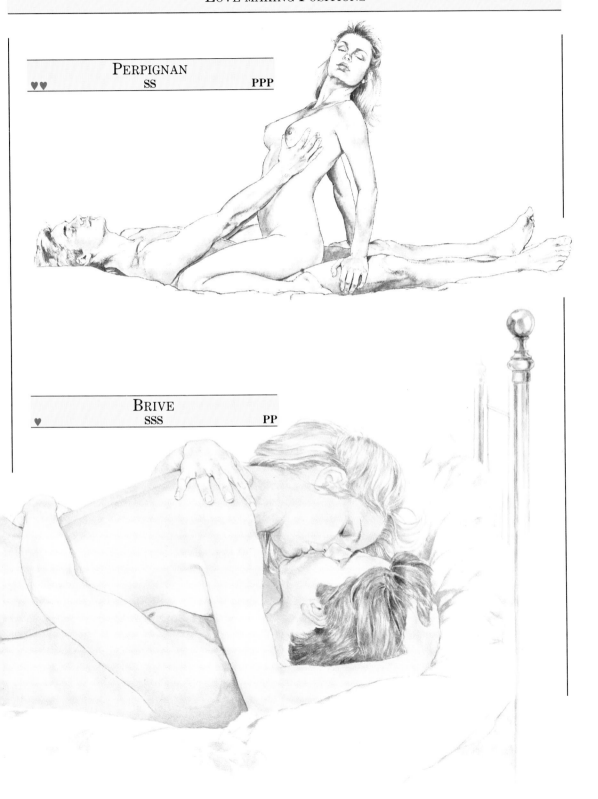

from the illustration, the woman has stretched her legs out in front of her, so that she's able to roll and bounce around quite freely. She can really move about in the most amazing way in this position, giving both herself and the man a lot of pleasure.

According to the world-famous sex authority Dr Alex Comfort, this position is known in parts of France as 'the Lyon stagecoach', because the movements are reminiscent of the bumping and jarring experienced by passengers in *la diligence de Lyon*. It must have been a remarkable vehicle.

Clearly, the woman can move herself from this position into several closely related ones—for instance, by turning her legs first through 45 degrees and then through 90 degrees in either direction. She can also turn to face away from the man, and then (if she likes) complete a full circle by returning to face him again.

I call the *Grenoble* position (see illustration) 'the lean back'. You can quite easily get into it from the positions mentioned previously. All you have to do is to lean backwards, until your head touches the bed. This should give you very pleasant and unusual sensations, as your partner's penis presses against the *front* of your vagina—and against the famous G-spot.

But do go a bit gently as you lean back, because you are putting your partner's penis under a fair amount of tension. This ought to be very agreeable for him—but a *sudden* lean back could produce pain, and (if you were really violent about it) the ultimate disaster of a ruptured penis. I suppose there are some blokes who *deserve* that sort of thing, but I'm sure you wouldn't want to go to bed with them.

Exotically-minded lovers can find all sorts of variants of the lean back position, by simply trying out the effect of straightening out various legs, and seeing what happens.

LYON	
♥ SSS	PP

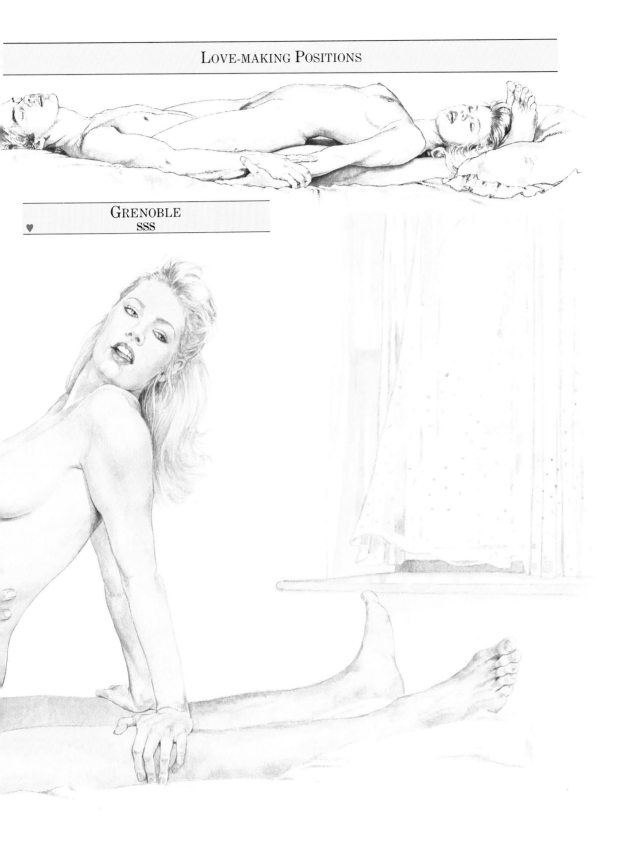

GRENOBLE
sss

♥

OLYMPIQUE DE PARIS
♥♥   SSS   PP

Olympique de Paris is a much less ambitious position—and one which is quite easy for most couples, provided the man is moderately supple. As you can probably imagine, the simplest thing here is for the couple to start in the ordinary female superior *Carcassonne* position shown earlier. The man then raises his legs so that his thighs are alongside the woman's bottom. He can then raise them even further so that they're up around her waist—and he can even cross them behind her back.

This is a pleasant, abandoned sort of position, in which the man can repeatedly pull himself up into the woman, creating sensations which both of them will find agreeable.

Biarritz is what might be called the 'Half

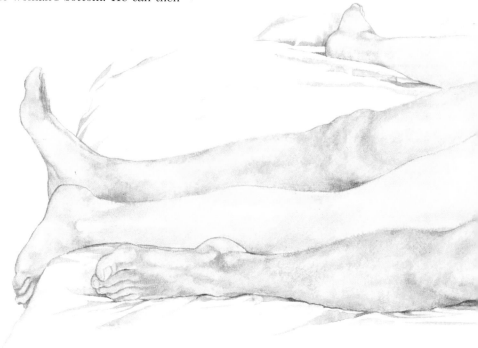

Cross Bum' position. As you can see, it's another female superior position—but she has turned herself through about 45 degrees on top of the man, a manoeuvre which will give her quite different sensations inside the vagina. This position does give the man a very good opportunity to caress her bottom (and, indeed, her breasts if that's what she likes).

The 'Full Cross' or *Vienne* (see illustration) is really just a development of the last one.

BIARRITZ
♥   SSS   PP

VIENNE
SSS   PP

The woman has turned through 90 degrees on top of the man. This certainly makes conversation difficult (which is why I've given this posture such an abysmally low romance rating), but the effect on the erotic nerve endings can be quite startling.

Face to face, sitting

A lot of people like to make love sitting in a chair—though I'd recommend that you choose a nice, comfortable one, which isn't likely to collapse. I'm slightly baffled by books which suggest that couples should make love on deck-chairs; if you try it, do be very careful!

Association Sportive (see illustration) a pleasant face to face sitting position. Some couples like to try out these chair positions first with their clothes on—since they feel that this is rather more risqué. Obviously, the woman just removes her pants and tights—or wears open-crotch ones.

Other chair positions are described later in this chapter.

♥♥♥	ASSOCIATION SPORTIVE	
	SS	P

Face to face, standing

Stade Français shows a couple making love in a standing position. If you have been making love horizontally in bed for years, and need something new to make sex more varied, then this could be the answer.

STADE FRANÇAIS
♥♥   SS   P

Standing sex has had a bit of a bad press—mainly because it tends to be used for illicit love-making by young couples who have no bedroom to go to. But in fact it can be very pleasant.

Since men are usually a bit taller than their female partners it's easier if the man can stand so that he's a little *lower* than his partner. If you're both on the same level, it can be a bit of a strain on the legs—and you may well find out why this position is often referred to as the 'dreaded knee-trembler'!

RACING CLUB
♥   SS

Racing Club (see illustration) is another version of face to face love-making while standing up. As you can see, the man has lifted the woman up so that she can wrap her legs round him. This is a most entertaining position, which tends to appeal to couples with a sense of humour—but it's best not attempted if the man has any back trouble.

Rear entry

Now we move on to the 'rear entry' positions. Some people don't like these, because they consider them undignified and rather too close to what goes on in the animal world.

Certainly, one of our most famous romantic novelists once complained to me that 'rear entry sex is *totally* unromantic'. (I hasten to add that there was nothing personal in her complaint; she was just rather shocked that I'd mentioned this type of intercourse in my column.)

She was quite right, of course: rear entry love-making isn't terribly romantic—and that fact is reflected in the low 'romance ratings'. But some rear entry positions can be very comfortable—particularly the 'Spoons' one, which we'll come to in a moment. Also, some of them are very practical during pregnancy.

Furthermore, these positions can help a lot of women who need extra clitoral stimulation during intercourse. For as you can see in the *Montauban* illustration, which shows a common rear entry position, one great advantage of this method of love-making is the fact that it would be easy for the man to reach round with his hand and stimulate the women's clitoris with his fingertips. Quite often, this can help her achieve orgasm during intercourse when otherwise she wouldn't have done so.

♥	MONTAUBAN	
	SS	P

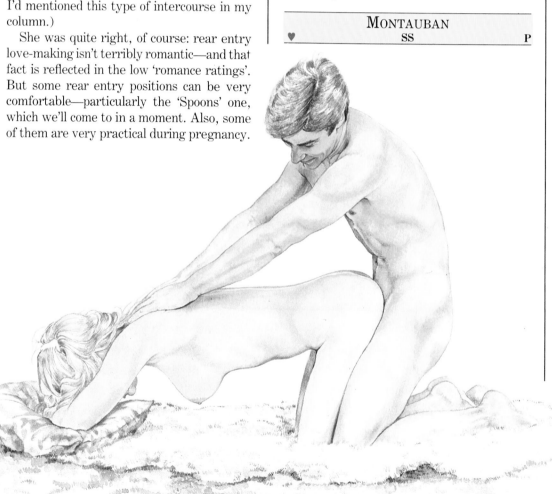

Finally, there's the important point that many couples do find these positions very sensually exciting! I recently had an extraordinary letter in my postbag from a woman who said: 'I get tremendous pleasure from being made love to "doggie fashion". Am I abnormal? Or is it, I wonder, because I was born in the Year of the Dog?' Could she, I wonder, have been sending me up?

BAYONNE
♥   SS   PP

We've seen one of the most common rear entry positions in *Montauban*—with the man above. But it's also perfectly possible to make love rear entry-style with the *woman* above—as you can see in the *Bayonne* illustration.

A very similar position, but this time on a chair, is shown in *Bègles* (see illustration).

Then there's the 'Spoons' or *Dax*—a comfortable, cosy position (see illustration). As you'll observe, this is a nice way for a couple to cuddle up together on a cold winter's night—and perhaps fall asleep afterwards cuddled up together like two spoons in a drawer. (This one is good in pregnancy too.)

Not illustrated, but very sensuous, are several variations on this theme. The first of these is similar to the Spoons—but with the woman bending the top half of her body right forward until it's at 90 degrees to the man's body. In a second variation, the man leans backwards. And similar to this last one is a

♥	BÈGLES	
	SSS	PP

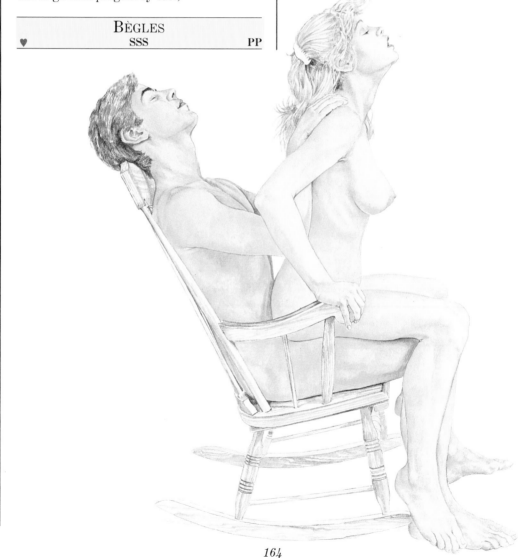

164

DAX

♥♥   **SS**   **PPP**

third variation, in which the woman thrusts her leg backwards between the man's thighs, as far as it'll go. Surprisingly enough, this produces strikingly different and pleasant sensations.

Finally, one rear entry position (not illustrated) which is worth trying is the standing one. The woman can 'develop' this by bending forward, if she wants to. If she's quite lithe and lissom, she may want to experiment with the sensations caused by bending very far forward until her hands touch the floor. Provided your lover isn't the sort of idiot who tries to drive your head through the carpet, this can be very agreeable. Also worth trying is bending forward over a comfortable sofa or armchair.

165

Sideways positions, including *cuissade* and *flanquette*

I always feel that the great thing about sideways positions is that they're so comfortable. Perhaps that's why couples who're a bit unsure of themselves find that making love in one of these positions is undemanding and builds up their confidence.

You can see what I call the 'ordinary sideways' position or *Châlon* (see illustration).

This one really is the easiest and most natural of positions—all the man has to do is lie beside his partner, and then curl his thighs up under her bottom. From there, a gentle entry (if necessary, aided by her hand) is delightfully easy.

From that simple and pleasant sideways position, you can readily progress to *Bergerac* (see illustration).

CHÂLON		
♥ ♥ ♥	SS	PPP

BERGERAC
♥ ♥   **SS**   **PPP**

This is what's impressively known as a *cuissade* position. I possess a very large French dictionary, and *cuissade* doesn't appear in it, but the word *cuisse* means 'thigh'. So I suppose that the term really means 'an approach round the thigh'.

And that's roughly what it is. As you can see from the illustration, the man is making love to the woman having first slipped his thigh under hers. Certainly, the pressure of thigh on thigh creates some very warm, intimate feelings.

MONT-DE-MARSAN
SSS

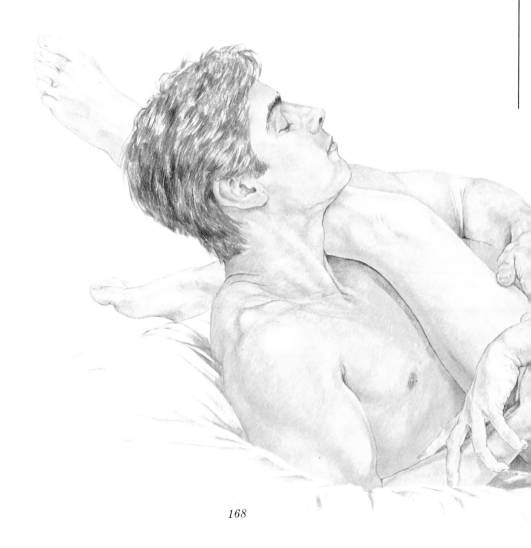

If you want to try a really exotic version of the *cuissade* position, have a look at the illustration of *Mont-de-Marsan*. It's also called the *cuissade* X-position, and it's certainly very sensuous, even if a trifle confusing.

One way of getting into it is for the couple to start in the previous position. The man then brings his top leg round so that it's up near the woman's shoulder. At the same time, he turns the rest of his body round so that he's facing her—and then slips his shoulder under her foot. If you can manage this correctly the very first time, you should probably be writing sex manuals instead of reading them.

Dacquoise (see illustration) is another type of sideways position, also called *flanquette*. What happens here is that the man again pushes his thigh between the woman's thighs, but this time from the front. So *flanquette* positions are sort of 'half facing' while *cuissade* ones are 'half rear'.

My large French dictionary doesn't include the word *flanquette*, but there *is* a word *flanc*, meaning 'side', so I suppose *flanquette* really means a little side position—doubtless the Gallic equivalent of having a bit on the side.

	DACQUOISE	
♥♥	SS	P

Our final side position is *Le Puc* (see illustration on p. 160). As you can see, it's simply another way of making love in a chair—and probably the most comfortable and stable way too.

There are those who claim that it's very exciting to use this position in public, making love under the woman's skirt so that in theory no one else knows what's going on. This strikes me as a good way to get arrested!

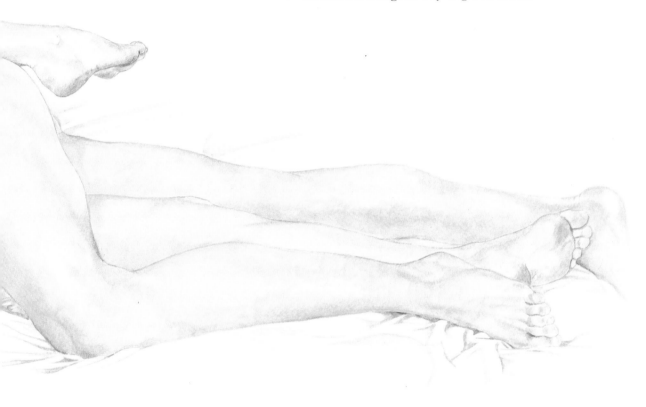

LE PUC

♥♥   SS   PP

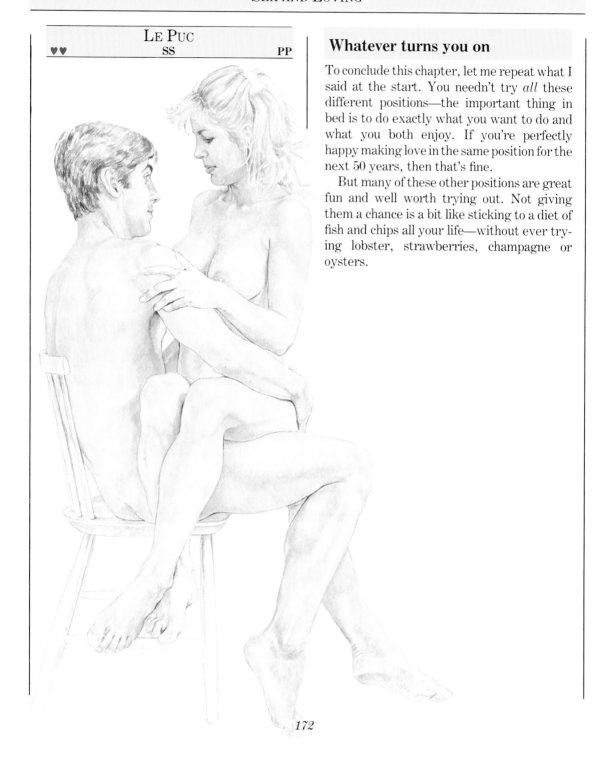

Whatever turns you on

To conclude this chapter, let me repeat what I said at the start. You needn't try *all* these different positions—the important thing in bed is to do exactly what you want to do and what you both enjoy. If you're perfectly happy making love in the same position for the next 50 years, then that's fine.

But many of these other positions are great fun and well worth trying out. Not giving them a chance is a bit like sticking to a diet of fish and chips all your life—without ever trying lobster, strawberries, champagne or oysters.

11

Sexual Difficulties in Women and Men

Have you ever had problems?

Have you ever had problems with love-making? The odds are that you have at some time or another—because such difficulties are very common indeed, in both women and men.

For instance, the famous American medical publication *The New England Journal of Medicine* recently printed a study of 100 marriages. The couples they surveyed were all well educated, comfortably off, apparently happily married, middle-class husbands and wives—people whose sex lives, you might think, should have been absolutely fine. So

you may be surprised to learn that *half* those husbands had sexual problems and three-quarters of the wives had one or more problems, ranging from difficulty in reaching a climax to general lack of interest in love-making. Incidentally, the survey also found that very often, the husband's didn't *know* that their wives had any worries! Perhaps not altogether surprisingly, the women were rather better at recognizing the existence of a difficulty or sexual worry in their men.

However, any doctor who works in the field of family planning and sexual medicine in any country in the world will tell you that these statistics come as no surprise at all! There's no doubt that many wives (and husbands) have difficulty with love-making—especially just after marriage, when they're a bit inexperienced and unsure what they're doing. The other very common times for problems to arise is after birth and during pregnancy (especially the first one).

> *Although nearly nine out of ten women can reach a climax, most of them don't do so during intercourse itself*

An interesting experiment was recently carried out by a British doctor. He took the time and trouble to ask every married woman who came into his surgery (for whatever reason) whether she had any difficulties or worries over love-making. A staggering 51.3 per cent replied that they had.

And if you have any doubts about that figure, then consider the fact that distinguished sociologist Michael Schofield found in his study of 25-year-old British men and women that 57 per cent of them have some sort of sex problem. He says that it may be something quite minor and easily corrected—but it's still a worry to the person concerned.

During recent years, confirmation that sexual worries are really common in the UK as well as the USA has come from large surveys carried out by women's magazines among their readers. The results—based on the experiences of many thousands of British women—showed that many wives aren't getting the satisfaction that they require from the physical side of their marriages.

Indeed, these surveys confirmed some very surprising work which was done by Ms Shere Hite in America—and published in her blockbuster of a book *The Hite Report*. Having met the redoubtable Ms Hite, I've developed the greatest respect for her. Ms Hite shattered a good deal of American complacency with her findings. Most stunningly of all, she found that although nearly nine out of ten women can reach a climax, most of them don't do so during intercourse itself. Indeed, Ms Hite says that only 30 per cent of wives achieve their climax during sexual intercourse, while the rest have to be content with experiencing it through oral or digital love-play—or self-masturbation.

When Ms Hite's astonishing assertion first became known, there were many people who declared that it was utter nonsense! I personally heard psychiatrists who are used to dealing with serious sexual problems say that this *couldn't* be true: after all, everybody knew that most wives easily reached a climax during intercourse. Those of us who had worked in Family Planning Clinics weren't so sure . . .

But large women's magazine surveys appear to have confirmed that Ms Hite's findings are right. Although about 90 per cent of wives can reach a climax by some other means, it seems probable that at least half of them can't do it during intercourse itself.

Now in fact, it's perfectly possible to have a good and satisfying sex life *without* having a climax during intercourse. But many women would prefer to reach orgasm during the time when they're closest and most 'at one' with their partners—and many men feel the same way.

What *are* the common problems?

So what are the common problems which worry couples? There's a great deal of talk about sex these days, but few people know what the more usual difficulties are.

So, first of all *in women*, these are the common problems:

- painful or uncomfortable intercourse
- general loss of interest in love-making
- inability to reach a climax
- inability to have a climax during inter-course—despite being able to manage it at other times
- general worries about one's own sex organs—their size, shape, aroma, colour, amount of hair and so on.

And what about the *men*? Their difficulties are these:

- reaching a climax far too soon (premature ejaculation) so that their wives aren't really satisfied
- loss of the ability to achieve an erection easily
- erection OK, but unable to reach a climax
- general loss of interest
- and (just as with women) general worries about the sex organs: size, shape, colour and so on.

To readers whose sex lives are already a success, some of these worries and difficulties must seem quite incomprehensible! But I do assure you that the problems I've been talking about do cause enormous unhappiness to an awful lot of people. In this chapter, we'll look at why these problems occur—and what can be done nowadays to put them right.

Women—painful intercourse and vaginismus

Is intercourse ever painful or uncomfortable for you? If so, you're very far from being alone! At any large Family Planning Clinic, several women will come in during the evening and complain of just this problem.

> *There's a great deal of talk about sex these days, but few people know what the more usual difficulties are*

To take a very typical case history: Susan is in her mid-twenties and had been married for about six months. She'd been going to her local Family Planning Clinic for about a year to obtain supplies of the Pill—and the doctors there had always got the impression that everything was fine with her sex life. After all, she seemed such a happy girl . . .

But in fact, bedtime with her husband Bill wasn't much fun for Susan. Right from the start, she'd found it uncomfortable when he tried to push inside. She knew she was 'dry' and that her muscles were held rather tight, but she didn't seem to be able to relax easily.

True, things were better some nights. If Bill went on gently thrusting inside her for five minutes or so, then her vagina seemed to relax and open up—and (most important) the 'love juices' which are essential for happy and successful intercourse began to flow from inside her. On nights like these, the discomfort disappeared, and everything finished up beautifully. But most nights, it seemed to be just a question of Bill battering away at the opening of her vagina until he got in, then reaching his climax very quickly—and that was that. No wonder that after six months of marriage, Susan often cried herself to sleep.

> *Some women find intercourse almost impossible because of pain*

One night she was at the Family Planning Clinic talking to the doctor when she broke down and explained through her tears just how awful she was feeling. Fortunately, the doctor—a middle-aged, motherly woman with plenty of experience of this sort of thing—was very kind and understanding. She examined Susan gently and found that there was nothing physically wrong: just a little spasm of the muscles of the vagina caused by Susan's understandable anxiety. The doctor showed Susan how to relax so that this spasm went away. Then she made an appointment for her to bring Bill in with her the following week.

At the next appointment, the doctor sympathetically explained to Bill something that regrettably few young men seem to know, even in these days of allegedly widespread knowledge about sex: that it's quite useless for a man to try to push his penis into a woman's vagina *unless he has spent at the very least a few minutes in preparing her both mentally and physically*. This is particularly true in the case of young women who have little experience of sex and who have never had children.

So the doctor briefly explained to Bill the importance of *romance* in the approach to a woman—rather than assault and battery—coupled with some basic instructions on the gentle art of love-play (see Chapter 8). Bill was a bit surprised at all this, but felt reassured when Susan told him that this gradual, loving approach was what she wanted.

That night they tried it—and it worked. In fact, Bill still had a lot to learn about love-play. But he bought books on the subject, and practised. He also used one of the many vaginal lubricants which are now widely available without prescription from pharmacists.

Susan took particular care to ensure that he didn't try to enter her until her vagina was really relaxed, and also well lubricated with 'love juices'. And before very long, the discomfort and pain which had been making such a mess of her sex life had disappeared.

More serious cases

There are many serious cases, however. Some women find intercourse almost impossible because of pain. And a few of them are the famous 'virgin wives' of whom you have probably heard—women who have been married for many months or years, yet who have never had intercourse!

I need hardly add that in these very severe cases, the marriage is invariably under the most tremendous strain. Even if the couple are managing some sort of intercourse, the pain involved is such that before very long, all kinds of stresses and antagonisms build up between the partners. A very common result is that the husband becomes impotent (that is, unable to achieve and maintain an erection), and naturally this makes things even worse.

Now what causes this trouble? Nearly always, the couple are sure that there's some *physical* difficulty—but they're wrong!

Again and again, doctors in Family Planning Clinics see wives who are convinced that their intense difficulty over intercourse is caused by something physical—perhaps a 'thick hymen' or the vagina being 'too small'. *This is nearly always nonsense.* No, the condition which almost always causes all this trouble is something called 'vaginismus'. The term isn't widely known, yet it's one of the most common disorders seen at Family Planning Clinics.

> *In these very severe cases, the marriage is invariably under the most tremendous strain*

What is it? Simply a violent tightening of the vaginal muscles (rather like Susan had, only more so) whenever any sexual approach is made. The many unfortunate women who have this disorder are basically terrified of anything being put in the vagina. And they get an intense and uncontrollable spasm of vaginismus whenever something comes near the vaginal opening.

So, not only do they tighten up whenever their husbands come near them, they also go into spasm when a doctor wants to examine them. And very typically, there's what I call a 'positive Tampax test'—in other words, the poor woman who has vaginismus literally shudders if the doctor even mentions the word 'tampon' to her!

So it was with Eva. She was 30, had been married for about five years, and was now only able to permit intercourse about four times a year because of the dreadful pain it produced. Quite understandably, she thought that the basic trouble was some physical obstruction in her vagina. Her husband Harry had accepted this explanation, and he was so depressed at the state of affairs that he had become partly impotent—so that even when Eva was willing to try to let him enter her, he had difficulty in getting a good erection.

Eva's trouble was actually spotted by her own doctor, who had been prescribing the Pill for her for some time. He realized that whenever it was suggested that she should have a routine vaginal examination, she 'dodged' it—usually by saying that she was menstruating.

Eventually, the doctor pointed out that she couldn't be menstruating *all* the time, and tactfully enquired whether anything was wrong. Eva was angry at first (there's a lot of anger, frustration and pain not far under the surface in most women with vaginismus), but she calmed down when she realized that the doctor only wanted to help.

'I just don't like being poked about,' she said, with the tears not far away.

'I see,' said her doctor. 'Tell me—do you use Tampax?'

Eva looked quite horrified. 'Oh no—I've never been able to put *those* things in, doctor.'

Her doctor knew for sure then that he was dealing with a case of vaginismus. And when he managed to persuade Eva to be examined, he found—as he expected—that there was intense muscle spasm: the same muscle spasm that was causing her terrible difficulties with intercourse.

He was able to reassure Eva that there was *no* physical obstruction present, as she had feared. With the aid of a mirror, he demonstrated to her that the whole cause of the trouble was the muscular contraction brought about by her deep emotional fear of anything going into her vagina. And with the aid of one of a number of psychological techniques which are now available to help women overcome this very common phobia, he was able—over a period of about six months—to help Eva get rid of this terrible fear. As her fear went, so did the spasm—and so did her pain. When last heard of, Eva and Harry had a much improved sex life—and they had successfully (and happily) conceived two children!

Physical causes

As I've explained, painful intercourse is *not* usually due to narrowness of the vagina nor to some sort of 'blockage', but to emotional causes. However, there are some important physical causes of pain or discomfort during intercourse, and they can be very distressing.

Here's another case history that had a happy outcome. Jenny had just had a baby. The delivery hadn't been too bad, but she'd needed rather a lot of stitches, and had been sore while she was in hospital. But her mind had been fully occupied with her baby, so she just assumed that the soreness would go in time. Unfortunately, when she and her husband John tried to resume intercourse, the results were disastrous. 'It hurt so much each time it brought tears to my eyes,' Jenny told her doctor. 'John's been very good and said he won't try again till I'm OK, but I wonder if there's anything wrong.'

> *Painful intercourse is usually due to emotional causes*

The doctor examined her and found that there was indeed something wrong. The stitching up had been left to a junior surgeon who had been rather too busy at the time, and the resulting needlework was far from perfect. It's not generally realized that stitching up vaginal tears is very difficult indeed—simply because the anatomy of the area is so distorted by the process of childbirth that it's really quite tricky to bring everything together. The outcome of all this in Jenny's case was good. Her doctor sent her back to the hospital where she was admitted for a day or two so that her vagina could be completely restitched in the operating theatre under general anaesthetic.

Another case history: Sheila had the same symptoms as Jenny—sudden inability to make love because of pain and discomfort. She was also a mother, but her little boy was now nine months old, and she and her husband had been able to have intercourse without any difficulty since about six weeks after the delivery.

But then things went wrong. The outside and opening of Sheila's vagina became sore and red. Any attempt at sex—even just petting—made her tighten up in an intense muscular contraction that made the pain worse and sex impossible. And she developed an unusual amount of discharge, which was yellowish in colour.

Fortunately, Sheila realized that she must seek professional advice—fast. She made an urgent appointment with her doctor for the following night and explained her symptoms. When she had a look at Sheila's vagina, the doctor found that the whole vagina was intensely inflamed and the sensitive area at the 'mouth' of the love passage was very sensitive to the touch. But the symptom which made clear what the likely cause might be was Sheila's discharge: it was yellow, with a tinge of green, and with lots of little bubbles in it. The doctor did a test which confirmed that the cause was something called trichomonas.

This is one of the most common of all infections—yet surprisingly enough, most people have never heard of it. It's a little 'bug' that lives on people's bodies. Fuller details are given in Chapter 5.

Sheila's doctor then gave her the standard treatment for this condition: some tablets called 'Flagyl' (metronidazole), which must be taken by both wife and husband to clear the parasite out completely. Two weeks later, Sheila and Steve's sex life was completely back to normal.

And now for yet another common cause of pain: Alice was six months pregnant when trouble struck. Again, it was pain on intercourse, vaginal discomfort and irritation, and some discharge.

Fortunately, she was going to the antenatal clinic that week, so she mentioned her difficulty to the obstetrician. He gave her an internal examination and found a thick, white curdy discharge, plus a lot of inflammation.

'I'm sending a swab to the lab just to confirm the diagnosis,' he said. 'But I'm quite sure that what you've got is thrush.'

> *Any attempt at sex made her tighten up in an intense muscular contraction that made sex impossible*

Thrush is the other very common vaginal infection of our time. Also known as 'candida' or 'monilia', it's a little fungus that likes warm, moist places—such as babies' mouths and women's vaginas (see Chapter 5).

'Put one of these little pessaries in the vagina each night and morning for 10 days,' the obstetrician told Alice. 'And here's some cream which both you and your husband should apply down below twice a day for a week. That should get rid of it.'

It did. Thrush is especially common in pregnancy, and Alice had a slight recurrence a couple of months later. But she got it treated promptly and it was soon gone again. There was an odd postscript to this story. Alice told her mother about her encounters with the dreaded thrush—who realized with amazement that this must be the same infection which years ago had plagued much of her own married life between the ages of 20 and 35.

'I was too embarrassed to do anything about it,' she said. 'And I don't suppose the treatment was so good in those days. Oh, how I wish I'd been born 30 years later!'

> *When we got into bed and made love, I felt absolutely nothing*

Lack of interest in love-making

'I've lost interest in my husband, doctor.' It's a statement made time and time again by distressed women sitting in their doctors' surgeries or in the Family Planning Clinic.

Ellen was 25 and had been married for four years. She had a little boy of two and a half, and she loved both him and her husband Keith very much indeed. Yet one day, when Keith suggested that they pop into bed for half an hour, she was alarmed to find that his touch actually repelled her!

'Every time he kissed me,' she recalled later, 'I wanted to turn my head away. And when we got into bed and made love, I felt absolutely nothing.'

Very often, a woman feels like this when she's tired or under stress or is having a difficult time—and then the next time it's all right. But that wasn't the case with Ellen: the same thing happened again and again over the next few months, every time Keith came near her. Of course, he realized that she'd lost interest in him and was quite naturally very upset by this.

Eventually, Ellen managed to find a local clinic where they were used to giving advice on this sort of problem. The female doctor there listened sympathetically to her story, and tried to identify the reason why Ellen should have lost interest. It would be nice to say that she discovered some important psychological factor that had caused all this, but very often in these cases no particular cause is found. And that was the situation with Ellen—the doctor could find nothing in her background that might have caused this distressing symptom.

But Ellen's chats with the doctor did help, as over a spell of about a couple of months, Ellen gradually became less and less tense about her problem. At one or two of her visits, she brought Keith along, and the doctor was able to help him to see that Ellen wasn't doing this deliberately, and that she loved him very much and wanted desperately to be able to give him physical love and satisfaction again. As the weeks went by, the tensions between Keith and Ellen gradually relaxed. And eventually their relationship suddenly 'came right'.

For the first time in months Ellen wanted to make love and from then on, their sexual relationship was fine again. All very mysterious, yet this is the way human beings are. Time and again, wives lose interest in sex for no apparent reason—and then, if some way can be found of relieving the tensions of the marriage, return completely to normal!

But there are also many instances when there's a clear-cut reason why a wife loses interest. Take the case of Jane and Kevin.

She had been married for six months, and had been going out with her husband Kevin for about two years before their wedding. They had had a good sex life right from the start, and Jane would have laughed at the idea that she could ever have a sexual problem. Then, one night when Kevin was making love to her, she suddenly realized that she felt absolutely no warmth or desire for him at all. She was so scared by this that she actually pushed him away—and he stormed off to spend the night on the sofa. This was repeated night after night for several weeks. By this time, Jane and Kevin were in a state of warfare.

Eventually Kevin dragged Jane along to the doctor to ask for 'some tablets that would make her sexy again'. The doctor told them: 'A lot of people think that we can prescribe tablets that will do that, but it just isn't true. Just occasionally, some women can be helped by injections of male hormones, which can pep up the sex drive.'

> Some women can be helped by injections of male hormones, which can pep up the sex drive

When Jane showed horror at the idea of male hormones, the doctor went on to explain that because the hormones are male and can often have unfortunate side-effects on a woman—like acne, excess hair on the face and a deep voice—doctors are reluctant to use them unless they have to. They prefer to try to find out what lies behind the loss of interest.

After two fairly long interviews with Jane and Kevin, he finally dug out what the cause of their trouble was. As is very, very often the case, it was something quite straightforward and simple: about a month before Jane's symptoms had started, the young couple had moved in with Kevin's parents. The walls of the house were thin and Jane was worried that their love-making would be audible. She also felt guilty about having sex in the house of her parents-in-law.

It sounds simple, but that particular worry—which the wife herself may scarcely be aware of—is a very frequent cause of loss of interest among young women.

Their doctor advised them to go away for a romantic weekend together. Naturally, she was still uneasy when they returned home but they were soon able to get a new flat and once they moved in there, Jane's troubles disappeared for ever.

Problems of pregnancy, childbirth and the Pill

One of the seemingly inexplicable things about women is the way their interest in sex can vary so greatly at different times. Men are constantly baffled by this. It's hard for a man to understand how a woman can be very interested in making love on one occasion, and quite the opposite on the next.

In the course of this section, I'm going to explain some reasons why this is so. But, in particular, I want to look at certain circumstances in which this normal female variation in sexual desire is so greatly exaggerated that distress and unhappiness result. The extraordinary loss of interest that some women suffer can occur at certain specific times; these are:

● during pregnancy

● after childbirth

● while on the Pill.

Let me make it absolutely clear at the outset that most women do *not* lose interest in sex when pregnant, or when they have just had a baby, or when they're on the Pill.

But a small minority do find that they've become unusually 'cold' toward their husband's advances at these times. And when this happens, it can put the marriage under very great strain. So if you have the misfortune to have this happen to you, do get something done about it!

Pregnancy

Marion was 23 and had always had a very satisfying sexual relationship with her husband. She and her husband Terry had been in the habit of making love several nights a week; but all that changed suddenly when Marion became pregnant.

> *Many women become much sexier when they're pregnant*

Not long after the doctor had confirmed that she was pregnant, Marion found herself inexplicably pushing Terry away at night. She didn't mean to do it, and she knew it made

Terry furious. But she couldn't help herself. Why had it happened? Well, there were basically three reasons for it.

First, when a woman becomes pregnant the changes in her female hormones are quite dramatic. During those nine months, the proportions of hormones circulating in her blood are very different from those at normal times. In most women, this change in hormone pattern doesn't have any significant diminishing effect on sexual desire. In many cases quite the reverse is true and many women become much sexier when they're pregnant! However, for a small number it does seem that the change in hormone pattern appears to lessen their interest in love-making for a while.

A second—and probably much more important—reason is that many wives don't feel well during long stretches of their pregnancy. This was so with Marion: when she was tired and under the weather and feeling a bit sick, the last thing she wanted to think about was sex.

The third reason some women get 'turned off' during pregnancy is a psychological one. It's very common for people to feel that love-making during pregnancy is somehow 'wrong'. Marion had picked up this notion during her childhood from something her mother had said to her. Later on, one of the girls at school had told her that intercourse during pregnancy could damage the baby—which is, of course, complete nonsense!

So those were the three reasons why Marion wasn't interested in sex—hormone changes, feeling rotten, and fear that sex in pregnancy was 'wrong' or dangerous. There's nothing anybody can do to alter a pregnant woman's hormones, but Marion's doctor was able to do something about the other two factors. He found that her tiredness and apathy were largely due to anaemia and treated that. And he also discussed with her the deep fears about sex during pregnancy which had played such a large part in her new-found lack of interest. Eventually, he was able to allay these fears and help her to realize that it was perfectly safe and normal to make love with Terry, even though she was pregnant.

So by the time she was about half-way through her pregnancy, Marion was very nearly back to normal. Thanks to Terry's love and understanding, and to her own common sense in seeking help from the doctor, their marriage survived this crisis—and by the time her little boy was born, their sex life was as good as ever.

> *It's very important for husbands to take things gently on resuming love-making after childbirth*

Childbirth

Melanie's problem was really the other way round. Her love-life was absolutely fine when she was pregnant, but as soon as she had had her much-wanted baby girl, things changed. When her husband tried to resume love-making after Melanie came home from hospital, she was just not interested. This is a very common situation—and a common cause of tears and marital trauma. Why does it happen? Again there are three possible reasons.

First, there's the hormone question. When a woman has a baby, there are very sudden, even violent, changes in her hormones over the next few days. Although it's difficult to prove, I think that in some wives these hormone changes can have an effect on sexual desire, making women rather uninterested in intercourse for several months or so. Happily, in such cases things usually correct themselves before very long, as the mother's hormone balance returns to normal.

Secondly, the soreness and discomfort which so many women have after delivery can make sex painful. That's why it's very important for husbands to take things gently on resuming love-making after childbirth.

And lastly, psychological reasons once again play a very important part. Melanie was a case in point: deep down, she felt that while sex was all right for young lovers, it wasn't part of being a respectable mother! As soon as she had had the baby, her subconscious guilt would not allow her to enjoy sex.

Oddly enough, this feeling is very common. Like many a wife before her, Melanie went along to the Family Planning Clinic when her baby was about three months old, and poured it all out in a flood of tears to the doctor.

The doctor spent two or three sessions reassuring Melanie that even women who've had babies are allowed to enjoy love-making, and (as is usually the case) this simple 'therapy' seemed to do the trick. The couple were back to normal love-making within a few weeks.

The Pill

It may come as a surprise to you that the widespread belief that the Pill commonly turns women off sex is quite untrue. The real truth of the matter is that there are tens of millions of women on the Pill worldwide, and with sex problems as common as they are, it's inevitable that from time to time a woman who's on the Pill will lose interest in her partner. *This is usually pure chance.*

Most research work involving comparing a large group of women who are taking the Pill and a large number of non-Pill takers seems to show that there's no difference in rates of 'loss of interest' between the two groups. But I have to add that most of this work has been done by Pill manufacturers!

It's certainly true that *occasionally* doctors come across a woman who feels totally anti-sex when she's on one brand of Pill, and then feels fine when she switches to another brand (or perhaps when she comes off the Pill).

And some recent research work seems to show that the increase in sexual interest which many women feel at about the time of ovulation—usually around 14 days before a period—is decreased by the Pill.

So if you happen to find yourself uninterested in sex when you're on the Pill, then it's not altogether impossible that it might be the effect of the hormones in the preparation. If your doctor or clinic feel that this might be the cause of the trouble, then it may be worth trying a change of brand.

But if you decide to try coming off the Pill altogether for a month or so to see what happens, do please choose some alternative means of contraception—otherwise, you may join the ever-increasing multitude of women who stop the Pill and promptly have an unwanted pregnancy. And that could put you off sex for a very considerable period of time!

Inability to reach a climax

It's the age of the orgasm, isn't it? Once upon a time, the words 'orgasm' and 'climax' (which mean exactly the same thing, incidentally) were never seen in magazines and newspapers. Today, you can't get away from them!

> *A lot of women are becoming increasingly worried about their orgasms—or lack of them!*

As a result, a lot of women are becoming increasingly worried about their orgasms—or the lack of them! For one of the most common appeals for help heard in Family Planning Clinics and doctors' surgeries is 'I can't reach an orgasm, doctor.'

I'm certainly not blaming the newspapers and women's magazines for making women much more interested in whether they're having climaxes or not. Personally, I think it's an appalling fact that, until quite recently, such a vast proportion of women just accepted the fact that they weren't having orgasms—and assumed that nothing could be done about it. For it's quite amazing how women's attitudes to the female climax have changed over the years. For instance, it's generally believed that at the beginning of this century, the great majority of 'respectable' ladies were not expected to have climaxes! Indeed, many people were quite unaware that such a thing as the female orgasm even existed.

Gentlemen who had had experience with 'fast' young women were aware that such ladies did seem to go into some sort of spasm of ecstasy toward the end of love-making, and they recognized that this was very like the male climax in its effects. But—and this is the important point—they seemed to believe that 'decent' women were quite incapable of such responses, and it was widely thought that only immoral ladies could have orgasms.

These ideas have changed only very slowly over the years, and even as late as the 1940s a lot of couples were quite unaware that there was any possibility of the woman having an orgasm.

As late as 1960, many—probably most—medical students were being taught that at least a quarter of women were 'constitutionally incapable' of having a sexual climax. And it was really only very recently that we reached the situation where virtually every woman expects an orgasm—even though quite a few of them are still disappointed!

Take the case of Rita. She'd had no sexual experience before she met her future husband, but she'd read all about it, and—like any modern girl—she knew that sex is supposed to be good for the woman too, and that a girl is entitled to her climax. Rita started making love with her fiancé shortly after she got engaged. But no orgasm! Things were no better when they got married, though Rita had naturally hoped that the security of being wed would help her reach that elusive climax. Six months after the wedding, she was feeling pretty depressed—and she was taking it out on her husband John.

He too had got a bit obsessed with climaxes, because he'd read an awful lot of novels in which the hero leaps on top of the heroine, gives a few magnificently virile thrusts and brings her to ecstasy just like that! He couldn't understand why his love-making wasn't having the same effect on Rita.

Rita was attending a clinic where she got her supplies of the Pill. And the doctor (having heard similar case histories several times that week already) wasn't particularly surprised. She just told Rita a few home truths about this whole business of orgasm.

'For a start,' she said, 'not many women have climaxes when they first begin love-making. Some do—but most don't. In fact, it often takes a few months of getting used to the other person before you can relax completely with him and let yourself go.'

'Yes,' said Rita tearfully, 'but I should have managed it by now.'

'Well,' said the doctor, 'that suggests that there's something wrong with the way that the pair of you are going about things. How long does John spend on love-play before he enters you?'

'Love-play?' said Rita, distractedly. 'He doesn't really go in much for that sort of thing.'

And that was the basic cause of the trouble. Like a great many young men, John simply hadn't the faintest inkling of the fact that nearly all women need careful preparation if they're going to be able to relax and enjoy an orgasm.

> *Nearly all women need careful preparation if they're going to be able to relax and enjoy an orgasm*

John was asked to come down to the clinic with Rita, and the doctor explained this basic fact to him. She advised him that—to begin with, at least—he should try to spend about 20 minutes on arousing Rita with love-play techniques before he actually put his penis inside her (see Chapter 8).

She also told him that he could use those same techniques to increase Rita's arousal during intercourse itself—and afterwards. Finally, she stressed to them that they must not regard the search for an orgasm as some sort of sexual Olympics.

'People who try too hard and who get uptight about it very rarely succeed,' she said. 'The best thing to do is to relax and really enjoy it!'

So, Rita and John went off, equipped with a book which detailed the various love-play methods that John was to use. And three weeks later, they came back full of smiles.

'We did it,' they said, more or less in chorus. Rita had come for the first time after only about a week of trying. She could now reach a climax fairly easily whenever John used the love-play techniques to get her excited. But she still had one worry.

'I'm only having the orgasm when he caresses me with his fingers,' she told the woman doctor. 'Shouldn't I be able to do it during intercourse?'

Now that's another very common query. About 90 per cent of women can reach a climax these days—but many of them are very concerned by the fact that they only come during petting—and not when their partners are actually inside them.

Until quite recently, most doctors who work in this field would have regarded the inability to reach a climax during intercourse itself as a 'disorder' requiring help. But as I said earlier, recent research has revealed the extraordinary fact that this isn't abnormal at all: most women find that they usually have their climax during love-play—but not during actual intercourse.

So the doctor explained this to Rita—adding that if she was keen to come during intercourse itself, then the best thing was for John to stimulate her clitoris area very intensively with his fingertips all the time he was inside her.

In fact, John and Rita did this—finding it easiest with him entering her vagina from behind, so that he could reach round and caress her clitoris—and their efforts were so successful that within a few months Rita was able to come just as he reached his own climax inside her. But if *you* can't manage to reach orgasm with your partner inside you and can only manage it through love-play, then you mustn't worry. You're certainly not abnormal, and anyway there's a good chance that you may acquire the ability as you get older.

> *Women do very definitely improve with age as far as sexual ability is concerned*

For women do very definitely 'improve with age' as far as sexual ability is concerned. And that's why there's great hope for the 10 per cent of women who can't reach a climax at all at the moment. Many of them find that, as the years go by, they suddenly develop the ability to come. Happily, the incidence of inability to reach orgasm is far less at 45 than it is at 25.

However, that doesn't mean that you shouldn't seek help if you can't reach a climax. Any woman who's been trying for six months or more without any success would probably benefit from a friendly word of advice from a doctor.

Often, just simple advice on technique is required (as in John and Rita's case). But very frequently, the wife has some minor emotional hang-up about love-making that's preventing her from reaching a climax. In such cases, gently talking the problem over will quite often help matters.

In some cases, common-sense relaxation exercises will do the trick—because the basis of the problem is simply that the woman can't 'unwind' and let herself go. (A dry Martini is not infrequently an additional help in these cases!)

Some doctors and psychologists use other techniques to help the wife overcome her emotional block. They may, for instance, suggest the use of sexy pictures, books or films—though, of course, these are *not* to everyone's taste!

But, if you happen to be one of the group of women who don't reach a climax and yet feel perfectly happy with sex, then there's no need to worry. If you and your husband are content with your style of love-making as it is, then don't let anybody talk you into feeling that you *must* have an orgasm at all costs. Remember—plenty of women can reach climaxes at the drop of a hat, yet are thoroughly miserable with their partners.

A warm feeling of love and togetherness in bed is far more important than 500 earth-shattering climaxes!

> *A feeling of love and togetherness in bed is far more important than 500 earth-shattering climaxes*

Worries about your body

After 13 years of being an 'Agony Uncle', I now doubt if there's ever been a human being who was totally satisfied with his or her body! And the bits of our bodies that tend to cause most dissatisfaction are the sexual areas.

The reason for this is quite simple: men and women don't have a lot of opportunity to compare those parts with those of other people. So they're especially liable to think that there's something wrong in those areas. Indeed any number of sexual problems are connected with these feelings that people have about their 'private parts'. Questions like 'Is it too big?', or 'Is it too small?', or 'Is it the wrong colour?', loom very large indeed in a lot of people's minds—and may prevent them from enjoying their sexual potential to the full.

For instance, take the case of Georgina. She loved her husband very much, but she'd never really hit it off with him sexually. The difficulty seemed to be that she couldn't relax. When he wanted her to be wild, abandoned and sensuous, she was usually lying flat on her back feeling all tensed up and quite unable to give herself as he (and she) wanted.

Why? The reason was fairly simple, though

Georgina had never been able to bring herself to talk to her husband about it. She was deeply ashamed of the size of her breasts. Ever since puberty, Georgina had thought of herself as flat-chested, skinny and 'mannish'. As a teenager, she'd convinced herself that boys couldn't possibly be interested in her, because of her Twiggy-like silhouette. (She'd totally failed to realize that many men found Twiggy irresistible.)

When Ralph had come along and not only taken her out, but eventually asked her to marry him, she'd been amazed. After five years of marriage, she still had this crazy (but all-too-common) idea that she was 'not really a woman'.

However, the encouraging thing about sex problems is that very often they get better. One day, Georgina found Ralph looking with some distaste at a picture of an enormous-breasted girl.

I'm glad you're not like that,' he said happily. 'I do prefer that lovely slim figure of yours.'

As Ralph wasn't normally the most communicative of men, Georgina had had no idea up till then that he felt like this. She promptly burst into floods of tears—and told him why. He in turn had had no notion of the fact that she had been so upset about her small breasts—and he had the sense to make a mental resolve to praise them regularly in future! All this made it a great deal easier for this rather reserved couple to communicate better with each other; as a result, their sex life improved no end.

Let's now take a brief look at the areas of the body over which women have the greatest worries. They are, of course, the breasts and the vaginal region.

> *The 'casualty rate' caused by this breast obsession is colossal*

Breasts

This is a terribly breast-conscious age, and the 'casualty rate' caused by this breast obsession is colossal. I get a lot of letters from women who—like Georgina—are convinced that their breasts are too small. I also get quite a few from ladies who feel that they're too big!

Let's look at the 'too small' problem first, because this is more common. The first thing to get clear is that the average woman is *not* supposed to be built like Raquel Welch. Again and again, doctors see ladies with absolutely splendid bosoms, who think they are too small. And it can be very difficult to convince them that an 86 cm (34 ins) bust is actually just about *average* in most western countries and is *not* abnormally small.

The other thing to remember is that—like Ralph above—lots of husbands really do prefer small breasts. And a final tip for women who are on the small side: don't fall into the all-too-common trap of hunching your shoulders and pulling your bosom in, because you feel ashamed of it. What you need to do is the reverse—just as actresses do—and throw your chest out! The way to make your bosom look bigger is to push those breasts forward (with shoulders back) as if you were really proud of them. After all, you *should* be proud of them!

Turning now to worries about over-large breasts, the problem here is also very often one of lack of self-confidence. While some women glory in a large bosom, others are highly embarrassed by it. If your bust is over about 97 cm (38 ins), you may perhaps feel that people are looking at you, or that your breasts are bouncing up and down too much whenever you move around.

I think that the remedy here is to try to accept that you have been well endowed by nature. Yes, people certainly will look at you—particularly men! But their looks will be of appreciation and admiration.

For it's an undeniable fact that there are many women who aren't particularly beautiful facially—but who are regarded as attractive by other people, simply because they have well-developed busts which they're not afraid to show.

Finally, a very few ladies with either very tiny breasts or really enormous ones may benefit from plastic surgery—especially if the embarrassment which they feel is making them extremely depressed or interfering with their sex lives.

The vaginal area

As with the breasts, so with the vagina. A lot of women worry about this area, and think that they are built too small or too large, or that they are somehow not like other women.

The real problem is that most of them have never really seen what other women are like—so they don't realize that they look pretty much the same. One thing you can do is to look at anatomical illustrations in order to reassure yourself that all is normal with you. Look back at Figure I in Chapter 2. If you have a look at yourself in the mirror, you'll find that you're built just the same. The outer lips or the inner lips may be slightly longer or shorter than the ones shown in the diagram in Chapter 2 but such variations are unimportant. (People often get very worried because they think that a long outer lip is some sort of tumour but, of course, this isn't true.) Similarly, the remnants of the hymen (or 'virgin's veil') may look a little different from the one shown in the diagram.

If you think that your vagina is too large after you have borne children, then you may possibly be right. A gynaecologist, GP or Family Planning Clinic doctor could tell you—and, if necessary, prescribe some exercises which will help you to tone things up, make the vagina less lax, and so improve your sex life. (Occasionally, an operation may be necessary instead, called a 'pelvic floor repair'.)

> *Sexual difficulties afflict so many men that they're actually a major cause of marriage break-up*

MEN: impotence

Does your man have any problems with sex? If not, then count yourself lucky! For sexual difficulties afflict so many men that they're actually a major cause of marriage break-up. These problems really do cause enormous unhappiness—for the husband and his wife.

All over the world, there are millions of women who are living lives of misery, simply because their partners have some kind of sexual difficulty. And the absurd thing is that quite often these difficulties *can* be helped, if the couple only realized it.

There are two male difficulties which are very common—so common that I'm sure that you have a friend whose husband suffers to some degree from one or other of them. These two difficulties are impotence and premature ejaculation.

Beginning then with impotence, what exactly does this mean? Let's be quite clear about this from the start—because a lot of women (and men) are hopelessly muddled about the very meaning of the word. It's *not* the same as infertility or the inability to have children, as so many people seem to think. What impotence means is just this: *the impotent male has trouble getting an erection when he wants to make love.*

Some men are *partially* impotent—that is, they're fine a lot of the time but sometimes find that they can't get their penis stiff enough to push it into their partner's vagina.

Other men are unfortunate enough to be *totally* impotent—that is, they can't manage it at all. Some have *never* been able to have intercourse, but most of them have been able to make love to their partners to begin with and have lost the ability over the years.

Let's take a typical case of impotence. James and Suzie had been married for about three years, and their sex life had been perfectly all right to start with. Suzie was now pregnant with their first baby—and was thoroughly delighted about the fact. However, there were some complications during the pregnancy: Suzie bled a tiny bit in the early months; she also suffered from excessive vomiting, and her blood pressure went up.

Suzie wasn't at all worried by these problems, but James was. He loved Suzie very much, and was terrified that he would lose her. In fact, he was so worried that at some point during her pregnancy he actually became impotent. Even when Suzie was very keen on love-making, he simply couldn't achieve sufficient stiffness to be able to penetrate her.

Like a lot of women, Suzie got completely the wrong message about all this: she assumed that James had lost interest in her—and even suspected that he might be having an affair. Nothing could have been further from the truth. It was because he loved Suzie so much that he'd got into this state. Deep within his mind, there was a confused idea that having sex with her during pregnancy might somehow hurt her. He was scarcely aware of this himself. For as is so often the case, his rational mind and the deep emotional part of his mind were working completely separately. And it was this emotional part that was saying to him: 'Don't have sex with her! You'll make her ill again! You musn't get an erection!'

Deep within his mind, there was a confused idea that having sex with her during pregnancy might somehow hurt her

How did it all work out? Fortunately, Suzie had the sense to take advice. She talked to a young midwife at the antenatal clinic about

> *The worst possible thing is for the woman to turn away in bed, feeling that she has been scorned*

her problems, and the nurse told her that this kind of reaction wasn't uncommon with young husbands during pregnancy— and that it was most unlikely that James was looking elsewhere for sex. She advised Suzie to go home and to talk the whole thing over with James; to reassure him that the midwife had said it was quite all right—even beneficial— for Suzie to have sex during pregnancy; and then physically to seduce him.

That's exactly what Suzie did; and her efforts were a great success. Once James had understood that there was no reason why he shouldn't make love to his wife, Suzie's undoubted charms did the rest. He never had any problems with his potency again.

That story indicates something very important about the causes of impotence, whether total or partial. It's this: the origins of impotence almost always lie in the emotions. It's often very difficult for people to appreciate this fact. The husband who can't get an erection will often assume that he has some dread-

ful physical disease—though this is virtually never the case. The brain is responsible for producing certain chemical changes elsewhere in the body—including the nerves which supply his penis. The chemical changes which occur within these nerves when a man is deeply worried, or frightened (or just very tired) make it almost impossible for him to get an erection.

So the really common causes of impotence are deep-seated fears, hidden worries, guilt about sex (very common this—even when it's sex with one's own wife!) and also general tiredness and strain. Don't forget this last point: far too many men work themselves into a state of emotional exhaustion and then wonder why they can't make love to their wives!

I should make it clear that an occasional episode of failure to 'make it' is usually of no significance at all. Virtually all men have found on at least one occasion during their lives that they've been unable to make love when they wanted to—usually because of excessive tiredness or perhaps over-indulgence in alcohol.

What should you do if your partner has persistent trouble in getting an erection? Well, the most important thing is to show him your sympathy and your love at this time of real crisis for him. The worst possible thing is for the woman to turn away in bed, feeling that she has been scorned. If her partner also rolls away from her, keeping his shame to himself, then the couple are well on the road to long-term trouble. A cheerful, loving attitude of 'Come on, let's beat this together!' will overcome many—if not most—cases of impotence.

Also, don't forget your sense of humour. If, instead of regarding a problem with erection as a cause for gloom and misery, you take the whole business fairly light-heartedly, then you'll help your partner a lot. But never laugh *at* him because of his problem—this wounds a man deeply: always laugh *with* him!

Next, remember that the cure for impotence is quite likely to be in your own hands—literally! For all too often, what happens when a husband can't get an erection is that the wife is so mortified that she does nothing to help him. Yet the skills of a woman's fingers (and lips) can almost be guaranteed to bring a man to erection sooner or later.

And—a final tip—having got him erect, it's usually best if you then straddle him, sitting across his body while he lies flat on his back. This enables you to 'put him inside you', and also to give him additional stimulation with your fingers whenever he feels a bit limp. I'd seriously recommend this useful technique—because all too often a husband who's having trouble with his potency finds that he loses his erection just at the very moment when he gets on top of his partner. The 'woman above' positions that I've described in Chapter 10 get round this difficulty.

If you can't sort out the problem by yourself, then there are now various agencies that offer counselling for both women and men. In general, I'd recommend that you begin by going to one of the Family Planning Clinics where counselling services are specially provided (though your doctor may perhaps know of some local therapist who can help). The addresses of organizations which can help are listed in Chapter 20. Doctors who work for these organizations can sometimes help with the (less common) *physical* causes of impotence.

Premature ejaculation

I recently saw a Canadian medical film which described this disorder as 'the commonest affliction of western man'. I think the film was pitching it a bit strong—but I did understand what they meant, because this particular disorder really is one of the most frequent causes of marital disharmony, and even marriage break-up.

In plain words, it means that the husband reaches his climax too soon. Why is that such a cause of trouble? Because the hundreds of thousands of women who are married to premature ejaculators are mostly pretty frustrated and unhappy.

As you know if you've read the earlier part of this chapter, it isn't always easy for a woman to reach a climax during intercourse—especially during the early years of a relationship. Women are specially likely to have difficulty in reaching a climax if their partners come too soon, because the majority of men (though not all) lose their erection within a few seconds of ejaculation and so can't continue thrusting into the vagina.

Admittedly, the husband who's sexually knowledgeable can stimulate his wife with his fingers after he has reached his own climax, and so prevent her from being totally frustrated. But many husbands don't know how to do this.

Many more are genuinely so exhausted after their climax that they find it difficult to raise the energy for any digital love-play. And, furthermore, a lot of wives find it rather unsatisfactory to be manually stimulated by a husband who has already 'shot his bolt'. So, all in all, if a man is a premature ejaculator, then there's a very high chance indeed that his wife will be unhappy and frustrated—and very possibly living on her nerves.

How do you know if your partner suffers from it? If he persistently reaches his climax before you do, leaving you 'high and dry' (well, not dry exactly, but you know what I mean), then it may well be that he has this condition. If he *cannot* prolong intercourse beyond about two or three minutes, then he almost certainly has it. In some poor husbands, the diagnosis is obvious: these unfortunate chaps have such difficulty with control that they usually reach orgasm the moment they enter their wives—and some even come *before* they get in!

I'd like to stress that this isn't the husband's *fault*. He doesn't mean to come too soon, thereby depriving his wife of sexual satisfaction. It's just that an awful lot of husbands seem to grow up with a sort of 'hair trigger' on their sexual responses. Any erotic activity—and in particular, any approach to the vagina—brings them dangerously near to the point of climax! The reasons why this should be so are a subject of some argument. The most popular view is that the unfortunate husband who suffers from this 'hair trigger trouble' has been conditioned into it during his teens or early twenties. The theory is that his first attempts at sex were probably a bit furtive and hasty—with the object being to get it all over as fast as possible! Psychologists theorize that this pattern stays with the man into his married life—making him reach his climax much too soon.

I'm not going to argue about that theory—because whether it's true or not is unimportant. What's important is that this common condition is now easily treatable in the vast majority of cases. So if your partner is unlucky enough to have this difficulty, then here's what can be done about it.

Very mild cases of 'PE' can usually be treated by the couple, without need of a doctor. What the wife needs to do is let her husband know that she's sympathetic and loving, and that she'll do her best to help him. She must avoid getting cross and saying hurtful things like, 'Oh you haven't done it *again*, have you?'

Instead, she should be sensitive to the fact that her partner is somewhat explosively triggered. She should ask him to give her a signal when his climax seems to be too near—and at that point she should lie still, and not make body or vaginal movements that would tip him over the brink.

As for the man, he can help himself in these mild cases by the following measures:

- thinking of something else—preferably something boring—during intercourse

- biting his lip or the pillows during intercourse—such 'distraction manoeuvres' will also tend to delay his climax

- applying a little local anaesthetic cream to his penis just before love-making so as to diminish sensation. A doctor can prescribe this for you—or there are commercially available products. There's a slight danger, however, of an allergic reaction to a local anaesthetic

- using a sheath, which will also diminish sensation a bit

- having a drink beforehand: a small amount of alcohol (not too much) often has a useful effect in damping down the urgent need to have a climax.

In more severe cases, however, these methods are quite useless. What's needed is some careful counselling from a doctor or other person experienced in treating this disorder. The counsellor helps the couple to sort out any tensions which are present in their relationship, and teaches them a simple technique which—over a period of weeks or months—gradually trains the husband to delay his climax until his partner's ready.

I'm not going to explain this technique in detail here, because it has to be taught very precisely and accurately—otherwise it won't work. But basically it depends on the couple making use of a discovery made by Masters and Johnson. They found that if the wife holds the husband's penis in a special grip, she can 'turn him off' whenever he tells her that his climax is near (see Figure A).

That may sound odd to you, but Masters and Johnson discovered that they could cure no less than 98 per cent of premature ejaculators with this technique. And all over the globe doctors have found that the method seems to work. I should add that as this book was being completed, news arrived that an Israeli team had discovered a way of treating premature ejaculation by giving one of the group of drugs known as 'alpha blockers'. But these are very powerful drugs with possible dangerous side-effects. Also, they make the man have a 'dry' climax with no seminal fluid. All in all, it seems a lot more sensible to use the Masters and Johnson 'grip' technique.

So let me close this section on premature ejaculation with a true case history—one which exemplifies the way in which so many

The special grip developed by Johnson and Masters for treating premature ejaculation.

serious problems can be helped these days.

Tom and Mary were in their early twenties, had been married for two years, and had a little girl called Jane.

But their love-making had always been a bit of a disaster—for poor Tom invariably came within 20 seconds or so of entering Mary. The result was that Mary was frustrated and unhappy, while Tom felt inadequate. Mary told the doctor at the Family Planning Clinic where she was getting the Pill—and the doctor got both of them in for a series of chats.

Mary was helped to see that it wasn't Tom's fault, and she resolved to do everything she could to put him right. The doctor taught Mary the special grip to use on Tom's penis, and she also gave the couple a 'bedtime programme' in which the Masters and Johnson grip could be used as part of Tom's re-training.

Three months later, Tom was completely cured. Instead of being a man who came after

Fig A

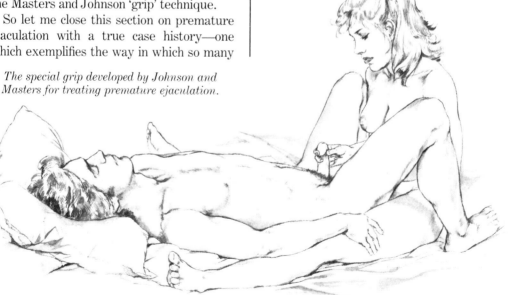

about 20 seconds, he'd become a skilled and tender lover who could make love to Mary for 20 to 30 minutes if he wanted to—and who could satisfy her more deeply than she'd ever thought possible.

In short, a marriage which might well have ended on the rocks had been saved.

Other male worries

What other common male worries are there? Well, there are three main ones: the inability to reach orgasm; loss of interest in sex; and worries about size and shape of the genitals.

Inability to reach orgasm

The medical name for this is 'ejaculatory incompetence'. What it means is that the man can have an erection and make love but he can't reach a climax. Fortunately, a simple treatment developed by Masters and Johnson cures most cases—*if* the couple love each other and are willing to co-operate in beating the difficulty.

The treatment programme should be administered by a skilled therapist. A major feature of it is simply teaching the woman how to rub her man's penis—for up to three hours at a time if necessary—until he reaches an orgasm. Once the mental barrier to orgasm has been overcome, it's usual for the man to acquire the ability to reach a climax during intercourse itself.

Loss of interest in sex

Though it's not as common in men as it is in women, some males do temporarily lose interest in sex. (Note the 'temporarily'—it's rarely permanent.)

In other words, the man may be potent and perfectly capable of making love—but he just doesn't want to. Possible causes include tiredness, stress, generalized debilitating illness, overuse of alcohol, psychological hang-ups, suppressed homosexuality—and just not being interested in his present partner any more. (Yes, this is common: you're not likely to want to make love with somebody whom you can't stand any more...) If there's no immediately obvious cause, then the couple should go and consult a doctor or psychologist who specializes in unravelling this kind of problem.

Worries about size and shape of genitals

Most men are permanently convinced that their penises are 'a bit on the small side'. Indeed, my postbag always contains a hefty bundle of letters from men who believe that their genitals are too small. If this worry applies to *you*, then you're probably wrong! Re-read what I have said about average measurements in Chapter 2 and, if necessary, measure yourself up with a ruler.

Again, if you think that you're differently *shaped* from other men, you're probably wrong. A brief wander across your local nudist beach should convince you of this. (Indeed, you'll probably see so many *frightful* looking people that the experience will be very good for your ego!)

In a few, rare cases, there's some genuine abnormality in the size or shape of a man's genitals. These days, this can very often be corrected by the skills of a urological surgeon.

To sum up, if you're worried about the size or shape of your sex organs, then don't hesitate to seek expert advice before the worries really get you down. Indeed, this is a principle which applies to *all* anxieties about sex.

12

Spicing Up Your Sex Life with a Naughty Weekend!

The joys of the naughty weekend—Accommodation—Romance—Hygiene—Sex

The joys of the naughty weekend

Ah, the joys of the naughty weekend! (I detest the expression 'dirty weekend'—there's nothing dirty about a nice, warm, sexy, romantic weekend away with the one you love.)

But can I tell you this? You really *do* need to plan and organize it properly.

20 years ago I was a young gynaecology house surgeon in Brighton—which has for decades been the naughty weekend capital of Britain. On Fridays and Saturdays, I used to see cheerful couples strolling along the pier or the promenade, exchanging loving glances. By the end of the weekend it was all too clear that in some cases things hadn't gone very well at all.

One extreme example, I recall, was the case of a couple who'd got a bit carried away with some very unwise sexual shenanigans. In the early hours of Sunday morning, she was admitted to our gynaecology ward—for the removal of a jar of vanishing cream which had, alas, vanished inside her. *He* stood in the background, wringing his hands and regretting what an idiot he'd been!

More commonly, weekender couples came in with rather more mundane problems. For instance, she might arrive in casualty bleeding quite heavily—simply because he had forgotten to trim his jagged fingernails before taking her to Brighton. And on several occasions, couples turned up at the hospital plaintively asking for help with the contraception which they had forgotten to bring with them on their romantic excursion to the seaside.

So my message is: *plan ahead*. If you want your weekend to be a superbly fulfilling emotional experience for both you and your partner (not to mention a lot of fun), then you've got to plan under various headings, viz:

- accommodation
- romance
- hygiene
- and . . . sex.

Accommodation

I'm not joking when I say that many a potentially good weekend goes hopelessly wrong because when the couple get to the—supposedly—romantic hotel or flat, it turns out to be awful.

For instance, a married couple who are friends of mine recently decided to have a second honeymoon at a hotel in Kent. They'd driven past it before, and they reckoned that it looked all right.

Well, when they arrived late on Friday evening, they found that the bedroom was freezing cold, damp and miserable, and the staff were unfriendly and churlish. I believe the food was awful too. Alas, it wasn't exactly the ideal setting for exploring the more *recherché* pages of the Kama Sutra!

So, if you're the one who's booking the accommodation. I'd strongly recommend that, wherever possible, you go and take a look at it first. Even if you can't vet it in person, make careful telephone enquiries. And above all, make sure the room has a double bed! There are few things more disappointing than to arrive at a hotel for a sexy weekend only to find·that you're supposed to sleep in separate beds. (Yes, you can shove them together, but you may find that they

drift apart at decidedly awkward moments.)

Similarly, one absolute essential for a successful naughty weekend is an *en suite* bathroom. Men sometimes forget that during long hours of love-making, a woman often feels the need to retire to a pleasant, warm and agreeable bathroom for a spot of hygiene, toiletry and refurbishment (at either end). If she has to traipse down the hotel corridor in her dressing gown to find a toilet and bathroom, both her feet and her emotions are liable to get a trifle chilly.

One final point about accommodation: if you can afford it, do consider booking a room with a four-poster. There's something about four-poster beds that has a delightfully erotic effect on most people.

> *There are few things more disappointing than to arrive at a hotel for a sexy weekend only to find that you're supposed to sleep in separate beds*

Romance

Now please don't forget this vital ingredient! It's no good taking your spouse (still less somebody else's spouse) to Brighton, Brisbane or Buffalo, and just concentrating on 'doing it' as hard and as often as possible.

No, remember that romance is the magic oil that makes love—and love-making—so much more delightful. Don't despise the traditional romantic props, because they really can work wonders. So I'd suggest that, if you can afford it, you arrange some of the following beforehand:

- a bouquet of flowers waiting in the bedroom (Interflora can easily arrange this)
- a bottle of Champagne waiting in a silver bucket by the bedside (ideal for soothing any slight pre-bed nerves)
- a candlelit dinner to be served the first night, in your room if you wish
- breakfast in bed: settling down to a really nice tray-for-two is so much better and more romantic than staggering down bleary-eyed to face a chilly dining room.

Hygiene

Though western men are a lot better than they used to be in this department, far too many of them are still not quite as clean (or as careful about body smells) as they should be. I say this from long experience of having to examine people!

So, if you're the man, do take care to present yourself to your ladylove in the best possible hygienic condition. You aren't going to improve her romantic mood if you lurch into bed half-shaven, smelling rather ominously around the armpits, feet and crotch—and with your fingernails dirty and jagged.

Bear in mind, too, that a recent survey showed that among the things women most detested about men in the bedroom were the habit of walking round dressed in socks (particularly smelly socks) and the habit of swanning about the place in an old singlet.

Sex

Finally, here are a few tips about that important ingredient of a cuddly weekend—sex.

First, take it gently to start with: just as with other forms of exercise, sudden bursts of unaccustomed activity (without a warm-up first) are inadvisable.

If you're a man, remember that women do get sore towards the end of a weekend of unusually hectic sexual activity. Be prepared to take things a little easy, and consider packing a tube of one of today's popular anti-soreness lubricants, such as KY or Durol (available without embarrassment at any large pharmacy).

If you want to try something fresh, why not take one of the new body lotions with you—and give your partner a nice, warm top-to-toe massage?

Once you've settled into your love-nest (as the popular newspapers call it), do experiment and see if you can find some special new erogenous zone which will give him/her unexpected pleasure! (It's alleged that a young lady who was weekending in Brighton with her Romeo said to him, 'Why don't you explore the erogenous zones?' And he replied, 'Aren't they down by the Palace Pier?')

For heaven's sake, don't forget to make sure that one of you is taking contraceptive precautions. No woman is going to enjoy a frisky weekend if she thinks she may have an unwanted pregnancy as a result.

One final practical tip: don't make the mistake of so many naughty weekenders and buy a vibrator to take to the hotel with you. As I said in Chapter 9 these things make a frightful racket, and will wake up everybody else on your corridor. Only take one if you're going to a country cottage—or an apartment with very thick walls.

13

The Dark Side of Sex

Why does there have to be a grim side?—Learning to cope with it—Rape—
Flashers—Frotteurs—Kerb crawlers—Sexual harassment at work—
Child abuse—Incest—Obscene phone calls

Why does there have to be a grim side?

Why indeed? Loving sex is such a delightful acitivity that it's a dreadful shame that in some men it can be twisted into an offensive, violent or cruel form. I say '*men*' rather than 'people', you'll notice—and I do so advisedly!

In these days of equality of the sexes, it's often considered old-fashioned or 'sexist' to suggest that there are great differences between male and female behaviour. *But of course there are.*

Nearly all sex crimes are, I'm afraid, committed by men. All of the sexual nuisances which I've listed at the head of this chapter are almost always perpetrated by males rather than females.

This fact does seem to be related to the greater aggression and 'criminality' of the male sex. (If you doubt that males are more criminal in their behaviour, then can I only remind you that in most developed countries, there are 40 men in jail for every one woman!)

But why on earth *should* some males behave in this warped way? That's hard to say. But as we'll see when we consider these abnormalities in greater detail, quite a lot of the men concerned are rather pathetic individuals who have grown up *unable to form a mature, loving sexual relationship with a woman.*

Instead, they can see sex only in terms of shocking, hurting or brutalizing somebody. You will probably not be surprised to learn that many of these men (though not all) come from childhood backgrounds where the father treated the mother in the most atrocious way, and where sex was regarded as something incredibly 'wicked', 'dirty' and 'shocking'.

When a female is brought up in such a family atmosphere, she very often grows up hating sex and totally unable to enjoy it. When a male grows up in that kind of environment, there is a considerable risk that he'll turn into the sort of individual who goes in for the kind of 'twisted' sex that we're going to deal with in this chapter.

By the way, don't misunderstand me: I'm *not* making any excuses for these men. Personally, I wish that the courts would give far stiffer penalties to rapists and other violent sex offenders, and take them out of circulation for a very long time indeed.

> *Quite often, the ordeal that these women are subjected to is far more brutal and disgusting than you would guess*

Learning to cope with it

From a practical point of view, the most important fact to appreciate is this. There's a lot of this kind of 'bent' sex around and I'm afraid it won't simply go away.

Therefore, we all need to know how to cope with it.

To be more precise, *potential victims* need to know how to cope with it. And regrettably, 'potential victims' are almost entirely women and children.

So, do read this chapter—repugnant though you may find it. It may perhaps help you and your family to protect yourselves against some of the really unpleasant aspects of sexual behaviour.

Rape

Rape is a hideous crime. In many cases, it's associated with terrifying violence. Some of the letters I've received in my postbag over the years from women who've been raped make it clear that being the victim of this sort of thing is a shattering experience which leaves the woman feeling dirty, degraded and (perhaps surprisingly) guilty.

And doctors who have treated rape victims are well aware that often they are psychologically scarred for life. Quite often, the ordeal that these women are subjected to is far more brutal and disgusting than you would guess from reading the reports in the newspapers.

Indeed, many cases are *never* reported in the papers—simply because a lot of women never report the attack to the police. This is partly due to a lack of confidence in the way the police will handle the matter. In the USA, a recent FBI survey estimated that only one in 10 rapes is reported.

Alas, it can't be denied that in Britain, Europe and America, police forces have a pretty abysmal record in dealing with women who have reported a rape. However, things *are* slowly improving—partly thanks to the widespread development of Rape Crisis Centres run by women.

I've tried here to set out some guidelines on how to avoid rape; what to do if somebody attempts it; and what to do afterwards.

> ● *Don't look submissive—a woman who looks alert and ready to fight back may put the man off* ●

Avoiding rape

Regrettably, no woman is entirely safe from rape. But here are a few rules which should help:

1. Don't walk along dark or lonely roads, or cross open ground when there's nobody about.
2. Be particularly wary at night—and especially in the hours after the pubs close (many rapes are alcohol-related).
3. At night, it's far better to take a cab than to walk—the expense may prevent you from having a dangerous experience (or even save your life).
4. Never accept lifts from men—especially late at night.
5. Never travel in single train compartments by yourself—pick an open compartment with other people in it, and sit near another woman.

6. Keep your doors and accessible windows locked, and put a chain on your front door.
7. If you *have* to go out at night, consider carrying a 'rape alarm'—a small canister that gives out a loud and alarming noise.
8. If the law permits it in your country (it doesn't in Britain), consider carrying a weapon for defending yourself.
9. Attend self-defence classes for women.

What to do if you're attacked

If a man, or group of men, starts being troublesome, you still have a good chance of avoiding rape. Follow the following rules.

1. At all costs, *don't look submissive*—women's anti-rape groups quite rightly teach that a woman who looks alert and ready to fight back may put the man off.
2. Yell for help—noise is a good deterrent and does actually frighten some men off.
3. Show active resistance: for instance, if a hand is put on you, grab the man's little finger (which is weak) and rip the hand away. Allowing a hand to remain on you will be interpreted as an invitation to go further.
4. If you think you have a reasonable chance of success, *fight back hard*—using any available methods (e.g. kicking him in the testicles, gouging him in the eye, ramming in a high heel or the tip of an umbrella).
5. As an alternative, it may be worth trying to *talk* your way out: some women have succeeded by striking up some sort of brief rapport and getting the man to discuss his problems.
6. Don't forget devious ploys like pretending you have womb cancer or VD—these have saved some women in the past.
7. At the point when all seems lost, remember that a man with an erection can be disabled for five or 10 seconds by grasping his organ firmly

and twisting it ferociously through about 90°.

8. If you do get free by violent methods, then for heaven's sake, *run*. (Kick off any high heels.) If you're caught again, you're going to get hurt.

9. If you're in fear of your life—e.g. if he has a gun or knife—then *give in:* at least you'll stay alive.

10. Finally, whatever happens, try to fix every detail about the rapist's appearance in your mind.

One final note: it may seem inappropriate to introduce humour into such a grim subject, but I thought you might like to know that one or two of the above points were included in a US magazine article entitled 'How To Say "No" To A Rapist And Survive'. Owing to a typesetting error, it appeared in print as 'How To Say "No" To A Baptist And Survive'.

> *Flashers are mostly rather silly inadequate males who seem to want to shock women*

What to do if you have been raped

It's a terribly shocking experience, but do your best to follow these guidelines.

1. Get to a phone and ring a Rape Crisis Centre (Rape Control Centre)—these are organizations run by women in many large cities. You'll find the number in the telephone book. Even if the nearest number is far away, ring it (reverse the charges if necessary).

2. Do exactly as the people at the Rape Crisis Centre tell you—they're used to handling this sort of thing.

3. Call the police: you may feel very much against the idea—but remember that if they catch the rapist, that should protect other women against his activities for quite a while.

4. *Don't* wash and *don't* change your clothes. If a conviction is to be secured, you'll have to have a forensic examination by a specially qualified doctor—and if you wash or change, the evidence will be gone.

5. Unless you're on the Pill or are otherwise protected against pregnancy, then within 24 hours of the rape make sure you find a doctor who will give you the morning-after Pill—see Chapter 7) to prevent you from conceiving.

6. A week or so after being raped you should, for your own protection, go to a doctor for VD tests (there's no point in going any earlier as the tests couldn't be positive).

7. If you become deeply disturbed as a result of what's happened, do keep in touch with the Rape Crisis Centre—and don't hesitate to seek psychiatric help and counselling.

Unfortunately, specific counselling for rape victims isn't easy to obtain. But some US cities, and at least five Australian ones and one Irish one (Dublin) have established special 'Sexual Assault Centres' where women can be both treated and counselled. There should be more of these places.

Flashers

Flashers are much less of a threat, annoying though they may be. They're mostly rather silly inadequate males who seem to want to shock women—or in some cases vent their anti-female fear or anger.

Despite this, most of them seem to be much less aggressive types than rapists and are unlikely to engage in violence. They're usually just a rather squalid nuisance, but they may of course badly upset some women (and children).

How do you cope with them? The best response to a flasher that I've ever heard of was that of two experienced nurses at London's St. Mary's Hospital.

They were making their way home across Hyde Park after a long night shift, when suddenly a flasher jumped out of the bushes. Both nurses took one look at what he was trying to shock them with—and then collapsed in contemptuous laughter. Exit one very chastened flasher!

Obviously, not everyone can just shrug off an episode of being flashed at in this way—especially if they're young, or if they've led fairly sheltered lives and aren't used to seeing naked men.

But the best way to react to being flashed at is to try not to take it too seriously. Concentrate on making a careful mental note of the man's appearance and clothing (if any). Then get to a phone and give the description to the police.

Frotteurs

Frotteurs are those frightful men who press themselves against women in crowded places (buses, trains, etc.)—or touch them sexually. The word comes from the French verb *frotter*—to rub.

Wimbledon tennis fortnight invariably brings them out (perhaps it's the combination of Champagne and short skirts), and after every All-England Championship the local constabulary have invariably incarcerated a rich haul of 'frotting' clergymen and retired officers. Unfortunately, in other circumstances and places the law is unlikely to catch those who 'frot'—mainly because they do it in very crowded locations.

So how are you going to cope with them? I'd suggest that the best response is a *very* loud and angry shout of something like: 'Keep your hands to yourself, you dirty old so-and-so!'

This will at least be very embarrassing for the frotteur. You could also stamp on him with one of your high heels (if you're wearing them). A jab in the stomach with a rolled up copy of a magazine can also be devastatingly effective.

But be wary of using violence, which can have unfortunate repercussions—especially if you accidentally attack the wrong man.

> *The best way to react to being flashed at is to try not to take it too seriously*

Kerb crawlers

These men really are a pain—and their activities can be very upsetting and frightening for women. Unfortunately, in many countries kerb crawling isn't actually against the law in itself. However, in Britain the law has recently been changed so as to provide ways of taking action against men who are being a nuisance to women.

Your best response to these characters is probably to ignore them—but also to write down their vehicle licence numbers and pass these on to:

the police
local women's groups
local residents and/or anti-prostitution groups.

> *Some women are subjected to the most disgraceful emotional blackmail by their bosses in order to pressurize them into giving sexual favours*

Sexual harassment at work

The issue of sexual harassment at work is a controversial one. Many men (and some women) take it for granted that there's bound to be a bit of sexual innuendo and *badinage* in most offices. I think it's fair to say that a lot of this is quite harmless.

However, in recent years, two things have become very clear: some women are quite genuinely very upset and embarrassed by the sort of sex-orientated joking which men tend to regard as 'jolly hearty fun'; and some women are subjected to the most disgraceful emotional blackmail by their bosses in order to pressurize them into giving sexual favours. In some cases, this virtually amounts to rape.

How can a woman handle this sort of problem? (There *have* been one or two cases in which a *man* was subjected to sexual blackmail by his female boss—but they're pretty rare!)

Here are a few hints:

> object *at once*—if you let things go on, they may get worse
>
> if you belong to a union, complain at once—preferably to a female official
>
> talk to other women at work about the problem
>
> if necessary, tell the man that you'll complain to higher authority about his behaviour
>
> if he *is* 'higher authority', then consider whether it's worth going to a lawyer—or the police
>
> if nothing can be done, don't stay in a job where you're miserable—leave.

Child abuse

Recent events make it clear how common child abuse is. The perpetrator is often a male relative or friend or male baby-sitter.

Regrettably, most child abusers get away with it again and again. A recent US survey suggested that the average child molester committed no less than 73 offences on children before being caught.

This is due mainly to two factors: firstly, many children are reluctant to tell their parents what has happened, especially if the man is a trusted family friend or relative who has pulled the common trick of swearing them to secrecy; and secondly, some parents are reluctant to make a fuss, or to believe that 'dear old Harry' (or Fred or Jim) really could be a child abuser.

Quite obviously then, there are two answers to this problem. Teach your child that there are a lot of silly men around who want to interfere with their private parts—

and impress on them that they must always tell you if anyone attempts this. And if your child tells you that an adult male (no matter how 'trusted' he is) has made a sexual approach, then take what the child says *seriously*.

It's not a good idea to follow the natural instinct of many parents—which is to go and splatter the man against the nearest wall.

You *should* however, inform the police. It may not be possible (or even necessary) for them to obtain a conviction. But the mere fact that they have taken an interest in the man may well deter him from risking assaults on other children in the future.

One final point: it seems to be generally agreed by experts in this field that you should do your best *not* to over-dramatize the situation when talking about it to your child. Discuss it with him or her sensibly and calmly—and make sure you don't make the youngster feel that what has happened was his or her fault in any way.

Incest

Sadly, there's quite a bit of incest around too—again mostly instigated by males, though there are a few cases of emotionally disturbed women who persuade nephews or even sons to have sex with them. However, studies in America seem to indicate that uncle-niece contact is the most common type of incest.

Incest is of course usually a form of child abuse, and most of what I've said above about that applies to it. However, there's no doubt that the experience of incest is especially damaging for a child and will probably have the most disastrous effects on his or her physchological and sexual development.

Also, incest (unlike 'ordinary' child abuse) usually involves actual intercourse. Quite apart from the psychological damage this causes there is of course the risk of pregnancy.

That in itself may seem bad enough—but there's the additional point that a child born of an incestuous relationship is highly likely to be abnormal. There's no doubt that quite a few doctors have taken the step of putting 15 or 16 year-old girls on the Pill in order to try to protect them against pregnancy caused by incest.

It's very difficult to know what to do if you suspect a case of incest. Fortunately, the Rape Crisis Centres mentioned earlier are willing to help, as are child-protection organizations like Britain's National Society for the Prevention of Cruelty to Children.

Also, an encouraging new step is the recent development of 'Incest Crisis Lines'— organizations which are run by former incest victims in order to provide telephone counselling for today's victims.

> *Quite a few doctors put 15 or 16 year-old girls on the Pill to protect them against pregnancy caused by incest*

Obscene telephone calls

A lot of these are just the idiotic actions of absolutely stupid people. Some are made by children or teenagers who dial a number at random and think it's a *great* joke to shout something rude into the instrument. Just hang up on them.

However, some obscene calls are much more sinister, and can be really frightening—particularly if you're on your own and if the calls are *repeated*.

How can you cope with these? Here are a few ground rules:

- tell the telephone company—if necessary they can intercept your calls and/or give you a new number

- tell the police

- in the case of repeated calls, think about hostile action

What do I mean by 'hostile action'? Well, you can cause appreciable pain to a 'heavy breather' by either:

- blowing a whistle loudly down the telephone

- or, better still, blasting a loud 'rape alarm' into the mouthpiece.

In the namby-pamby world in which we live, some people claim that to hit back at an obscene telephone caller in this way might be 'unfair' to *him*! Indeed, some even say that legally it might be regarded as an assault by *you* on *him*!

All I can say is that if any jury convicted you under these circumstances, they would be out of their tiny minds. (And, what's more, I would gladly pay your fine.)

14

The Love Relationship and the Stresses on it

What is love?

No, I don't know the answer to that question! All I know is that, thank heavens, most people *do* have love in their lives—in other words they have somebody (whether it's a parent, a child, a wife, a husband, a mistress, a lover or just a dear friend) for whom they feel this remarkable emotion called 'love'.

People who *don't* have love of any sort in their lives tend—quite understandably—to become miserable and anti-social. They may develop neurotic illnesses, or just go round doing things like mugging old ladies or attacking Poland.

So far, we've just been talking about love—which, of course, is often non-sexual, as in the case of a parent and a child. Sexual love is even more complicated and incomprehensible. For as well as the warmth and tenderness experienced in other loving relationships, there's also the extraordinary and potent contribution of sheer sexual *desire*.

And what a strange thing *that* is! If you were a visitor from outer space, you couldn't fail to be astounded at the bizarre way in which these human beings seem to keep wanting to poke bits of their own anatomy into bits of other people's anatomy (and *vice versa*, if you see what I mean).

Anyway, I'm afraid that we just have to accept that we don't really know what sexual love is. We're no further forward than we were when the 30s song plaintively asked:

'What is this thing called "Love"?' (And you have to be very careful how you punctuate that sentence, otherwise it sounds rude.)

This chapter will explore some aspects of the orthodox love relationship and, most importantly, the stresses on it. (For less orthodox relationships see Chapter 15.)

> *Many young adults have led very restricted lives before marriage—and indeed some have found it very difficult to meet the other sex at all*

Finding a partner

Finding a loving partner (one hopes for life) isn't easy. A surprising number of people *do* manage it—but a lot *don't*.

And, of course, vast numbers of people find the *wrong* partner. Hence the appalling divorce rates in western society: in Britain, one in three marriages now ends in divorce—and in some US cities, the annual divorce rate is actually exceeding the marriage rate.

So, finding a life's partner is something to which you need to devote considerable care. A surprising number of people don't realize this, and just take the amiably fairy-story view that it must be written in the stars that sooner or later the one 'true love' will appear over the horizon. (Oddly enough, he or she quite frequently does!)

Some of them blithely marry the first person they go out with at perhaps 17 or 18, cheerfully assuming that young love will conquer all. However, having seen so many marriages—particularly teenage marriages—break up, I do think that young people should try to meet and to out with quite a wide range of partners before eventually deciding to settle down. After all, you wouldn't buy a suit of clothes without trying on at least half a dozen other suits first!

I'm *not* implying that you should sleep with all these partners. Contrary to what some people think, that isn't a necessary preparation for choosing a wife or husband.

But meeting a wide range of people does seem to be a good preparation for deciding on the sort of person you would like to settle down with for life. From talking to patients, it's all too clear to doctors who work in the field of marriage relationships that many young adults have led very restricted lives before marriage—and indeed some have found it very difficult to meet the other sex at all.

This is particularly common in people who are shy or working in a job where the employees are virtually all of one sex. If this is *your* situation, then it's very important that you should make the effort to:

- join clubs
- take part in sports
- go to dances, discotheques and so on
- go on holidays for the 18–30 group
- if necessary, sign up with a *reputable* dating agency.

Finally, I have to admit that it *is* possible to

have a happy and loving married life even though you've had virtually no experience of social contact with anyone of the opposite sex apart from your spouse.

For much to the amazement of us westerners, the 'arranged marriages' of the east do often work—with the couple coming to love each other in a way that is practically incomprehensible to those brought up on the traditions of romantic wooing! The fact remains, however, that for most people, finding a partner should be regarded rather like visiting a street market: have a good look round before you buy!

> *Don't rush into matrimony just to give the baby a name*

Living together

One of the amazing changes of recent years has been the vast increase in the habit of living together. Twenty years ago, you couldn't publicly admit that you were living together: yet nowadays, every other pop star seems to have a 'live-in lover'—and a very high proportion of young adults are doing the same thing.

In some instances there is a definite case for living together. When I survey the shattered marriages of people who only managed to make it through the first three or four months of matrimony (and then found out they couldn't *stand* one another!), I seriously wonder why they didn't avoid all the trouble and legal complications by living together on a trial basis first.

I note that there is one world-famous female media pundit whose views on marriage are avidly quoted in newspapers and TV. *Her* only marriage lasted three weeks! Why couldn't she just have moved in with the man for a month or two, discovered they were incompatible, and saved the vicar all that trouble for nothing?

Also, there is a widespread feeling today that living together is at least 'stable' and therefore preferable to the promiscuity which so many young adults adopt. On the other hand, there are difficulties and dangers in the 'living together' relationship. They can be summed up briefly like this:

- parents and relatives may still be very upset

- you need to be very clear about what happens if somebody gets pregnant—which they frequently do. (If it happens, *don't* rush into matrimony just to 'give the baby a name'—a hurried marriage is *never* a good idea.)

- sordid and commercial though it sounds, you've also got to be very clear about what your *financial* arrangements are going to be—regrettably, many live-in couples run into all sorts of bitter financial disputes when they break up. It's a pretty awful business when two former lovers meet up in court to fight over who gets half the house or—in the USA—who pays 'palimony'.

So, think twice before you accept that tempting invitation to 'move in with me, darling!' You could be letting yourself in for a lot of happiness—or for a lot of trouble.

Engagement

Being engaged can also be either a very happy or a very difficult time. Unfortunately, there are often stresses from all sides—from parents, relatives, friends and (if it's a second marriage—as it often is these days) from former wives and/or husbands!

There are also difficult financial pressures—unless you're very rich! There can be tricky social obligations, with the need to keep all sorts of people happy.

And there's the major stress (at least, it's a major stress for a lot of people) of having to be the central actors in that emotion-charged theatrical event: a wedding. No wonder so many brides (and grooms) do a bunk on the day and just fail to turn up for the ceremony at all!

The important things to remember during an engagement are these:

1. Be patient with your partner—because he or she is probably under a lot of stress too.

2. Be nice to your partner's family (even if it's the ex-wife or ex-husband!). The family bitterness that so frequently arises at or before a wedding will all too often last a lifetime.

3. If you become doubtful about marriage, *for heaven's sake put it off!* It doesn't matter what arrangements have been made or how much money will be lost (it doesn't even matter if you're pregnant): the fact is that you should never embark on the frail ship of matrimony unless you're absolutely *sure* that this is the sailor you want to spend the rest of the voyage with. Because the rest of the voyage is *life*.

4. Similarly, if the two of you seem to be sexually incompatible—or if one or other of you has serious sex problems—then think very carefully before going ahead with the wedding. Far too many people think that 'it'll be all right when we're married.' It probably won't.

Marriage

Obviously, this book can't be a complete and infallible treatise on marriage. But from the experience of watching a large number of savable marriages break up—mainly because one or both parties persisted in behaving in a way that was silly, immature and selfish—I would suggest these few almost laughably simple ground rules:

- when you have problems, *talk* to your partner: 'bottling it up' is likely to lead to disaster

- try every day to *praise* your partner—not to criticize him or her

- if things are going wrong sexually, *seek professional help* before matters get any worse

- don't commit adultery—it's awfully common, but the troubles it can bring are enormous

- if you *do* commit adultery, keep quiet about it; if you must unburden some guilt, find a good friend, doctor, priest or counsellor to talk to, but don't shift the unhappiness onto your poor old spouse

- if you suspect or find out that your partner has had an affair, try not to regard it as the end of the marriage—see below

- don't seek answers to marriage problems in drink or drugs—a very high proportion of divorces are related to alcohol abuse

- don't involve your children in difficulties

between you and your spouse—and never try to 'recruit' them onto your side

- if the going's getting rough, always go and see a trained marriage guidance counsellor

- try to ensure that your partner is sexually happy: an awful lot of men and women pay no real attention to their spouses' sexual needs—and then wonder why the said spouse goes off with somebody else.

If all that advice sounds a bit trite, I can tell you that I have known quite a few couples who've managed to save their marriages by deciding to stick to rules like these, after a period in which they had been very close to breaking up.

If you suspect or find out that your partner has had an affair, try not to regard it as the end of the marriage

Coping with infidelity

Unfortunately, we have to face the fact that infidelity is very common. Various US and British surveys have suggested that as many as 50% of all husbands are unfaithful to their wives at some time.

And recent surveys in the USA and Britain have now confirmed that infidelity is alarmingly common in women too. For instance, studies carried out on the readers of what are generally thought of as highly respectable and conservative women's magazines indicate that about three out of 10 wives have been unfaithful.

These studies are open to one major criticism, and it's this: women who have very strict and puritanical moral views *tend to refuse to take part in such surveys*, whereas women who are very 'easy-going' sexually are likely to have few inhibitions about answering the questions. So this factor may, of course, artificially inflate the apparent proportion of wives who have been unfaithful.

Nonetheless, any doctor or marriage guidance counsellor will tell you that it's very common to have to cope with a person who's terribly distraught because he or she has found out about his or her partner's infidelity.

This section of the book isn't about adultery (which is dealt with in the next chapter). It's about *how to cope with your partner's adultery.*

So how *are* you going to cope with it? Well, the old way of 'coping' with infidelity was to set about divorcing your partner immediately—or possibly to make arrangements for shooting him or her!

That really doesn't seem awfully sensible these days. If *everyone* divorced (or, indeed, shot) his or her spouse solely because of infidelity, there wouldn't be that many marriages left (and rather a lot of bodies around, too).

There's no doubt that finding out that your partner has been unfaithful can be a very shattering experience. Unless you're running some sort of 'open marriage' (see Chapter 15), you're likely to be extremely upset—to say the least—if you discover that your wife or husband has been having a love affair with someone else.

Indeed, for some people the 'hurt' of this

can last for life. In the past, I've seen quite a few women and men who've simply never recovered from the shock of their spouse's infidelity: many years later, they're still depressed and resentful.

But if you're going to make a go of your marriage, then clearly you have to try and react in a more positive way than this, difficult though it may be.

Here are a few basic suggestions as to how you might deal with the situation:

- although it may be terribly hard, try to be generous-minded; have a blazing row if you wish, but always keep in your mind the possiblity of forgiveness

- think coolly and clearly about just how common such silly affairs are (see above)

- once you've vented your feelings, try to think—in what is quite genuinely a Christian spirit, even if you aren't a Christian—about the *temptations* which have made your partner go astray. (Was it during a business trip abroad by one of you? Was she or he lonely and fed up when sudden 'consolation'—in the shape of sex—was offered?)

- painful though it may be, try to think about what *you* have done which might have pushed your partner towards infidelity. (If you don't think you've ever done anything like that, you must indeed be a remarkable and saintly person!)

- think particularly about whether you've been tender and loving enough recently

- think about whether you've been understanding and sympathetic, and whether you've listened to your partner's problems and worries and tried to help her or him

- think about whether you've made yourself *attractive* enough to your partner lately— banal though it sounds, the fact is that again and again, people go off and have sex with somebody else because their own partner has let her- or himself go. I wish I had £10 for every time I've heard a really unwashed and scruffy-looking person saying 'I just can't understand why she/he did it . . .'

- finally, think about whether you've taken the trouble to be *sexually pleasing* enough to your partner recently. Again, that sounds trite: yet time and again, wives take lovers because their husbands won't make love to them often enough; or husbands go with other women because their wives aren't sexually adventurous enough in bed.

I know that what I've said will irritate many people, because it puts so much responsiblity on the *innocent* party. But if you want to keep the marriage going, then clearly *both* of you (not just the guilty party) have got to work hard at it.

Two final 'no-nos': firstly, don't respond to your partner's infidelity by confessing some past unfaithfulness of your own (if you've had one)—still less by flinging it in his or her face!

Why not? Studies indicate that human beings (i.e. people like your partner) are so idiotic that they tend to regard their own infidelities as 'not very important'—but they tend to regard their spouse's affairs as 'very serious indeed'!

So resist the urge to shriek 'Well—*now* I can tell you that you're not the only one: I did it with the Head Buyer at the office Christmas party!' This won't get you anywhere at all, and it may put another nail in the coffin of the marriage.

Secondly *don't*, if you can avoid it, react to your partner's infidelity by refusing point blank to make love ever again. It's quite natural to want to refuse to make love with someone who's just let you down. On the other hand, you have to remember that love (*including* physical love) is exactly what's needed to 're-cement' your marriage.

Refusing to have sex after things have calmed down might just drive your spouse away for good. Remember that you may well now have competition from 'the other woman' or 'the other man' (in a few cases, from both!).

> ## *Don't react to your partner's infidelity by refusing point blank to make love ever again*

You need to fight this with all the weapons at your command if you want to retain your spouse. And those include your sexual weapons . . .

Good luck—and I hope you keep your relationship together.

Coping with divorce

It's a pretty awful thought that (in most western societies) at least one in three of all those who get married will some day have to face marriage breakdown.

Although I've been divorced myself, I get more and more depressed when I read the divorce statistics each year!

Although there are variations between countries, it seems that almost everywhere, the trend towards divorce is on the increase. Repeated divorce—or 'serial monogamy', as they call it in California, has now become quite socially acceptable.

Britain is fairly typical of most western societies: 80% of all divorces occur in first marriages. Which means, if you think about it, that one in five of all divorces involves somebody for whom this was already the second marriage!

Indeed, in nearly one in 10 cases, *both husband and wife* have been married before, and are going through their second divorce. This lends new weight to Dr Johnson's famous statement that second marriages represent 'a triumph of hope over experience'!

Obviously, I can only hope to deal in this book with the sexual side of coping with a divorce. But if divorce does strike your marriage, how are *you* going to cope with it sexually?

The first thing to say is this. *Don't assume that your love-life is over!*

Although I've said that a second marriage should be regarded with caution, there's no reason to feel that matrimony is 'out' for you from now on.

Nor are enjoyable romantic relationships with the opposite sex by any means over. It's very easy for a divorced person—particularly a woman—to think, 'My love-life is finished.' But that's not necessarily true: life still holds plenty of romance—and *divorcées* (and *divorcés* too) are socially very much in demand these days!

Indeed, the problem for both *divorcée* and *divorcé* may be quite the reverse. Enthusiastic would-be lovers tend to swarm round any recently divorced person who is even half-way attractive, and there may be very real difficulty in keeping all these characters out of your bed!

I have to say that there's a terrible tendency among many newly-divorced people (both men and women) to give in to the temptation to partake 'not wisely, but too well' of all these offers. As this book was being completed, I received in my postbag a fairly typical letter from a recently-divorced woman who had been quite 'bowled over' to find out, after all these years of monogamy, that she was highly attractive to men.

The poor lady had (according to her letter) slept with all the handsome men who flocked round her, and had (I quote) 'a fantastic time', as she discovered that most of them were far better lovers than her husband. This experience is common.

Unfortunately, in the end (literally) she had got herpes. Naturally, she was now pretty distraught. She'd been particularly distressed at the idea that she'd 'never be able to make love again'—which fortunately isn't really true: see Chapter 5.

This kind of wild over-indulgence often occurs after divorce. It may result in:

- sexual infection

- emotional hurt

- unwanted pregnancy

- difficulties with existing children—who may understandably be very upset that a parent keeps coming home with a replacement Daddy or Mummy on Saturday nights.

So, play it a bit cool. *Don't* rush headlong into unwise affairs. *Do* remember that contraception is (usually) still necessary. *Do* remember that one-night stands tend to bring infection. And above all, bear in mind that *you must not let your love-life upset your children.*

> *Enthusiastic would-be lovers tend to swarm around any recently divorced person who is even half-way attractive*

However, never forget that you do still have a chance of finding a life-long loving relationship. Despite Sam Johnson's dictum about repeat marriages being 'a triumph of hope over experience', they do quite often succeed. Why, you've only to look at President Reagan and Nancy!

Coping with bereavement

Unfortunately, one person in virtually every loving couple has eventually to face bereavement from their partner—sometimes tragically early.

If this happens to *you* early in life, it's absolutely devastating. Many people feel like killing themselves—and a few actually do.

But the fact is that most people who are bereaved early in their married lives do (often much to their amazement) manage to get things back on an even keel. Many of them do eventually start going out with other people— and a lot get married again. Such marriages are often highly successful—though you should *never* rush into one just 'to give the children a father/mother'. As you're doubtless well aware, almost all stepchildren are wary of (and potentially hostile toward) any step-father or stepmother.

A far more common situation, of course, is for a loving couple to survive 30 or 40 years together, and then to be split up by death quite *late* in life. Though it's common, it doesn't make it easier to bear.

I get a lot of letters from people who've recently been bereaved. The main hope I can offer is something every doctor knows: that eventually most of them *do* find a purpose in living, particularly through their interest in their children and grandchildren. Some who have *no* children find fulfilment in helping others.

What about the sexual aspect of bereavement? I receive an amazing number of letters from people who have lost their partners—but who still have very strong sexual feelings. Most of these letters are from women—which is partly a reflection of the fact that women tend to outlive men.

Obviously, it can be very distressing if you're a widow of 65 or 70 and you find that you're still troubled by strong sexual urges (a common situation judging by my postbag). I think the first thing to say is that—in answer to a question frequently raised by grannies (!) who write to my column—yes it's perfectly acceptable to relieve these tensions by masturbation.

However the fact is (however awful it may sound to someone who's recently been bereaved), *you're never too old to get married again*. Many people who've had happy and loving marriages, and who eventually lose their loved ones, do later remarry at 65 or 70. I've even seen people remarry at 90—which gives one fresh hope, I must say!

Finally, I would like to stress that there is an encouraging new trend in the development of organizations which counsel those who've lost their loved ones. These are bodies like the Compassionate Friends in Britain (see Chapter 20), who try to help people through the cruel loss of the person they have loved for life.

15

Other Relationships

Adultery—Open marriage—Wife-swapping—Group sex—Troilism—
Bisexuality—Homosexuality

Adultery

'Infants', as somebody once remarked, 'don't have nearly so much fun in infancy as adults do in adultery.' And that's the trouble with adultery. It's awfully tempting—and it always looks as though it would be such fun, and wouldn't do any real harm, would it?

Unfortunately, the trouble is that adultery quite often *does* do harm—to marriages and families, and to people's physical and emotional health.

Of course, it may well lead to divorce. Even today (when adultery is rather less 'frowned on' than it was) about a third of all divorce petitions are brought on grounds of infidelity. Admittedly, the infidelity is often the *symptom* of a marriage collapse, rather than its cause.

But there's no doubt that in most cases, if an innocent party finds out about his or her partner's adultery, this is likely to lead to a great deal of emotional upheaval—and sometimes even to violence. The trouble and bitterness may spill over and affect the children of the marriage, which is something which no one in their right mind would want.

You must also bear in mind a couple of simple basic medical facts, which are so often forgotten by people who trip down the agreeable primrose path to adultery. First, there may well be a good chance that the affair will result in a woman becoming pregnant by the wrong husband. And secondly, there's always the risk that if your fellow-frolicker in bed is promiscuous, you may wind up with a sexual infection—which you in turn may pass on to your spouse.

Having said all that, I have to admit that people are only human and that they do very often stray from the path of virtue—and frequently get away with it.

As I said in Chapter 14, adultery is incredibly common these days. Even in staid, respectable Britain, it seems likely according to recent surveys that:

- three out of 10 wives have committed adultery

- half of these have had multiple lovers

- at any given time, about one in 10 wives is having an affair.

So if you *are* unwise enough to give in to temptation, what's the best way to manage things and keep the situation from getting out of control? Here are some pointers:

- firstly, try to bring the affair to an end if you can—the longer it goes on the more the likelihood of trouble

- just because you slipped between the sheets with somebody *once* in a moment of weakness doesn't mean you have to do it again

- try at all cost not to turn a sexual affair into a genuine love (i.e. loving) affair. I'm afraid there's a terrible tendency for people who fall into bed out of sheer lust to decide before long that they love each other—and that really can be bad news

- laughably simple though it sounds, make sure someone is taking contraceptive precautions. You really are going to mess up a marriage (perhaps two marriages) if it looks as though there's going to be a little cuckoo in the nest

- if there's the slightest chance that your frolic might have led to infection (and this is very common with one-night stands and business trip romances), then for heaven's sake have a confidential check-up at a clinic. It would be totally unfair to give an infection to your innocent spouse—which is, unfortunately, what quite often happens

- finally, unless there's some really overwhelming reason why you have to, *don't confess*. Few people want to be told that their partner has two-timed them: if you *must* confess to someone, see a priest, doctor or marriage guidance counsellor.

Quite a few people these days are perfectly agreeable to their partners sleeping with other folk

Open marriage

Quite a few people these days *are* perfectly agreeable to their partners sleeping with other folk. Where a couple reach such an arrangement with each other, it's called an 'open marriage'.

It all sounds very civilized and sophisticated, but often it *doesn't* work out: maybe

> *Open marriages are likely to end up in open divorce*

one partner gets jealous or even violent, or perhaps one or other party will fall in love with someone they've bedded. And then there are dangers of infection and 'outside' pregnancy.

Furthermore, if you have children, it can be very unsettling for them to observe—as they're almost certain to do—that some nights Mummy sleeps with Bill, or Fred, or Jim, or Pierre, or Helmut ...

Rather reluctantly, I have to say that some open (or, at least, fairly open) marriages work. A famous example was that of the late and much-loved Lord Louis Mountbatten and his immensely-admired wife Edwina. But the success of that highly unusual relationship depended on the fact that Mountbatten was almost totally devoid of jealousy, and really didn't mind in the least whether his wife actually decided to give herself to their close friend Prime Minister Nehru or not.

From personal observation of people who have tried to work an open marriage policy, I'd say that very few couples could have achieved that kind of non-jealous harmony. I'd even go further and say that most open marriages are likely to end in open divorce.

Wife-swapping

Everything I've said about the dangers of open marriage applies with even more force to wife-swapping. This practice is now endemic in the relatively affluent suburbs of cities in the USA, Britain and Australia. (I don't think it's reached Ireland yet, but you never know.)

What usually happens is that a couple advertizes in a 'contact magazine', and then selects a husband and wife from the replies they get—and I gather they get many.

They then meet up in a pub or bar, and see if they like the look of each other. If they do, they then simply swap partners for the night.

The risks involved—particularly that of VD—are considerable. By going in for this kind of thing, you also put yourself in jeopardy of blackmail. A small number of couples who have indulged in it have been horrified to find their names splashed over the racier newspapers. Also, in some countries (and in some states of the USA), advertizing and taking part in wife-swapping can actually land you in trouble with the law.

All of this makes it *very* dangerous living indeed (like 'feasting with panthers', as Oscar Wilde used to say in a different context).

Group sex

Group sex is also very popular these days: you'd be amazed how many discreet orgies are arranged in well-appointed London town houses, or in 'respectable' Californian ranch houses. But everything I've said about the dangers of wife-swapping and open marriages applies with about 50 times more force to group sex.

For a start, the multiplicity of sexual contacts in a single evening is just an open invitation to germs to have a ball (if you'll pardon the expression). When I worked regularly at a London VD clinic, I used to see men who had ... er ... 'embraced' 25 ladies the previous Saturday night—and who now had to telephone these 25 ladies (and their husbands) to tell them that they urgently needed to go to a clinic for a check-up.

Quite seriously, outbreaks of thrush, gonorrhoea and NSU (see Chapter 5), of jealousy and even of violence have forced the activities of many an enthusiastic wife-swapping circle to grind—so to speak—to a halt.

If AIDS were ever to get a hold among the devotees of wife-swapping orgies (as it has among the *gay* orgy set), then the results could be monumentally disastrous.

Troilism

This is an activity, common in some quarters, in which three people go to bed together. I make no moral comment on this, because that's not my brief. It's clear that troilism appeals to a lot of people for a variety of reasons. There are two types:

The two women in bed with one man situation

This appeals to most males' sexual fantasies, of course—since studies show that secretly, most men are very attracted by the idea of going to bed with as many women as possible—50 or 100 perhaps. Girlie magazines encourage this sort of fantasy with the more girls the merrier, all of them eager to be satisfied! In reality, this wouldn't do the man a lot of good, since one man usually has enough trouble satisfying *one* woman—let alone two (or 100!).

It's also a little difficult to see what the two women are supposed to get out of this kind of troilism, unless they have lesbian tendencies. My suspicion—based on talking to a number of people who've gone in for troilism—is that what the girls usually get out of it is *money*.

The two men in bed with one woman situation

As far as I can make out, this definitely does have an appeal for some women (though emphatically *not* for most) because of the higher chance of sexual satisfaction—and the feeling of being admired and wanted by not just one man, but two.

Why this situation appeals to some *men* isn't entirely clear. But there does seem to be a tendency for some men to feel that their own sexual efforts to satisfy their partners aren't really sufficient, and should be augmented by those of good old Charlie down the road.

I have to say that I think there's a very real danger that if good old Charlie is any use in bed, he might end up going off with the woman (or, for all I know, with the other man!).

Bisexuality

Although many people find the whole idea incomprehensible and distasteful, it's undeniable that a good many 'happily married' husbands and wives are bisexual—in other words, they have the urge to obtain sexual pleasure from both men and women.

My eyes were opened to this fact years ago when I worked in a busy VD clinic—where we'd see Mr Jones, respectable banker and father of four, who just *happened* to have a boyfriend in Chelsea. Since then, the bisexual lives of rather a lot of famous people have been revealed, and we've actually reached the extraordinary stage where some pop stars seem to revel in it.

However, finding that your partner is bisexual is no fun (as Mrs Oscar Wilde discovered). Quite apart from anything else, if the bisexual partner is male there is the ever-present danger of bringing infections—possibly even AIDS—into the home.

In many such marriages, the 'straight' partner quite understandably gives up and gets a divorce. Astonishingly though, I have encountered some cases in which a loving spouse was somehow or other willing to make an effort to cope with his or her partner's bisexuality, and make a go of the marriage. This was, of course, the case with the celebrated and eccentric partnership of Harold Nicolson and Vita Sackville-West.

Homosexuality

With no offence to gays I have to say that this book wasn't intended for them—so I include a brief comment on homosexuality just for completeness, and to try to help those who find that their partners are basically homosexual.

It now seems generally accepted that at least one in 20 men and women *is* homosexual. We don't know the cause of this, despite many ingenious theories.

It's important for 'straight' people to realize that gays do *not* regard themselves as 'ill' and are deeply insulted at any suggestion that they might be 'cured'. (In fact, conversion to heterosexuality by medical means is very nearly impossible, and fraught with emotional dangers.)

In general then, gays should be left to lead their own lives in their own way. Contrary to widespread myth, they don't often make any unwelcome approaches to 'straight' people—after all, there are plenty of other gay people around.

Occasionally, a 'straight' person finds him- or herself married to someone who has only just realized that she or he is totally 'gay'. This is usually a pretty hopeless situation and divorce may be the only way out. However, there have been rare instances where a loving and compassionate 'straight' spouse has somehow managed to maintain a worthwhile, but of course platonic, relationship with a gay husband or wife.

16

The New
Role for Men

The old attitudes—The new attitudes—Male emotions and sexual response—Male responsibility for women's sexual fulfilment—Male responsibility for contraception

The old attitudes

What's the traditional view of what a man should be like? Well, everybody knows that he should be strong, dogged, tough and *macho*. He should be brave as a lion, fearless and bold, never flinching in the face of danger, ever-ready to fight if someone insults him—or his woman—and, of course, ever-ready to leap into bed and thrust away with pulsating virility, probably siring triplets in the process. ('Ah, señor—he is much *hombre*, that one . . .')

In short, the stereotype male is the sort of man who's traditionally been played in the movies by John Wayne, Charlton Heston, James Cagney, Clint Eastwood or Humphrey Bogart. (Did he *really* say: 'I never knew a dame who couldn't be fixed by a smack in the mouth or a slug from a .45'?) I wouldn't deny that *some* of the characteristics of the male stereotype are good ones. For instance, I find it impossible not to admire courage, determination, and a willingness to protect women from physical danger.

But I think you'll agree that there are also some pretty awful aspects of the old male stereotype. For instance, the admired male is traditionally portrayed in many books and films as:

- aggressive

- prone to violence

- loud and brash

devoted to swearing

far too 'manly' to show any emotion

likely to treat women as inferior beings

likely to take sexual pleasure from them without worrying about the consequences (yes, James Bond again!).

It's the last three of these points that I want to concentrate on in this chapter—because these three are the specific attitudes which have ruined so many couples' sex lives and made their relationships one-sided and unequal.

Did you know, by the way, that John Wayne's real Christian name was *Marion?*

A new movement to encourage men to be more caring and sharing in their sexual and family relationships has emerged

The new attitudes

Thank heavens, things are slowly beginning to change. In Britain, the USA and quite a few other reasonably civilized countries, a new movement to encourage men to be more caring and sharing in their sexual and family relationships has emerged.

In the USA, this change seems to have arisen largely as a result of the feminist movement—after all, nobody really likes being called a male chauvinist pig! In Britain, it has been stimulated by organizations such as the Family Planning Association, who were deeply worried about the wildly irresponsible sexual behaviour of young males and the large number of resulting unwanted pregnancies, venereal infections, and emotional disasters which that kind of sexual behaviour led to.

In the mid-1980s, the FPA created much interest by launching a long-term campaign to encourage male sexual responsiblity—the well-known 'Men Too' project. To quote the FPA, the campaign aims to foster: 'equal respect for the value of women and men alike, openness and integrity in personal relationships, and in taking contraceptive action ... sharing responsiblity for emotional well-being and sexual health, for the planning and spacing of children, for sub-fertility problems, for childbirth, parenting and maintaining a caring environment in the home.'

Good stuff, certainly—and in sexual terms what the new attitudes mean is that men should:

be willing to show emotion and tenderness and love

make a point of regarding a sexual partner as an *equal*—not as someone to be exploited

take the trouble to ensure that she too receives erotic pleasure and sexual fulfilment

help to make certain that she doesn't become the unwilling recipient of an unwanted pregnancy.

Male emotions and sexual response

It's very important, then, that a man should be able to show his emotions in bed—that he should be able to say 'I love you' to his partner without embarrassment, and that he should be able to talk to her tenderly and romantically about his feelings towards her.

Unfortunately, many men still *can't* do this—in fact they can't talk *at all* in bed, and just communicate in grunts. If *you* have a man like this, dear female reader, then the only thing you can do is to keep on chatting to him till he responds!

The other big emotional drawback of the *macho* man at bedtime is this. *He can't admit the possiblity that his sexual response will be anything less than perfect.* In other words, he assumes that a 'real' man must produce an instant rampant erection (which, of course, must be *very* big), and must also be capable of ramming it in with great power and virility.

If any of this *fails* to happen, he's hurt, desolated, ashamed, fearful that he's not a real man any longer, or that he's turning into a homosexual! Worst of all, he usually can't talk to his partner about it—because real men have such stiff upper lips that they never do that sort of thing.

In other words, the old *macho* man is terribly vulnerable if things start going wrong in bed. There's now a widespread feeling that it would be far more sensible if every young male grew up taking a more laid-back attitude to sex, with much less emphasis on proving himself (as if it were an Olympic event) and much more emphasis on being tender and loving to his partner, and on giving her warmth, cuddling and sexual pleasuring.

In other words, he shouldn't have to feel that he must demonstrate himself to be a 'stallion'. (In general, women are in any case not much interested in stallions—except the kind that romp home first in the Grand National!)

Male responsibility for women's sexual fulfilment

One of the most important things which has happened in recent years is the increasing acceptance of the fact that it really is a man's duty to make sure that his partner has a good time in bed! This is a quite new trend: at the beginning of the twentieth century, the general idea was that women weren't entitled to any sexual pleasure, and should just lie there and take what was (literally) coming to them!

These ideas persisted far into the '60s and '70s, with many men—including some doctors—still holding such amazing attitudes as these:

- women aren't usually very interested in sex, are they?

- a woman's sex drive is far less than a man's

- women don't need climaxes

- most women don't have orgasms.

Even today, at the medical journal for which I work, we *still* (in the mid-1980s) receive indignant letters every time we mention female orgasm. The doctor who writes them claims that 'there's no such thing as a female climax—and women who claim that they're having one are deluding themselves!'

There are plenty of other men who do at least admit to the *possiblity* of their partners getting sexual pleasure and of female orgasm—but who then reveal in the doctor's consulting room that they seriously believe that a woman who doesn't reach a climax after a quick bit of penile thrusting 'must be abnormal'. (Some of them even think that their wives must be lesbians!)

But the 'New Man'—as some magazines now call him—has the sense to realize that it's up to *him* to romance and pleasure a woman, using the agreeable love-play methods described in Chapter 8 to give her the enjoyment (and, indeed, orgasms) to which she's entitled.

Male responsibility for contraception

Similarly, the 'Old Man' (if I can call him that) couldn't care less about contraception. In his youth, he may happily swan around getting all and sundry pregnant.

When he gets married he cheerfully 'screws' his wife without the least thought for the consequences—or the least notion that *he* might do something to prevent unwanted pregnancy. When the poor woman has had so many babies in a row that he's beginning to get irritated by the sheer volume of nappies around the place (*he* will never offer to change them—or wash them!), he then says to her: 'Oy! Why don't you go down to the clinic and get something done about it?'

One well-known man of this ilk who features regularly in English newspapers has two 'wives' and over 20 children—all of whom are supported by the State. It's an interesting comment on our society that the papers usually call him 'Superdad'.

The New Man, on the other hand, (saintly fellow that he is) realizes that contraception should be a *shared* decision. Even if he himself doesn't end up using one of the male methods outlined in Chapter 7, he will have had the sense to talk over all the available contraceptive techniques with the woman he loves—and to reach a reasoned and reasonable decision with her as to what's best for them.

To sum up, the New Man—both in bed and out of it—knows that *it's perfectly possible to be masculine without being macho*.

17

The New Role for Women

The emancipation of female sexuality—New choices and new dangers—
New attitudes to masturbation—New expectations
– and new demands on men

The emancipation of female sexuality

There's no doubt that there has been the most dramatic change in women's sexual behaviour during recent years. This is particularly the case with single women—most of whom think it perfectly reasonable to behave in a way that would have had them labelled as 'loose women' in their grandmother's day!

This change has been partly due to the liberating influence of feminism. Women have, quite rightly, said to themselves *Why should there be one standard for men—and a totally different one for us?*

Another major factor has been the advent of the Pill—and also other highly effective contraceptive methods, such as the IUD (see Chapter 7). It's a little difficult to remember that, just a generation ago, the only really widely-used and effective method of contraception was the sheath. No wonder that when young, single women discovered that they could be totally protected against pregnancy by the Pill, they started to take their sexual pleasure in a way that no generation of women had ever done before.

And the sexual revolution hasn't just been confined to single females, either. Married, divorced, separated and even widowed women have become far more sexually liberated during the last 20 years or so. Women expect far more in bed from their partners—and I'm afraid that if they don't get it, then they tend increasingly to look elsewhere for sexual satisfaction.

So there have been bad as well as good effects of this emancipation of female sexuality. We shall be looking at the new dangers—as well as the new choices—in the next section of this chapter.

New choices—and new dangers

What are the new sexual choices which are available to today's woman? Let's look at them as they apply to various *groups* of women: the single; the married; the divorced; and the widowed.

> *Today's single woman has the choice of doing once-forbidden things without risk of incurring disapproval from society*

Single women

Research by sociologists in various western countries has confirmed that although quite a number of single women do still lead the chaste and virginal lives which were once the norm, most young women don't. Most of them regard sleeping with a fiancé or even a steady boyfriend as perfectly acceptable morally.

Indeed, many of them lead far more adventurous sexual lives than *that*—and the British sociologist Michael Schofield has shown that at least 25% of them go through a distinctly promiscuous phase before (in most cases) settling down to matrimony.

To sum up, today's single women has the choice of doing the following once-forbidden things without serious risk of incurring disapproval from society:

- she can have sex with her fiancé or boyfriend (sometimes even both)

- in most circles, she can fairly openly stay the night with him if she wants to

- as a rule, she can unashamedly go off on holiday with him

- she can—provided she's discreet—have a relationship with a married man (in one recent woman's magazine survey in Britain, a startling one in eight of all readers were having affairs with married men)

- provided she doesn't overdo things and flaunt herself as being too widely 'available', she can cheerfully take a string of lovers. Some of today's younger women have actually slept with 30 or 40 men before they settle down

- she can even meet a man at a party or at a disco or in a bar, and choose to sleep with him that night—and then leave him in the morning. Such one-night stands are amazingly common.

But there are great dangers in this new lifestyle—particularly at the promiscuous end of the scale. For instance:

it doesn't seem to be generally known that single women frequently end up *infertile*, as a result of unnoticed infection picked up during a promiscuous phase of life (see Chapter 6)

multiple partners do increase the risk of cervical cancer (see Chapter 5)—though so, admittedly, do several other factors

despite the availability of contraception, vast numbers of single women get pregnant (often by an unknown father)—and end up having an abortion or an unwanted baby

huge numbers of single women catch VD as the result of their promiscuous life-style

today's easy-going attitude to sexual contact has caused the emergence of 'new' types of sexual infection—most notably herpes (which has caused great distress to many people) and AIDS (which so far has mainly affected the promiscuous wing of the homosexual community). If single women and men continue to go in for promiscuous sex, I'm afraid that other new infections will probably emerge

finally, there are many emotional casualties of today's easy-loving singles life-style. Admittedly, some women would contend—probably with justification—that there were many emotional casualties as a result of the old, puritanical life-style, with its unfair double standard which discriminated so grossly against women.

Married women

What about married women? The sexual revolution has affected them too, though perhaps not so dramatically.

However, today's freer and easier sexual code has, in most western countries, given them options which they didn't have before:

if they want to, they can have a drink, or lunch or (even!) dinner with another man without serious risk of arousing comment

again, if they want to, they can enjoy light-hearted caresses and kisses with other men, especially at parties, without really straying outside the social guidelines of their group

if they're *very* careful, they can indulge in a discreet affair; in some circles, it's even considered acceptable to discuss this with one's girlfriends (or, indeed, to borrow their apartments in the afternoons)

in *very* 'liberated' marriages, a wife may sleep around quite a lot, and even go in for 'husband-swapping' and group sex (see Chapter 15).

But . . . yet again there are dangers. And they're not all that dissimilar from the ones we mentioned while discussing the perils of the single woman's life. Here they are:

sleeping around and having affairs may be all very agreeable, but does increase your chances of ending up in the divorce court

you may become pregnant by someone who is not your husband—this is common, and not easy to cope with. (Have you ever tried explaining a positive pregnancy test to a husband who's had a vasectomy?)

you may easily catch VD—and almost inevitably pass it on to your husband. Still worse, ordinary family contact (through face flannels, etc.) can occasionally pass it on to your children.

Divorced and separated women

I must say that the 'new morality' does seem to me to have been a godsend to divorced and separated women, even though it has brought its own problems. *Divorcées* (and *séparées*) no longer have to feel embarrassed about their marital status, nor pretend that they're really married.

Neither do they have to feel sexually frustrated. In most societies, it's now socially acceptable for them to find a boyfriend—or even, in some cases, to take a much younger lover. Masturbation is also widely used to relieve sexual frustration, and this is considered perfectly acceptable by most people nowadays.

The drawbacks? Well, they're much the same as those we've discussed—the risk of pregnancy (in those who haven't yet reached the menopause), the risk of VD, the risk of cervical cancer (though many women of 'a certain age' very wisely give themselves some protection against this by using a diaphragm).

You could say that there's a risk of emotional hurt too. But I suspect that most divorced and separated women—particularly those who are no longer young—are only too grateful for the fact that they don't have to endure the emotional frustration which previous generations of *divorcées* had to put up with.

Widows

Rather surprisingly, I get a lot of letters from widows who still have very strong sexual feelings. For the relatively small proportion who still want to have a fling with the opposite sex, the advent of the permissive society has meant that they can take the opportunity.

A few 'merry widows' (especially affluent ones) actually find themselves very much younger lovers—sometimes irreverently known as 'toy boys'. But most of the widows who write to me about their sexual feelings are older, and not interested in the pursuit of young lifeguards on Bondi Beach or wherever!

What they want to know in most cases is, quite frankly: is it all right to relieve sexual tensions by masturbation? Of course it is—and we'll be dealing with *that* aspect of women's emancipation in a moment.

And to be honest, I can't really see that the permissive society has done any harm at all to these women: quite the reverse in fact. It's given them the freedom to acknowledge their sexuality—I can't imagine that *before* the advent of the permissive society, many grandmothers would have written to advice columnists saying, 'Is it all right to buy a vibrator, doctor?'

New attitudes to masturbation

Yes—a curious aspect of the sexual emancipation of women is that masturbation has suddenly become respectable. Women have at last realized that it's all right to do it—particularly when they are without a current partner, or when they're away on a business trip or a holiday. They've also appreciated that the great thing about it is that it can't get you pregnant or give you VD—and also that you don't have to worry whether your lipstick is straight!

In some ways, I think that this has gone just a little too far. I'm now beginning to get letters from women who think that they're abnormal because they do *not* masturbate! This is nonsense, of course: nobody *has* to masturbate, and a lot of women get through life without ever doing it.

But there's no doubt that for a lot of women, the fact that this way of relieving sexual tension is now 'OK' has been a great boon. It can be a considerable solace when you're lonely or frustrated. And I must make the point that a lot of women now use self-masturbation as a way of ensuring that they reach a climax when they're in bed with a man. (Some men find it difficult to cope with this—but that's *their* problem. Others are actually turned on by it.)

It's because female sexual emancipation has made self-stimulation respectable that there has been such a massive and continuing boom in the sales of vibrators. Literally millions of women now have them, and customs officers no longer raise an eyebrow when they come across one in a woman's luggage.

(Mind you, an airline pilot did tell me about one extraordinary occasion when a woman air traveller was highly embarrassed by the fact that her vibrator 'went off' in her baggage—and caused a bomb alert!)

The subject of vibrators is dealt with more fully in Chapter 9, but I would like to make the important point that if you're going to go in for this sort of thing, you should use only *safe* vibrators—preferably those which are designed for the job.

Do *not* put vibrators inside your vagina unless the instructions specifically state that this is safe. The woman in Figure A is using a vibrator in a safe and correct way, simply running the 'head' over and alongside her clitoris, without using undue force.

In recent years, the greater use of vibrators and masturbatory objects by women has led to one or two silly injuries and accidents—for instance, abrasions caused by an electric toothbrush (ye gods!) or internal bleeding in the clitoris, caused by manipulation with rough objects. When either your own (presumably) soft finger or a purposebuilt vibrator is available, it's obviously crazy to use anything which might cause you harm.

Fig A

The gentle use of a vibrator for safe self-pleasuring.

New expectations—and new demands on men

Finally, let's admit that the 'New Woman' is certainly making demands on men—and that not all men can cope with those demands. Indeed, many men are very worried about the way in which women are now frankly expressing their sexual needs.

During the launch of the British Family Planning Association's campaign for more sexual responsibility among men, I was several times asked by anxious TV presenters: *'But aren't women now demanding too much of males?'*

Well, what *are* women demanding? I think you could sum it up like this:

today's woman expects a man to respect her

she expects him to treat her as an equal in bed

she expects him to show concern for *her* sexual pleasure, as well as his own

she expects him to show at least some interest in making sure that she reaches a climax—or at any rate, in making sure that she doesn't finish the evening in a state of total sexual frustration

she expects him to try to *prolong* love-making and love-play beyond about two minutes flat. (I see that I was recently quoted in a French newspaper as saying that British women now insist on *'une bonne demi-heure'*—which is an interesting translation of the English phrase 'a good half hour!')

she expects him to share the responsiblity for contraception—or, at least, not just to assume that 'she must be on the Pill'

she expects him not to regard pregnancy as 'her fault'—and not to walk out on her if she *does* have an unwanted pregnancy

she expects him to take care not to give her VD

she expects him not to brag to his friends about what they did in bed together

and she expects him not to kick her emotions around as though they were a football.

All in all, I really don't think that's too much for today's woman to expect—do you?

18

Common
Sex Questions

My postbag of questions

I receive a massive number of readers' questions in my postbag each month—not just from Britain but from Australia, Jamaica, America, the Middle East, New Zealand, Hong Kong, Canada, and most countries in Europe.

Some time ago, I did an analysis of a large number of letters, and found that the most common of all topics were vaginal soreness and discharge—particularly when these symptoms interfered with love-making.

But people have a very wide range of worries about sex and sexual health. This chapter focuses on some of the most common questions, which cover an extraordinary breadth of subjects, some bizarre and some mundane. I hope that some at least will be of help to *you*.

Questions on health

Q Can you help me with an embarrassing problem? I go to the clinic quite often for Pill check-ups and I have no objection to being examined. But when I get off the examination couch, I always find—to my shame—that I have left a large 'puddle' behind. Is there any way I can avoid this?

231

A No need to, really. It's a simple fact of life that if a woman has a gynaecological examination, she usually drips a bit afterwards—especially if the doctor has used some lubricant on her/his gloves or instruments.

Quite a few women are embarrassed about the fact that they always leave damp patches—but their worries are quite unnecessary. After all, the doctors and nurses aren't remotely interested in these patches.

Indeed, in well-conducted clinics it's always the case that a woman lies on a sheet of disposable, absorbent paper—which is whipped away by the staff after they get up. I'm appalled to say, however, that in a few hospitals you may be asked to lie on a couch without any disposable paper covering. This is rather insanitary, and decidedly unaesthetic too, and you should protest.

—◆·◆·◆·◆—

Q Is it really true that you can contract VD from a loo seat?

A It is most unlikely—but you could pick up certain other infections. Personally, I wouldn't dream of sitting on a public toilet seat—especially in central London.

I understand that in ladies' toilets it's common for the attendant to attempt some primitive form of 'hygiene' by wiping the seat for you before you sit down. Frankly, if the cloth has been used to wipe other toilet seats, then this practice is more likely to spread infection than to prevent it.

If you feel that you have to sit down in a public convenience—and many women find it almost impossible to 'go' without being seated—I'd recommend that you first cover the seat with clean toilet paper (assuming there is some!).

Q My husband has suddenly developed an obsession with 'three-in-a-bed' fantasies. While we're having sex, he talks constantly about either me having sex with two men at once; or him having sex with two women at once. I'm not keen on this at all. Do you think this is just a phase which men go through? If so, how soon can I expect him to grow out of it?

A 'Three-in-a-bed' sex is called 'troilism'. I've never found out how to pronounce this word since—as you can imagine—it's not something that often comes up in polite conversation. And I gather that, in practice, troilism is even more difficult to go in for than to pronounce. For a start, there aren't many men around who are capable of satisfying two ladies—many men have enough trouble satisfying one. I suppose that troilism with two men and one woman could be more successful, though it all sounds a bit confusing to me. ('Oops—sorry, George!'—'Not at all, Simon.')

Anyway, the important thing to grasp is that troilism is a common male fantasy, though not many people actually indulge. (Admittedly, the recent massive Playboy sex survey reported that 36% of American men and 34% of American women had tried it, but it appears to me to be less popular in other countries.)

Your husband may fancy the idea but—I hope—wouldn't actually do anything about it. I am, however, a little bothered by the fact that he seems 'obsessed', to use your word. In general it's not a good idea for people to let themselves get obsessed with one particular sexual fantasy—since there's a tendency for that fantasy to take over their entire sex lives if they're not careful. Even now, your husband's constant talk of troilism is clearly driving you wild.

So, all in all, I think it would be a good idea if you yourself thought up some other powerful fantasy and whispered it into his ear in bed. For instance (to borrow an idea from the Reverend Sydney Smith), what about making love to a glamorous TV news-reader while eating *pâté de foie gras* to the sound of trumpets?

Questions about infections

Q *I am a gay woman—a Lesbian. I have been terrified to hear that gays are very much at risk of catching serious kinds of VD, especially AIDS.*

What are my chances of picking up one of these horrible infections?

A Practically none—especially if you don't sleep around.

It is *male* gays and bisexuals who are unfortunate enough to be at increased risk of getting these serious infections, if they go with a lot of fellers.

But I do find it encouraging to see that there are already signs that the male gay community is taking steps to protect itself against these awful new infections, partly by adopting a less promiscuous lifestyle.

Q *I felt miserable when I read a joke about herpes in your column. I have herpes myself, and when I get attacks my confidence disappears and I have terrible feelings of guilt and shame. I have received no sympathy from my doctor.*

A I'm so sorry about this. The reason why I've printed a couple of jokes about herpes is to try to 'de-fuse' the ridiculous media panic about this infection—panic which has unnecessarily alarmed a lot of people.

From the rest of your letter, it's clear that you've had herpes very badly, and that it's given you a rotten time. I know you'll find this hard to accept, but I think it's important that people should realize that a lot of women and men don't have severe attacks—and find to their relief that (for them at least) herpes turns out to be a relatively bearable infection.

I don't think that you should feel guilt and shame at having acquired herpes; I would regard it as sheer bad luck. After all, there but for the grace of God goes virtually anybody who hasn't led a totally monogamous life with a totally monogamous partner.

Finally, you say that you're not getting any sympathy from your own doctor. I much regret this, but in fact herpes should be treated by a venereology specialist, not a GP. As far as I can see, there's no venereology clinic in the town where you live, but there is one in the huge city just a few miles up the road, and I think you should go there.

Q *I have been taking antibiotics for an ear infection. Now I have developed a vaginal discharge.*

Are the two connected?

A Yes, I should think so. Antibiotics make a woman much more liable to the very common condition called thrush (or candida).

233

Q *Is it true that there's some sort of organization for people who've had herpes?*

A Yes, write to the Herpes Association, c/o Spare Rib, 29 Clerkenwell Close, London, EC1 0AT.

General questions

Q *I have very small breasts. My girlfriend wants me to go to a 'non-textile' (i.e. nudist) beach with her this summer. Do you think I will feel terribly embarrassed?*

A Probably! I speak from personal experience because some time back, I reported on a naturist camp for a medical magazine, and had to strip off to conduct the interviews.

However, I can tell you that the embarrassment lasts *about two minutes flat*—by which time you've realized that no one's paying any attention to the size and shape of your personal bits and pieces!

Incidentally, I found naturists a jolly, friendly lot. They run things like sponsored nude swims in aid of leukaemia. And the organizer of their British Singles Club keeps writing to me to say that they need a lot more female members. Interested readers should write to CCBN, Assurance House, 35-41 Hazelwood Road, Northampton, NN1 1LL for a leaflet called *Bare With Us!*

Q *I have fallen deeply in love with a married man who works with my husband. I see him for a chat every day when I pick my husband up from work.*

It seems a bit crazy really, because I love my husband too. Do you think there is any future in having a relationship with this other man?

A Nope. In fact, I reckon it'd be crazy to let things go any further. Since your husband and this bloke are workmates, your hubby would be almost certain to find out.

Married people do often fall for someone they've met casually like this, but usually the infatuation is soon over.

Meanwhile, I suggest you stop picking your husband up from work, so that you're not exposed to this chap's obvious charms!

◄═◆◆◆═►

Q *This sounds crazy, but I am a man of 25, and I think I have fallen in love with another man.*

I have long suspected that he is gay. Now I am beginning to feel that I am too.

A Well, perhaps you are. Lots of people don't realise they're gay until they're in their mid-twenties.

If you *are* gay, it's best to accept the fact. But you're obviously not quite sure yet! So I wouldn't go dashing in and telling this guy that you think you're in love with him. (For a start, it could be very embarrassing if he's *not* gay!)

I suggest you wait a while, and see how your emotions develop. If your basic sexual inclination is homosexual, I think you'll soon be aware of the fact.

Q *I found a letter in my husband's coat which showed that he was unfaithful to me many years ago. Should I make a fuss about this?*

A I'm sure this was very upsetting for you. And you may well feel like sloshing your old man with a rolling pin—but you have to appreciate that males often do very silly things.

A recent survey suggested that almost half of all married men had been unfaithful at some time or other.

From, what you say, it sounds as though this affair was a long time ago—and presumably it's just a distant memory to your husband.

So, if you can forgive and forget, I should try to do so—though it may not be easy.

Q *My husband was brought up to think that girls should be virgins when they get married.*

He made a great fuss on our wedding night about how marvellous it was to be 'the first one'.

The only trouble is that, to be honest, he wasn't the first one.

I feel a little bit guilty about this. Should I tell him?

A No, I don't think so. If he hasn't found out by now, he's not likely to in the future.

Although it's better to have no secrets from your husband, the fact is that telling him about your previous boyfriend (or boyfriends) would certainly upset him, in view of his feelings about virginity. To cause him pain just in order to clear your conscience would be vergin' on the ridiculous.

Q *I was upset when I learned recently that I was born illegitimate. Is there any way that I could alter my legal status?*

A This would be very unlikely unless you could persuade your mum to marry your dad.

But cheer up. Most of the prejudices against illegitimate people have gone these days—which is only fair.

Incredibly enough, one in six British babies is now born out of marriage. While I think it's regrettable that the illegitimacy rate is so high, this does mean that you're very far from being alone.

Q *I dearly love my husband, so I can't account for what I've just done.*

I went to London on a weekend break with three of my girlfriends. We had a great time shopping and going to the pictures, and we met some nice guys in a bar on the Saturday night.

To my shame, I spent the night with one of them. He vanished in the morning, not leaving an address.

Should I tell my husband?

A No—why make another person unhappy? You've got it off your chest to me, so leave it at that.

Be thankful that (presumably) you'll never see this fella again. So you're lucky that there should be no complications from your brief affair—assuming, that is, that you're not pregnant.

And be wary of future shopping trips to London without your husband—they can get a girl in an awful lot of trouble!

Q *My doctor says I conceived when making love just as my period was coming to an end. Would this make the baby abnormal?*

A No, not at all. So you've nothing to worry about. Relax—and I hope you have a good pregnancy.

———◆·◆◆·■———

Q *Please don't think this question foolish. My son is about to marry a Chinese girl. Is it true that they are built different to us, and that intercourse between the two races is impossible?*

A No, ma'am—that's a stupid myth: they're just the same as us. Many members of Her Majesty's forces who served in the Far East can testify that both marriage and intercourse between British and Chinese can be highly successful.

———◆·◆◆·■———

Q *Can you advise me about a family problem? I have discovered that my son, aged 20, sometimes masturbates.*

A He'd be quite an unusual 20 year old if he didn't. This is quite normal and harmless. I don't know how you found out about his activity, but I think you have to face the fact that it isn't really any of your business, is it?

Q *I would very much like to learn how to massage correctly—for use on my husband. How can I find out what to do?*

A I presume you're talking about non-sexy massage. (If not then send for a book called *The Joy of Sex*, by Dr Alex Comfort, available in the UK from the FPA Bookshop, 27-35 Mortimer Street, London, W1N 7RJ.)

But for ordinary relaxing/therapeutic massage, I suggest you try a good new Penguin paperback called *The Massage Book*. by George Downing, price £2.50 from most bookshops.

A quick tip for either type of massage: use a little baby oil or talcum powder on your hands. You'll be surprised at the pleasant results.

———◆·◆◆·■———

Q *I read what you wrote in your column about how women shouldn't feel that their vulvas were ugly or abnormal. Well, I'm not happy about the appearance of mine, because the labia are far to long.*

I would like to get them operated on before the summer holidays. Is this possible?

A What sort of summer holidays are you going on? You'd have to get your skates on in order to have your labia shortened by bikini-time, but it can be done.

I honestly wouldn't recommend this operation for most people, though. I am told by a cosmetic surgeon that there's a procedure which is known in the plastic surgery trade as a 'fanny-plasty'. It costs about £500 in the UK, and it's possible to get it done through the British Association of Cosmetic Surgeons, mentioned earlier.

Please note that I can't guarantee the

results of such an operation to re-shape your vulva, though I do understand your reasons for asking about it. After all, as Keats says in *Endymion*, 'A thing of beauty is a joy forever . . .'

Q *I am 31, male, heterosexual—and suffering from an embarrassingly itchy bottom.*

I've been seeing my doctor for months, but he can't find anything wrong with me, and neither can a pile specialist. So now my doctor says it's 'stress'—which it isn't.

A An itchy bottom is fantastically common—especially in the male half of the population. It's often difficult to diagnose, and I must admit that, once we've ruled out things like piles and eczema, we doctors are a bit prone to suggest that it must all be down to stress.

There are even some doctors who hold that an itchy bottom can indicate suppressed homosexuality. I suspect that this suggestion may have been made to you—judging by the challenging way you announce right at the top of your letter that you're hetero!

I have two proposals to make. First, a lot of cases of mysterious itching turn out to be due to fungus infections (like the thrush which so many *women* get). So try a mild anti-fungal cream, which your pharmacist will be only too delighted to sell you.

If this doesn't work, ask your GP about going to a skin specialist.

Q *My fiancé wants me to use cocaine with him, and says it will improve our sexual satisfaction. What do you think?*

A I think he's insane. He'll probably end up impotent—and you'll probably end up in jail or in the cemetery (neither of which places is particularly noted for sexual satisfaction).

Q *I am a widow of 53, and I let out several rooms in my house to students.*

Just lately, a very handsome boy of 19 was renting a room. I really took a fancy to him, silly though it seems, and one night when he came home from a party I let him come to bed with me.

He has now moved on to another part of the North of England, but he left me his address. Do you think I would be foolish to try to keep touch with him?

A Frankly, yes! You must be quite a lady to be able to 'pull' a lad of less than half your age, but I really think there's no future in this relationship.

It seems that you're still a pretty romantic and sexy female, so why not look out for a more suitable younger man—say, one about 49 or 50?

Q *I am a man of 25, and I have always thought I was sexually normal. But my mates have always laughed at me because when I go into a public toilet to pass water, it ends up going on the floor. Should I see a doctor?*

A Definitely. It sounds as if you have a condition called 'hypospadias', which occurs in about one in every 200 men.

In this condition, the opening is on the underside of the penis, instead of at the end. As a result, there is this problem with going to the loo.

The disorder is unlikely to stop you having children, but it would be worth having it checked out—since it may be possible to have a small operation to correct it.

So do see your doctor who will probably send you to a specialist called a urologist.

Q *My wife has one breast slightly smaller than the other. Would massage help make it bigger?*

A No—it might be fun, but it wouldn't make it bigger.

Seriously, most women have breasts of very slightly different sizes. This is nothing to worry about.

19

Glossary
(with pronunciation)

Many people find it difficult to communicate with their doctors (and, indeed, with their partners) because of the simple fact that they don't understand what certain anatomical and physiological terms mean—and, furthermore, they don't know how to pronounce them! This is quite understandable. Anyway, in this chapter you will find a glossary of over 100 words and expressions, which I hope will help clear up any misunderstandings.

Certain words give people particular difficulty with pronunciation, and in these cases I've given an indication in brackets of how to pronounce the word.

One more thing about pronunciation: the way of pronouncing medical words does vary considerably in different parts of the globe. For instance, some anatomical terms are pronounced differently in Scotland from the way they are in England! There's even more difference between British medical pronunciation and American pronunciation. However, if you pronounce the words in the way shown in this glossary you should be clearly understood in *any* part of the world, except possibly Outer Mongolia.

ABORTION: premature ending of pregnancy. Confusingly, doctors in Britain and some other countries still use the word to include *miscarriage* (spontaneous ending of pregnancy), but to most people it means the deliberate termination of pregnancy.

ANUS (AY-nuss): the opening of the rectum ('back passage').

ARTIFICIAL INSEMINATION BY DONOR (A.I.D.): insertion in the woman's vagina of sperm 'donated' by a man who's not her partner.

BALANITIS (Bal-an-EYE-tiss): inflammation and soreness of the end of the penis.

BARTHOLIN'S GLANDS: small glands located near the opening of the vagina; infection of these can cause pain and swelling.

BONDAGE: sexual habit in which pleasure is derived from one or other partner being tied up.

CAP, CONTRACEPTIVE: birth control device which provides a barrier to stop sperm reaching the woman's cervix—see Chapter 7.

CARUNCLE: painful swelling which sometimes develops at the opening of the female urinary pipe; treated by surgery.

CERVIX: neck of the womb—see Chapter 2.

CHANCRE (SHAN-cur): painless 'sore' which is the first sign of syphilis.

CIRCUMCISION: removal of the male foreskin. The same word is applied to a barbaric ritual, in some third-world countries, involving the removal of the female labia and/or clitoris.

CLIMAX: peak of sexual pleasure.

CLITORIS (CLIT-orr-iss): main pleasure centre in women—see Chapters 2 and 3.

COIL: type of intra-uterine contraceptive device (I.U.D.)—see Chapter 7.

COITUS INTERRUPTUS (CO-it-uss in-terr-UP-tuss): withdrawal—a wildly dangerous form of do-it-yourself birth control in which the man 'withdraws' just before reaching his climax.

CONDOM: see 'SHEATH'.

COPPER 7: a popular form of intra-uterine device (see Chapter 7)—also known as the Gravigard.

CYSTITIS (Sis-TIGHT-uss): inflammation of the bladder—see Chapter 5.

D AND C: dilatation and curettage—a very common operation in which the neck of the womb is dilated so that the surgeon can insert an instrument to 'scrape' the lining of the womb.

DIAPHRAGM: the most common type of cap (see CAP)—explained in Chapter 7.

DILDO: an artificial penis.

DISCHARGE: any abnormal amount (or abnormal type) of fluid produced by the vagina or penis. Confusingly, in some countries the word is used to mean 'climax'.

DYSPAREUNIA (Diss-par-YEW-nya): pain or discomfort on intercourse.

DYSURIA (Diss-YEW-rya): pain on passing urine.

EJACULATION: production of seminal fluid at a man's climax; also now used for the production of *female* sexual fluid which is alleged to occur after stimulation of the 'G-spot'— see Chapter 3.

ERECTION: stiffening of an organ (e.g. the penis or clitoris) as a result of engorgement with blood.

FETISHISM: sexual habit in which there's unusual interest in an object or part of the body—commonly the foot.

FIBROID: benign swelling in the wall of the womb.

FORESKIN: the prepuce, or 'loose' skin at the end of a man's penis.

GLANS (rhymes with 'Hans'): the rounded end of the penis.

GONORRHOEA (gonn-orr-EE-ah): major venereal disease—see Chapter 5.

HERPES GENITALIS: one of the relatively 'new' sex infections, caused by a virus similar to the one which causes cold sores on the mouth—see Chapter 5.

HOMOSEXUALITY ('Homm-o', not 'Home-o'): attraction to the same sex, whether male or female.

HORMONES: chemical 'messengers' produced by the sex glands; they travel round our bloodstream and produce effects on various parts of the body.

HYMEN: the 'virgin's veil': a thin membrane which partly closes off the lower end of the vagina in virgins.

HYPOSPADIAS (Hy-po-SPAY-dee-ass): a common condition (1 in 200 men) in which the urinary pipe opens onto the *under* side of the penis.

HYSTERECTOMY: removal of the womb—see Chapter 5.

IMPOTENCE (IMP-o-tense): inability to achieve a good enough erection to make love.

INFERTILITY: partial or complete inability to have children.

INTRA-UTERINE DEVICE: the I.U.D.—a widely used contraceptive device which is placed in the womb; see Chapter 7.

LABIA (LAY-bee-ah): the 'lips' of the vagina. The singular is 'Labium'.

LIBIDO (usually lib-EYE-doh—sometimes LIB-id-oh, but also lib-EE-doh): interest in sex.

LOOP: a type of INTRA-UTERINE DEVICE—see above.

LOVE-PLAY: sexual caressing or 'petting'.

MASOCHISM: a deviation in which the person takes pleasure in having pain inflicted on him or her.

MASTECTOMY: partial or complete removal of the breast—see Chapter 5.

MASTURBATION: stimulation of the sex organs with the hand to produce erotic pleasure; traditionally the word is used to indicate *self*-stimulation—but it can mean 'petting' of another person.

MENOPAUSE (either MEN-o-pause or MEAN-o-pause): the time when the periods stop; the change of life.

MINI-PILL: term used in Britain and other Commonwealth countries to indicate the (single hormone) progestogen-only Pill. *Not*, as often thought, a low-dose version of the ordinary Pill. See Chapter 7.

MONILIA (Mon-ILL-ya): see THRUSH.

MORNING-AFTER PILL: a tablet taken shortly after unprotected sex (especially rape) in order to try to prevent a pregnancy. See Chapter 7.

NON-SPECIFIC URETHRITIS (Yew-reth-RIGHT-iss): NSU or NGU—one of the most common sex infections around today. See Chapter 5.

ORGASM: see CLIMAX. (*Note:* orgasm is a *noun*; there's no verb 'to orgasm'.)

OVARIES: the two female glands which produce (a) eggs (ova); and (b) female sex hormones. See Chapters 2 and 3.

OVULATION: the process in which an egg (an ovum) is released from the ovary. See Chapter 3.

OVUM: Latin name for an egg. The plural is 'ova'. See Chapter 3.

PAP TEST: see SMEAR TEST. (Pap is short for Papanicolaou—the name of a Greek-American doctor who pioneered the test.)

PENIS: if you don't know what this is, you're reading the wrong book!

POLYP (POLL-ipp): any kind of benign (harmless) wart-like growth. Polyps occur in many parts of the body, including the cervix and the male urinary pipe.

PREMATURE EJACULATION: a tendency in males to 'come' too quickly; also known, particularly in the US, as 'hair trigger trouble'. See Chapter 11.

PROGESTOGEN (pro-JEST-o-jenn): also spelt 'progestagen'. An artificial hormone which produces similar effects to those of the natural female hormone progesterone. One of the two hormones in the pill.

PROLAPSE: a descent of the internal female sex organs (especially the womb). Mainly due to slackness of the pelvic tissues as a result of childbirth. See Chapter 5.

PROSTATE GLAND (PROSS-tate): male gland, about the size of a chestnut, through which the urinary pipe passes. See Chapter 5.

RHYTHM METHOD: technique for getting pregnant. (See Chapter 7 for a slightly less cynical view.)

SCROTUM (SCRO-tumm): wrinkled retainer forming a pouch of skin, within which are the testicles.

SHEATH: very common form of male birth control—see Chapter 7.

SMEAR TEST: simple test which should protect almost all adult women against cancer of the cervix; in practice, many women don't have the test regularly—and some die as a result. See Chapter 5.

SPECULUM (SPECK-yew-lumm): metal or plastic instrument, inserted into the vagina so that doctor or nurse can inspect interior of vagina or cervix. Complain if it's not warmed before use.

SPERM: one of the hundreds of millions of small tadpole-like cells which are found in a man's sex fluid—a single one of which can unite with an OVUM (q.v.). See Chapter 6.

SPERMICIDE: any chemical which will kill sperms. Spermicides are used as a method of contraception along with a barrier (e.g. the sheath or diaphragm). See Chapter 7.

STERILIZATION: operation to make a man or woman infertile. Male sterilization is more usually called 'vasectomy'. See Chapter 7.

SURROGATE (SURR-o-get or SURR-o-gate): a substitute. Can mean either (a) a substitute sex partner, who tries to help someone with a sexual difficulty; or (b) a substitute mother, who bears a child for someone else.

SYPHILIS: a very serious venereal disease—see Chapter 5.

TAMPON: an internal sanitary protection. Although primitive tampons have been used since ancient Egyptian times, the modern tampon was invented by the American physician Dr Earle Haas in the early 1930s. His invention was immediately denounced as wicked and immoral.

TERMINATION OF PREGNANCY: deliberate ending of a pregnancy, either legally or illegally.

TESTICLES: the male sex glands, which produce (a) sperm; and (b) male hormones.

THROMBOSIS: a clot, usually in a vein or artery. Can be associated with the Pill—see Chapter 7.

THRUSH: a very common fungus infection which affects women's vaginas and babies' mouths. See Chapter 5.

TRANSVESTISM: a desire to dress up in the clothes of the opposite sex (other than for money).

TRICHOMONAS VAGINALIS (Try-ko-MOAN-ass vadge-in-AY-liss): very common vaginal infection. See Chapter 5.

URETHRA (Yew-REETH-rah): urinary pipe. See Chapter 2.

UROLOGIST (Yew-ROL-o-jist): surgeon specializing in disorders of the urinary apparatus, and the male genital apparatus.

UTERUS (YEW-terr-uss): see WOMB.

VAGINA (Vadge-EYE-nah): pink female passage, devoted to love.

VAGINISMUS (Vadge-inn-IS-muss): common condition in which spasm of the vaginal muscles makes intercourse difficult or impossible. See Chapter 11.

VAS (usually VASS): the vas deferens, or tube which carries sperms from the testicle to the penis. See Chapter 2.

VASECTOMY: male sterilization, by cutting through the vas (q.v.) on each side. See Chapter 7.

VENEREAL DISEASE (VD): sexually transmitted infection. In some countries— e.g. Britain—the term is only used for a few *legally-defined* sexually transmitted diseases.

VIBRATOR: an electrically-powered device, used to give sexual pleasure.

VIRGIN'S VEIL: see HYMEN.

VULVA: the opening or 'mouth' of the vagina. See Chapter 2.

VULVITIS (Vulve-EYE-tiss): inflammation of the vulva (q.v.). Common causes are thrush and trichomonas—see Chapter 5.

WITHDRAWAL METHOD: see COITUS INTERRUPTUS.

WOMB: the uterus—the hollow organ in which the baby develops. See Chapters 2 and 3.

20

A Directory of Useful Organizations

This chapter lists a number of organizations which could be useful to you if you need help in the areas of love, sex and health. Many of them are charities, so please remember to enclose a stamped, addressed envelope when you write to them.

The directory begins with organizations in the United Kingdom, but international addresses are provided in the latter part of the chapter.

United Kingdom

Family planning and infertility

British Pregnancy Advisory Service,
Austy Manor, Wootton Wawen, Solihull, W. Midlands B95 6BX.

Brook Advisory Centres,
153a East Street, London SE17 2SD.
(Advice for young people.)

Natural Family Planning Clinic,
Birmingham Maternity Hospital, Queen Elizabeth Medical Centre, B15 2TG.

Family Planning Association,
27–35 Mortimer Street, London W1N 7RJ.
(All aspects of birth control and related subjects.)

National Association for the Childless,
Birmingham Settlement, 318 Summer Lane, Birmingham B19 3RL.

Pregnancy Advisory Service,
11–13 Charlotte Street, London W1.

Pregnancy and childbirth

Association for Postnatal Depression,
7 Gowan Avenue, Fulham, London SW6.

Birth Centre (London),
101 Tufnell Park Road, London N7.
(More natural childbirth.)

Caesarian Support Group,
Lyn Hallett, 9 Nightingale Grove, London
SE13 6EY.

La Lèche League,
BM 3424, London WC1 6XX.
(Support for breast feeding.)

Miscarriage Association,
4 Ashfield Terrace, Thorpe, Wakefield, W.
Yorkshire WF3 3DD.

The National Childbirth Trust,
9 Queensborough Terrace, London W2.

Adoption

**British Agencies for Adoption and
Fostering,**
11 Southwark Street, London SE1 1RQ.

Parents for Children,
222 Camden High Street, London NW1
8QR.
(Adoption—especially for older and
handicapped children.)

**Parent to Parent Information on
Adoption Services,**
Lower Boddington, Daventry, Northants.

Children

**National Society for the Prevention of
Cruelty to Children,**
67 Saffron Hill, London EC1N 8RS.

Bereavement

The Compassionate Friends,
6 Denmark Street, Bristol BS1 5DQ.

**Cruse, The National Organisation for
the Widowed and their Children,**
Cruse House, 126 Sheen Road, Richmond,
Surrey TW9 1UR.

National Association of Widows,
54–57 Alison Street, Digbeth, Birmingham
B5 5GH.

Gender problems

Beaumont Society,
P.O. Box 3084, London WC1N 3XX.
(Transvestism.)

Gay Switchboard,
BM Switchboard, London WC1N 3XX.

Women victims

London Rape Crisis Centre,
P.O. Box 69, London WC1X 9NJ.

Women's Aid Federation England,
52–54 Featherstone Street, London EC1.
(Temporary accommodation for victims of
rape and/or battering, and their children.)

Women's health

Endometriosis Society,
65 Holmdene Avenue, Herne Hill, London
SE24 9LD.

**Breastcare and Mastectomy
Association,**
26 Harrison Street, King's Cross, London
WC1H 8JG.

Disabled

S.P.O.D.,
286 Camden Road, London N7 0BJ.
(Sexual and personal relationships of the
disabled.)

Australia

**Family Planning Federation of Australia
Inc,**
Suite 3, LUA House, 39 Geils Court,
Deakin Act 2600.

**The Australian Marriage Guidance
Council,**
6 Morton Road, Burwood, Victoria, 3125.

**The Marriage Guidance Council of
Western Australia,**
32 Richardson Street, W. Perth, 6005.

Austria

**Osterreichische Gesellschaft fur
Familien-planung (OGF),**
Universitatsfrauenklinik II, Spitalgasse
23, A-1090 Vienna.

Belgium

**Fédération Belge pour le Planning
Familial et L'Education Sexuelle,**
28 rue Hesbroussart, 1050 Brussels.

Bermuda

Chief Medical Officer,
Department of Health, P.O. Box HM 1195,
Hamilton HM EX.

Teen Services,
P.O. Box 1324, Hamilton 5.

Bermuda Marriage Guidance Council,
Bungalow Bay Cottage, Spanish Point,
Pembroke.

Brazil

**Sociedade Civil de Bem Estar Familiar
no Brasil (BEMFAM),**
Avenida Graca Arañha 333, Rio de Janeiro,
RJ, CEP 20030.

British Virgins

**British Virgin Islands Family Life
Association,**
P.O. Box 1064, West End, Tortola.

Canada

Family Services,
P.O. Box 224, Richmond Hill, Ontario.

Marriage Counselling,
United Church House, 85 St. Clain Avenue
East, Toronto, Ontario.

Family Life Education Council,
223–12 Avenue SW, Calgary.

**Family Service Association of
Edmonton,**
9919–106 Street, Edmonton T5K 1E2.

**Family Service Association of
Metropolitan Toronto,**
22 Wellesley Street, East, Toronto M4Y
1G3.

Family Service Centre of Ottawa,
119 Ross Avenue, Ottawa K1Y 0N6.

Family Services of Greater Vancouver,
1616 West 7th Avenue, Vancouver V6J
1S5.

Family Services of Winnipeg Inc.,
287 Broadway Avenue, Winnipeg R3C
0R9.

**Ontario Association of Family Service
Agencies,**
1243 Islington Avenue, Toronto.

**Ontario Association For Marriage and
Family Therapy (OAMFT),**
3080 Yonge Street, Ste 5082, Toronto M4N
2K6.

**Associated Marriage and Family
Therapists,**
200–419 Graham Street, Winnipeg.

**Planned Parenthood Federation of
Canada (PPFC),**
430–1 Nicholas Street, Ottawa, Ontario
K1N 7B7.

Cyprus

Family Planning Association of Cyprus,
Boumboulina Street 25, Nicosia.

Denmark

Foreningen for Familieplanlaegning,
Aurehojvej 2, 2900 Hellerup.

Egypt

Egyptian Family Planning Association,
5 Talaat Harb Street, Cairo.

Finland

Vaestoliitto,
Kalevankatu 16, 00100 Helsinki 10.

France

**Mouvement Français pour le Planning
Familial,**
4 Square St-Irenée, 75011 Paris.

Greece

**The Family Planning Association of
Greece,**
121 Solonos Street, Athens, 10678.

Holland

Rutgers Stichting,
Postbus 17430, 2502 CK s'Gravenhage.

Hong Kong

**Family Planning Association of Hong
Kong,**
Southern Centre, 130 Hennessy Road,
Wanchai.

India

Family Planning Association of India,
Bajaj Bhavan, Nariman Point, Bombay 400
021.

Israel

**Institute for Sex Education, Counselling
and Therapy,**
Shelta Medical Centre, Tel Hashomer,
Israel.

Israel Family Planning Association,
9 Rambam Street, Tel Aviv 65601.

Jamaica

Jamaica Family Planning Association,
P.O. Box 92, 14 King Street, St. Ann's
Bay.

Department of Psychological Medicine,
University of The West Indies, Mona, St.
Andrew.

Family Planning Board,
48 Church Street, Montego Bay.

Kenya

Family Planning Association of Kenya,
Harambee Plaza, Room 2, 5th Floor,
Nairobi.

Luxembourg

**Mouvement Luxembourgeois pour le
Planning Familial et L'Education
Sexuelle (MLPFES),**
18–20 rue Glesener, Luxembourg-Ville.

Mexico

**Fundacion Mexican para Planificacion
Familiar (MEXFAM),**
Calle Juarez 208, Tlalpan, Mexico 22 DF.

New Zealand

**The New Zealand Family Planning
Association Inc.,**
P.O. Box 11–515, Manners Street,
Wellington.

**National Office, Marriage Guidance
Council,**
P.O. Box 2728, (150 Featherston Street),
Wellington.

Family Planning Association Inc.,
National Office, 214 Karangahape Road,
Newton, Auckland, 1.

Norway

**Norsk Forening for
Familieplanlaegging,**
c/o Ellen Lindbaek, Grakam Vgien 18a,
0389 Oslo 3.

Pakistan

**Family Planning Association of
Pakistan,**
Family Planning House, 3A Temple Road,
Lahore.

Portugal

**Associacao para o Planeamento da
Familia (APF),**
Rua Artilharia Um, 38-2°, Dto., 1200
Lisbon.

Puerto Rico

Asociacion Puertorriqueña Pro-Bienestar de la Familia (APPBF),
Apartado Postal 2221, Calle Padres las Casas No. 117, El Vedado, Hato Rey, Puerto Rico 00919.

Singapore

Family Planning Association of Singapore,
Singapore Council of Social Service Building, 11 Penang Lane, #05-02, Singapore 0923.

South Africa

Family Planning Association of South Africa,
412 York House, 46 Kerk Street, Johannesburg 2001.

Department of Obstetrics and Gynaecology,
University of Cape Town.

National Council for Marriage and Family Life,
114 MBA Building, 413 Hatfield Street, Pretoria.

Sri Lanka

Family Planning Association of Sri Lanka,
P.O. Box 365, 37/27 Bullers Lane, Colombo 7.

Sweden

Riksforbundet for Sexuell Upplysning (RFSU),
Box 17006, Rosenlundsgatan 13, Stockholm 17.

Switzerland

Centre d'information familiale et de regulation des naissances,
47 Boulevard de la Cluse, 1205 Geneva.

Centre Medico-Social de Pro Familia,
Avenue du Theatre 7, 1005 Lausanne.

Familienplanungstelle,
Universitatsfrauenklinik, 4031 Basel.

USA

The International Planned Parenthood Federation,
902 Broadway, 10th Floor, New York, NY 10010.

Planned Parenthood Federation of America Inc. (PPFA),
810 Seventh Avenue, New York, NY 10019.

The American Association of Sex Educators, Counselors and Therapists,
435 North Michigan Avenue, Chicago, Illinois 60611.

The American Association for Marital and Family Therapy,
924 West Ninth Street, Upland, California, 91786.

US Virgins

Virgin Islands Family Planning Association,
P.O. Box 9816, 49–50 Kogens-Gade, St. Thomas 00801.

West Germany

Pro Familia: Deutsche Gesellschaft fur Sexualberatung und Familienplanung e. V.,
Cronstettenstrasse 30, 6 Frankfurt am Main 1.

Zimbabwe

The Child Spacing and Fertility Association,
P.O. Box ST220, Southerton, Harare.

For all countries

International Planned Parenthood Federation (IPPF),
International Office, Regent's College, Inner Circle, Regent's Park, London NW1 4NS.
(Valuable help on all matters connected with family planning, addresses of Family Planning Clinics in various countries, brand names of pills in different areas, useful publications, etc.)

Index

abortion, 14, 116, 240
acne, 12
adoption, 96, 100
adultery, 210, 216–217
AID, *see* artificial insemination by
 donor
AIDS, 76, 128, 219, 220, 227, 232
 causes of spread of, 87–88
 course of HIV infection, 80
 defined, 79
 development, 82–83
 in Europe, 86–87
 men, 84, 85–86
 myths about, 77–78
 people at risk of catching, 76–77
 protection against, 88
 symptoms, 80–81
 women, 84–85
AIH, *see* artificial insemination by
 husband
alcohol, 62, 63, 128, 191, 193, 210
anal area, 35, 42
anal sex, *see* rectal sex
anti-fungal cream, 75
anus, 42, 240
aphrodisiacs, 63, 135
Arab Strap, 135
areola, 26
arthritis and sex, 131, 141
artificial insemination by donor
 (AID), 87, 96, 97–98, 240
artificial insemination by husband
 (AIH), 95, 97

baby, 9, 43
 trying for, 91, 140–141
balanitis, 240
Bartholin's glands, 240
baths, hot, 62, 75
beard development, 12

bereavement, 215
Billings method, 91, 111–112
birth control, *see* contraception
bisexuality, 219–220
 AIDS, 77, 82, 86
 in teenagers, 14
bladder, 49, 71–72
Blakoe energising ring, 135
blocked tubes, 93–95, 98
blood transfusion, 79, 82, 87
body hair, 11, 12
bondage, 144, 240
Boob Drops, 138
bottom play, *see* rectal stimulation
breast-feeding, 112
breasts, 24–26, 119, 124
 benign swellings of, 25
 cancer of, 25, 64–65
 development of, 11, 24
 lumps, 232
 plastic surgery for, 25
 size, 188–189
buttocks, 35, 41–42, 49

candida, *see* thrush
cantharides, 134–135
cap, *see* diaphragm
Capsule, the, 107–109
caressing, general, 119
caressing, sexual, 119
caruncles, 240
cervix, 24, 29–30, 106, 240
 cancer of, 30, 66–67, 74, 104, 113–
  114, 227, 233
 erosions of, 30
 polyps of, 30
 stimulation of, 122
chancre, 240
change, the, *see* menopause
Chlamydia, 69–70, 75

child abuse, 9, 204–205
childbirth, 30, 35–36, 178, 182
children, 8–13, 211, 214, 215
 abuse of, 204–205
 molestation of, 9
circumcision, 75, 76, 83, 238
climax, 13, 14, 17, 35, 38, 47–48,
  52, 54–56, 117, 120, 129, 170,
  174–175, 183–187, 192, 223–
  224, 242
 inability to achieve, 183–187
 multiple, 17, 48, 117, 120
clitoral stimulators, 133
clitoris, 21, 32, 33, 40, 53, 240
 stimulation of, 49, 120, 124, 131,
  133, 170, 187
cocaine, 237
coil, *see* intra-uterine device
coitus interruptus, 102, 240
Compassionate Friends, The, 215,
  246
complexion, 11, 12, 14
conception, 44, 90, 91, 92, 95, 217
condom, *see* sheath
condom, female, 109
contraception, 90, 101–106, 198
 getting advice on, 14
 male responsibility for, 224
Copper, 7, 240
Cowper's gland, 52
cross-buttock position, 141, 148–
  149
crushes, 14
cuddling, 57–58, 223
cuissade position, 143, 167, 168–169
cystitis, 71–72, 240

D & C, *see* dilation and curettage
Dalkon Shield, 105
delay creams, 137–138

252